A GUIDE

to the

HISTORY

of

SCIENCE

GEORGE SARTON was born in Ghent, East Flanders, Belgium, on 31 August 1884. His formal education was completed at the Athénée and the University of his native city. Soon after obtaining his doctorate in mathematics (1911), he decided to devote his life to the study of the history of science. He founded *Isis* in 1912. During the first World War he emigrated to America. After a few difficult years, Dr. SARTON was appointed a research associate of the Carnegie Institution of Washington, an appointment which enabled him to accomplish his mission. He held it from 1918 to 1949. Dr. SARTON taught the history of science at Harvard University from 1916 to 1918, and from 1920 to 1951. At present, he does not teach any longer but he is still very active in his chosen field and hopes to continue his work for many more years.—Dr. SARTON is honorary president of the *History of Science Society* and of the *Biohistorical Club* of Boston, and an honorary member of the history of science societies of Belgium, England, Germany, the Netherlands, Italy, and Israel.—More information will be found in the biography included in the *Studies and Essays in the History of Science and Learning*, edited by M. F. ASHLEY MONTAGU, offered in homage to him, on the occasion of his 60th birthday (New York: Schuman).

Main Publications: *Introduction to the History of Science* (From Homer to the end of the xivth century), 3 vols. in 5, 4332 p. (Published for the Carnegie Institution of Washington by Williams & Wilkins, Baltimore, 1927-48).—*The History of Science and the New Humanism* (New York: Holt, 1931). Revised edition (Harvard University Press, 1937). Spanish translation (Rosario, 1948). Japanese translation (Tokyo, 1950). —*The Study of the History of Science* (Harvard U. Press, 1936).—*The Study of the History of Mathematics* (Harvard U. Press, 1936).—*The Life of Science: Essays in the History of Civilization* (New York: Schuman, 1948).—*The Incubation of Western Science in the Middle East* (Washington, D. C.: Library of Congress, 1951).—*Ancient Science to the Time of Epicuros* (to be published in 1952 by the Harvard U. Press).

Founder and Editor of:—*Isis, an international review devoted to the history of science and civilization* (Vol. 1, Wondelgem, 1913). Vol. 43 is being published in 1952 (Widener Library 189, Cambridge 38, Massachusetts, U.S.A.).—*Osiris, commentationes de scientiarum et eruditionis historia rationeque* (Vol. 1, Bruges, 1936). Vol. 10 including Table of vols. 1-10, will be published in 1952 by the St. Catherine Press of Bruges, Belgium.

A GUIDE
to the HISTORY
of SCIENCE

A First Guide for the Study of the History of Science
With Introductory Essays on Science and Tradition

by GEORGE SARTON

Editor of Isis and Osiris
Professor in Harvard University

THE RONALD PRESS COMPANY

New York

PREFACE

IVIDED into two parts which are very different yet complete each other, this Guide may attract and serve two kinds of readers; on the one hand, scientists and scholars, on the other hand, historians of science. The first and shorter part explains the purpose and meaning of the history of science in the form of three lectures delivered at various European universities; the second, much longer part, is a bibliographic summary prepared for the guidance of scholars interested in those studies. The first part is meant to be read, the second to be used as a tool.

The lectures of the first part were originally thought out at the request of the University of London, and they were first delivered in the Anatomy Theatre of University College in March 1948. The University had invited me twice previously but I had not been able to accept its flattering invitations more promptly, because I could not leave the United States before the printing of the third volume of my Introduction to the History of Science (*Science and Learning in the Fourteenth Century*) was completed. Freedom to leave Cambridge was not in sight until the end of 1947.

When a man has devoted the best part of his life to definite studies, he may be forgiven if he interrupts his real work for a while in order to explain it to others. It is for that reason that when the University of London invited me, I yielded to the temptation.

The problems dealt with in these London lectures were dealt with again in other lectures delivered on the Continent. The ideas of the first lecture were discussed in English before the Vlaamse Club of Brussels, and in French at the Institut d'histoire des sciences (Faculté des Lettres) of Paris; those of the second lecture were explained in French at the University of Liége and at the Collège de France; those of the third were summarized in French before the annual meeting of the Association française pour l'Avancement des Sciences in Geneva.

As all my lectures, whether in English or in French, were delivered with but a minimum of written notes and recreated to some extent for each occasion, the text which is printed below does not reproduce them except in a general way. The text contains much less than the lectures, but also something more, and it differs from each spoken lecture at least as much as each spoken lecture differed from the others dealing with the same subject.

To the lectures has been added a general bibliography meant to provide a kind of vade mecum for students. The lectures try to explain that it is worth while to study the history of science, and indeed that general history is utterly incomplete if it be not focussed upon the development of science; the bibliography appended to them gives the means of implementing the purpose which they advocate.

The history of science is slowly coming into its own. Its study has been delayed by administrators without imagination, and later it has been sidetracked and jeopardized by other administrators having more imagination than knowledge, who misunderstood the discipline, substituted something else in its place and intrusted the study and teaching to scholars who were insufficiently prepared. Historians of science must know science *and* history; the most perfect knowledge of the one is insufficient without some understanding of the other. A historian of culture is not qualified to discuss the history of science if he lacks any kind of scientific training, and the most distinguished men of science are unqualified if they lack historical sense and philosophical wisdom.   Good intentions are never enough, and they are not more acceptable by themselves in this field than in any other.   There are but few historians of science completely qualified for the task of teaching it (the whole of it) today, but it is possible and even easy to create more of them.   That is simply a matter of training, a training different from the other kinds of scientific or historical training, but not more difficult.   As the need of the new kind of scholars increases, the necessary training will be better organized, and more historians of science will be ready to cultivate the new field, and in their turn to train other investigators, perhaps better ones than they are themselves.

To conclude, I wish to thank the scholars and men of science who sponsored my European lectures: first of all, Professor HERBERT DINGLE of University College, London, then, Prof. F. MOREAU, President of the Société belge d'Astronomie and M. PAUL VER EECKE, President of the Comité belge d'histoire des sciences in Brussels; Prof. FRANZ DE BACKER of the University of Ghent and Major-general Dr. IRÉNÉE VAN DER GHINST* of the medical service of the Belgian army, Prof. ARMAND DELATTE and HENRI FRÉDERICQ of the University of Liége, Professor GASTON BACHELARD of the Sorbonne, Professor MAURICE JANET of the Faculté des Sciences of Paris, president of the Société mathématique de France, Professor ANDRÉ MAYER of the Collège de France, M. HENRI BERR, president of the Foundation "Pour la Science" and of the Centre International de Synthèse, Professor PIERRE SERGESCU, president of the International Academy of the History of Science, and his predecessor Professor ARNOLD REYMOND, of the University of Lausanne.   My thanks are due also to many other men and women who made the accomplishment of my task more easy and more pleasant, in their several countries, but it is impossible to name them all here and now.   I am very grateful to all of them, and this book is published in part to express my gratitude and to justify their confidence in me.

The three lectures of Part I have already appeared in French translation, the first and third in the *Archives Internationales d'Histoire des Sciences* (no. 5, p. 10-31, Paris 1948; no. 10, p. 3-38, 1950), the second in the *Revue d'Histoire des Sciences* (vol. 2, p. 101-38, Paris 1949).   These translations written by myself during a vacation in Switzerland and Belgium are relatively free.   As I was my own translator, I could take liberties with the text without the risk of betraying myself.

The brief bibliographic guide which constitutes the second part of this book was enriched by my friend, Dr. CLAUDIUS F. MAYER, Editor of the *Index Catalogue*, Chief Medical Officer of the Army Medical Library in Washington.   Not only did he fill many gaps passim, but he rewrote Chapter 11 dealing with General Scientific Journals, added Chapter 12 enumerating the main Abstracting Journals, and enlarged considerably Chapter 20 on the Journals and Serials devoted to the History of Science.

The proofs of the whole book were kindly read by Mrs. JEAN P. BROCKHURST and Mrs. FRANS VERDOORN who suggested many corrections.

The chapters dealing respectively with publications, societies, museums, institutes are bound to include duplications, because research, collections, exhibitions, publications are but different functions of the same entities.   These duplications do not matter.   Omissions are more serious; some are deliberate, others, maybe the worst ones, are not.

The citing title, *Horus,* was chosen for the sake of convenience.   Such a title should be as brief as possible; the briefer it is the easier it is to refer to the book.   In this case, it will not even be necessary to mention the author's name; it will suffice to say "Horus, p. 145," or "Horus 145," without ambiguity.   A name should be brief, but it should not be arbitrary.   *Horus* was the son of *Isis* and *Osiris;* this book is the offspring of the two serials, *Isis* and *Osiris,* a collection of fifty volumes.   It has many of the defects as well as the qualities of its parents.   What could be more natural and more justified than to call it *Horus?*

---

* My old friend, IRÉNÉE VAN DER GHINST, born in Bruges 1884, died at Watermael, near Brussels, on 30 April 1949.

The falcon reproduced on page iii and elsewhere represents *Horus;* it is the symbol of the God and to the expert that symbol is much clearer than the very word *Horus.* The model which was here reproduced, thanks to the courtesy of the Metropolitan Museum and of Dr. AMBROSE LANSING, Curator of the Department of Egyptian Art, is one of the magnificent hieroglyphics of the Carnarvon collection,* hieroglyphics which were used for monumental or decorative purposes. The author hopes he will not be considered immodest for his own use of it.

The Renaissance tail pieces have nearly all been reproduced from PLANTIN publications, the few earlier, as well as the Baroque vignettes, from various sources in the Chronica Botanica Archives, while the head piece on page xiii was taken from Mém. Ac. Roy. Sci. of 1750.

Cambridge, Massachusetts
Widener 185   THE AUTHOR

* Polychrome faience inlay, late dynastic period; height 15.7 cm. *See* ALBERT M. LYTHGOE (Bull. Metropolitan Museum, Feb. 1927). It has often been reproduced in books dealing with Egyptian art, or with pottery and porcelain, *e.g.,* JEAN CAPART: Documents pour servir à l'étude de l'art égyptien (vol. 2, p. 92, pl. 99, Paris 1931).

TOME I, FASC. 1.   N° 1

ISIS

REVUE CONSACREE A L'HISTOIRE
DE LA SCIENCE, PUBLIÉE PAR
GEORGE SARTON, D. SC.

WONDELGEM-LEZ-GAND

(BELGIQUE)

—

MARS 1913

TITLE PAGE OF THE FIRST NUMBER OF *Isis* ISSUED IN 1913.
— The list of associate editors illustrates the journal's international character. As will be shown in this *Guide,* the history of science is, indeed, a truly international discipline.

CONTENTS

Part I—Introductory Essays

SCIENCE and TRADITION

(Lectures delivered at University College, London, 1948)

Part II

A FIRST GUIDE for the STUDY of the HISTORY OF SCIENCE

A. History

D. Organization of the Study and Teaching of the History of Science

ABBREVIATIONS

Archives.—Archives internationales d'histoire des sciences. Paris 1947f. Continuation of MIELI's Archivio di storia delle scienze, later called Archeion (1919-43).

Introd.—G. SARTON: Introduction to the History of Science and Learning (3 vols. in 5, Carnegie Institution, Washington, D. C., 1927-48).

Isis.—Isis: An international review devoted to the history of science and civilization. Founded and edited by GEORGE SARTON. Vol. 1, 1913; vol. 43, 1952 (Harvard University Press, Cambridge, Massachusetts).

Mitt.—Mitteilungen zur Geschichte der Medizin und der Naturwissenschaften (40 vols., Leipzig 1902-43).

Osiris.—Osiris: Commentationes de scientiarum et eruditionis historia rationeque edidit GEORGIUS SARTON. 10 vols. (St. Catherine Press, Bruges 1936-1952).

Symbols like (IV-2 B.C.), (XIII-1), mean second half of the fourth century before Christ, first half of the thirteenth century of our era; their use implies that the subject is dealt with in my Introduction to the History of Science and Learning.

Part I

INTRODUCTORY

ESSAYS

SCIENCE

and

TRADITION

I. SCIENCE AND TRADITION

The title of this group of lectures and particularly of the first one is paradoxical. It would seem natural to twist it a little and instead of saying Science *and* Tradition, to say Science *versus* Tradition. Indeed, the two terms are to some extent antithetical. The word tradition suggests preservation and continuity; on the other hand, science is the most revolutionary force in the world. That is obvious enough on the material plane. Why are our domestic and industrial affairs, the rhythms of our life, essentially different, say, from those of the Napoleonic times, or even from those of the Victorian age? The fundamental cause of those differences is the fantastic increase of our mechanical power and that increase is due to the development of science. The main "cuts" in social history are due to inventions and discoveries—such as the compass, typography, improvements in mining and navigation, the discovery of the new world, steam engines, locomotives and steamships, dynamos and motors, telephones and telegraphs, moving and speaking pictures, broadcasting, airplanes. These things are too well known to require description. Moreover, those of us who were fortunate or unfortunate enough to be born in the last century, the members of this audience who were "fin de siècle" children, need not undertake special investigations to be aware of the almost incredible changes which have taken place under their own eyes. These changes can be symbolized by a series of revolutionary discoveries, all of which were the fruits of science.

If we turn our attention from the material world to the spiritual one, the changes are equally revolutionary; they may be less obvious, but they are deeper. Think of the "Weltanschauung" or scientific outlook before and after COPERNICUS, before and after GALILEO, before and after NEWTON, before and after DARWIN. Each of those great men made a new gigantic "cut" in our fundamental conceptions. They did not change the world, but they changed so profoundly our viewing of it, that it was as if they had moved us into another one. The change might be one of size, or structure, or meaning. The Ptolemaic world was much larger than that of ANAXAGORAS, the world of KEPLER was much larger still, that of HERSCHEL immeasurably larger; this last one, which seemed to challenge human imagination beyond the limit, is hopelessly dwarfed by the astronomical theories of today. All these changes be it noted are purely spiritual ones, not material. The world wherein we actually live has not changed its dimensions, or rather it has changed them in the opposite way, becoming smaller and smaller as our means of communication were accelerated.

The changes of structure were equally upsetting. Our distant ancestors conceived the possibility of gradual transformation of one kind of substance into another, yet their world was relatively stable and continuous. When they knocked their fists on a table, they had no doubt that that table was solid and without holes. The conception of vacuum was repugnant to them, but a day came in 1643 when it became impossible to duck it. Later the theory of gravitation and the wave theory jeopardized the integrity of that vacuum. Later still the new atomic theory broke the continuity of matter. It took almost a century to establish that theory on a sound basis and no sooner was it established than the atoms disintegrated into smaller and smaller particles. For a short time it had seemed as if the atoms were the only solid things left in the vacuum, and then suddenly the vacuum was rediscovered within the atoms themselves. It is not necessary to extend these remarks. Our conceptions of the world structure were modified so often with increasing frequency, that the wisest children of men hardly knew where they were.

The most revolutionary change of all and the one which might be used above all others to define "modern" man concerns the very idea of science or knowledge. It would take too long to describe how it came about, for the revolution, deep as it was, was gradual. Between a science ancillary to theology or to divine revelation and one aimed at discovering the truth irrespective of consequences, the distance is prodigious, yet it was bridged by an infinity of small steps. The man of science of today loves the truth above everything else and is prepared to sacrifice everything to his quest. He is not anxious, however, to discuss epistemological difficulties with philosophers, because he is satisfied with his own intuition of truth (vs. error) and with his experimental verifications of it. He knows that absolute truth is hopelessly beyond his reach, but that he can come gradually closer to it by the method of successive approximations. Coming closer implies the possibility of having to reject old conceptions as well as that of accepting new ones, but the honest man of science is ready for that and used to it, so much so that it does not hurt him any more to have to abandon some of his ideas. That is a part of the game which he is playing with so much joy. There are no dogmas in science, only methods; the methods themselves are not perfect but indefinitely perfectible. There are no certainties in science, but in a sense there are no doubts. Or looking at it from another angle everything is doubtful except the feeling that the margin of error decreases gradually, asymptotically. The fact that that margin will never be equal to zero does not disturb the man of science but causes him, if he be wise enough, to be very humble.

Men and women untrained in scientific training might believe that the conception of science which I have outlined is simply a personal matter, somewhat like a personal religion, but it is much more. In spite of its gentleness that conception prepares him who harbors it for the acceptance of the most shocking conclusions and the most revolutionary deeds.

Let us see what happened in the past. There has been much discussion apropos of the causes of the French Revolution. Some of the causes were purely material, hunger and misery, others were spiritual, misery and hunger. The influence of writers such as VOLTAIRE and ROUSSEAU, that is, the influence of their social writings, has been exaggerated, while the influence of science has been underestimated. The Old Regime could function only in the darkness; as soon as light was being poured into the dark corners, the defects and diseases became visible and obnoxious, and the thought of correcting them almost unavoidable. During the eighteenth century science, pure science, grew steadily, slowly at first, then faster and faster. The new intellectual temper which has been referred to above, was shaping itself. The Old Regime was established on superstitions, such as the divine right of kings, the excessive privileges of the aristocracy and of the high clergy, the identity of state and crown. Men of science did countenance such superstitions, just as long as they themselves were inhibited by them, but not much longer. Their own ideas, scientific ideas, did not have much currency to begin with and their field of activity was at first very restricted, but in that field, which was steadily growing, their power was irresistible. Moreover, these ideas were gradually vulgarized, not only by the Encyclopédistes and by VOLTAIRE, but by such inoffensive people as BUFFON and the abbé PLUCHE.

Diseases, whether of the human body or of the body politic, can exist and flourish indefinitely as long as they are hidden, but throw the light of knowledge upon them and the situation begins to change; aye, it may change so fast that a revolution occurs. The diseases are recognized and their danger acknowledged; they are described with increasing precision, remedies are contemplated and tried, the experiments are published, the victims are counted and the damages evaluated, the determination of fighting the evil and overcoming it is strengthened. The struggle becomes more intense and sooner or later the diseases are cured if they be curable, or they are abated if they are not.

Before the Revolution a few personal diseases could be alleviated but social diseases were practically incurable, because it was impossible to investigate them and to know them sufficiently. In the second half of the nineteenth century the conditions of research and healing were decidedly better. Among the benefactors to whom we owe that improvement I would like to commemorate one, the Belgian ADOLPHE QUETELET (1796-1874). QUETELET did not declaim against social evils but he undertook to make a scientific investigation of them and he was one of the first to realize strongly that when the elements to be considered are far too numerous to be studied individually, the only method of approach is the statistical method. He had been trained to appreciate the value and limitations, the difficulties and pitfalls of that method by his studies of meteorology and phenology. He discovered that the average number of robberies, murders, suicides, births out of wedlock, etc., is constant in a given community (under normal conditions) and drew the conclusion that these crimes and delinquencies must needs divulge realities comparable to physical realities, and that the most secret behavior of men is submitted to social laws of the same kind as the laws of physics. It follows that those crimes and delinquencies are caused partly by the community and hence that a reform of the community might reduce their number.

QUETELET published his observations in a book entitled "Sur l'homme et le développement de ses facultés ou Essai de physique sociale" (Paris 1835). The book was remarkably successful,[1] but it fluttered the dovecotes of respectability and raised considerable opposition; it gave hypocrites a fine opportunity to illustrate their exceptional virtue. Nevertheless, LEOPOLD, first king of the Belgians, invited the author soon afterwards (in 1836) to teach mathematics to his nephews, the young princes, ERNEST and ALBERT of Saxe-Coburg and Gotha, and when the princes were sent to the University of Bonn in the following year, QUETE-LET continued his teaching in the form of letters dealing with the theory of probability and its social applications. One of these princes became the husband of Queen VICTORIA. The letters were published in French in 1846 and in English translation in 1849.[2] A young man who read them in English, FRANCIS GALTON (1822-1911), was deeply impressed and the directions of his thought were modified accordingly.[3]

I have told this episode at some length, because it deserves to be meditated. Though QUETELET found many collaborators and emulators and the efforts of other sociologists converged with his, the results which have been obtained down to our days fall considerably short of our hopes and aspirations. It is true that some diseases, personal or social, have been cured or alleviated by the use of scientific knowledge and technical means combined with sincerity and moral courage; it will suffice to quote venereal diseases, the abuse of intoxicants and narcotics, tuberculosis, slavery . . . Victories have been won but so much remains to be done, which could have been done, that honest men of science feel humbler and more contrite than ever. There are still millions of men and women who are the victims of our greed and hypocrisy rather than of their own shortcomings.

We should not be disheartened, however. It is not quite fair to compare the present situation with that of our dreams which may be realized (or not) at some future time; or at least we should compare it also with

---

[1] The Paris edition of 1835, was followed by a pirated one (Bruxelles 1836), and by German and English translations (Stuttgart 1838, Edinburgh 1842). In the new edition published in Bruxelles, Paris, Saint-Pétersbourg in 1869, the title was modified, the challenging words "Physique sociale" being printed in large type at the beginning of it. Facsimiles and additional information in the Preface to Volume XXIII of Isis (1935).

[2] Lettres sur la théorie des probabilités appliquée aux sciences morales et politiques (Bruxelles 1846), dedicated to ERNEST who had become in the meanwhile the reigning duke of Coburg.

HARRIET H. SHOEN: Prince ALBERT and the application of statistics to problems of government (Osiris 5, 276-318, 1938).

[3] Later in life GALTON tended to minimize QUETELET's influence upon him. He was struck by the fact that QUETELET's promises of 1835 did not bear as much fruit as one might expect, but honestly recognized the immense difficulties involved. See a letter of his to FLORENCE NIGHTINGALE, dated 1891. KARL PEARSON: Life, letters and labours of FRANCIS GALTON (vol. 2, 420, 12, Cambridge 1924; Isis 8, 181-88; 22, 253-55).

past situations. The application of scientific methods and points of view is still enormously short of what it might be, yet thanks to QUETELET and many others so much has already been accomplished that the political world in which we are living to-day is as profoundly different from the political world of the eighteenth century, as the material equipment of today is different from that of the earlier one. By the way, this offers another justification for historical research. In order to go forward, we must look not only forward, but also backward. The backward view gives us confidence and helps us to straighten our course. Every man of science knows deep in his heart (and the history of the past is there to confirm his knowledge) that diseases, superstitions, undeserved privileges can only thrive in darkness and ignorance. In order to eradicate them it is necessary to project enough light upon them, but that is not enough. Knowledge remains insufficient and sterile if it be not implemented by corrective deeds and those deeds require an abundance of good will, generosity and tenacity.

* * * * *

Turning our attention now to another aspect of the matter, I would like to point out that in spite of the revolutionary nature of science, or rather because of it, if we wish to live good and noble lives, we should never break with the past. The traditions of evil must be stopped of course, but many of our traditions are not evil; they are good, they are what is best in us, the accumulated goodness of centuries. Having done what we could to destroy the evil traditions we must make certain that the other traditions, the good ones, the noble ones, be safeguarded and strengthened. That is far from easy but it must be done. I felt so deeply the need of it some thirty-five years ago that I dedicated my life to that purpose.

Why is it so difficult? Simply because the very progress of science has driven the majority of men of science further and further away from their inner citadel, from their city of God, into investigations of greater speciality and technicality, of increasing depth and decreasing field. A good many of our men of science are not men of science any more in the broad sense, but technicians and engineers, or else administrators and manipulators, go-getters and money-makers. Those men look forward in their own narrow sector; they will not look backward. What is the good of that?, they would say. The past is past and dead. Those hard-boiled technicians would fain reject the whole past as "irrelevant." And if we make the honest attempt to look at the past with their eyes we must admit that they are right, or at least that they have a right to their opinion; that it is not irrational and arbitrary. Looking backward would hardly have helped the STEPHENSONS, the EDISONS, the MARCONIS to solve their particular problems, and to solve them as brilliantly as they did. They were definitely breaking with the past, turning their back to it and welcoming with open arms a future as glamorous as the rising sun. The reading of history could not recommend itself to them except as a diversion, and they perhaps knew simpler ways of relaxing their minds. When a tough technician tells us that he does not care for history, that it is all "bunk"—there is really nothing that we can answer him. It is as if a deaf man told us that he had no concern with music. Why should he concern himself with it? And why should the technician bother about history if his mind and heart are closed to it?

The technician may be so deeply immersed in his problems that the rest of the world loses reality in his eyes and that his human interests may wither and die. There may then develop in him a new kind of radicalism, quiet and cold, but frightening. PLATO wished that the world were guided by philosophers, we often wish that it were guided by wise men of science, but God save us from technocrats![4] If unchecked and unbalanced by humanities, technical radicalism would undermine civilization—whatever there was left of it—and turn it against itself. In order to show that I am not exaggerating I invite you to contemplate for a moment the terrifying example (and warning) which some German technicians have given us during the war.

Many of us have asked ourselves with anxiety, "How is it that the spirit of science, so highly honored in Germany, did not protect that country from the Nazi aberration and its inhuman consequences?" You might even say to me, "You spoke so warmly of the love of truth and the new world which it opens, a world of higher morality and brotherhood. That spirit of truth-seeking and truth-loving was abroad in Germany and stronger there perhaps than anywhere else. And yet what did it lead to?" How did Germany succumb to Nazism, how did its proud scientists and professors abandon so readily their own lofty ideals to accept those of an ignorant mahdi? It is certain that the latter could have done nothing without the explicit or implicit confidence and complicity of the German elite. How could he secure that complicity? Its reality has been established beyond the possibility of doubt and its mechanism carefully analyzed by Dr. WEINREICH, who concluded: "Many fields of learning, different ones at different times according to the shrewdly appraised needs of Nazi policies, were drawn into the work for more than a decade; physical anthropology and biology, all branches of the social sciences and the humanities—until the engineers moved in to build the gas chambers and crematories."[5]

---

[4] "Technocracy" is a movement which achieved a flare of popularity in the United States some fifteen years ago. It is defined as "government or management of the whole of society by technical experts, or in accordance with principles established by technicians" (Webster Dictionary). The main apostle of it was the physical metallurgist, HOWARD SCOTT; see his Introduction to technocracy which began to appear in 1933. (Fourth printing, 53 p., New York 1940). I do not know whether that movement caused as many ripples on the surface of English opinion as it did on that of American opinion. At any rate, it did not last very long, even in the United States, but the commotion left mental scars. The "technocrats" were obviously right on many technical matters, but the happiness of individuals and societies depends very largely on matters which are not amenable to technical treatment. The very best of life cannot be "processed" in that way. Mr. SCOTT is still alive and full of propaganda (The New Yorker, June 14, 1947, p. 18).

[5] MAX WEINREICH: HITLER'S professors (291 p., New York, Yivo, 1946, p. 7; Isis 37, 240).

The question remains and we ask it with more anxiety than ever. "How could such a complete perversion of humanity happen in one of the most enlightened countries in the most enlightened age?" I have thought long and often on that question and my answer is—I hope it will not shock you too much—that the German scientists and engineers were partly the victims of their "technical" infatuation. They were "technocrats" with a vengeance, and one can see how some of Mr. HIT- LER's problems may have excited their technical minds. Absolutely new problems, such as this one "What is the simplest and cheapest way of destroying human beings, not individually, nor by the hundred, nor by the thousands, but by the millions?" The problem included enough difficulties, with no precedents for guidance, to challenge the ingenuity of the most resourceful technicians. For example, how could one sal- vage precious metals? The managers of ordinary slaughterhouses need not worry about that because cattle, hogs and sheep do not have gold teeth. One of the main difficulties was to establish the human slaughter- houses and make their functioning possible without causing too much curiosity and without discommoding and infuriating the neighborhood. (For after all the majority of Germans were not mad technicians, and we may assume that they were not more cruel than the rest of us; more- over, even ogres would dislike the smell of slaughterhouses.) German technicians solved that problem and gave the means of destroying ruth- lessly and unobtrusively millions of innocent people. Their technical concentration and the benumbedness and insensibility which proceeded from it were carried to such a point that their minds were closed to hu- manity and their hearts dulled to mercy.[6]

I beg to apologize for awakening memories, which are perhaps the most gruesome in the whole history of mankind. I would prefer to drive them out of my mind, or rather out of reality but that cannot be done. I feel we should try to forgive them if possible, but it is not desir- able that they be forgotten. The past is not dead, it never dies; the things that were ever done were done forever, nobody, not even God, could undo them. I spoke of those unspeakable atrocities, because they afford the most telling example of the inhumanity which can be created or at least condoned by the kind of technicians who do not look back- ward, who do not care for history (they call it "irrelevant") and can no longer be restrained by political or religious traditions.

---

[6] The reader might stop me here and say "What about the atomic bomb?" The atomic bomb is an instrument of warfare, the latest and deadliest weapon invented by men. In a sense war is criminal; it is the greatest moral bankruptcy, yet when we are involved in it, there are no alternatives but to beat the adversary or be beaten. There is an immense difference between killing men in warfare and mur- dering them as a civilian policy. The Nazi slaughterhouses were not instruments of war, but instruments of civilian destruction. The fact remains that we have many "technocrats" in our midst, an increasing number of technocratic brutes, with- out sensibility and without imagination, who do not hesitate to make drastic deci- sions on the grounds of technical efficiency alone without any regard for the feel- ings of the individuals involved.

The French mathematician, HENRI POINCARÉ, once remarked, "I do not say, Science is useful because it helps us to build better machines; I say, Machines are useful because as they work for us they will leave us someday more time for scientific research." Unfortunately, these hopes of his have not yet materialized; the machines have perhaps enslaved more men than they have freed. This suggests another score against Science; many who greeted her with blessings dismissed her with curses. It would seem easy to ward off those maledictions. It suffices to distinguish between men of science and even technicians on one side, and business men, industrialists, men of prey on the other. The inventors cannot be held responsible; they themselves would protest, for the criminal abuses which have been made of their inventions. This type of controversy has reached a dramatic climax recently apropos of the atomic bomb; if the latter were used for the destruction of mankind should we condemn or exonerate the physicists and chemists who brought it into being?

That question is too difficult to be solved here. Instead of that let us see what could and should be done to vindicate the spirit of science, to purify it, and to make sure—or bring nearer—its redemption and ours.

We have recalled at the beginning of this lecture that science is the most powerful agency of change not only in the material world but also in the spiritual one; so powerful indeed that it is revolutionary. Our *Weltanschauung* changes as our knowledge of the world and of ourselves deepens. The horizon is vaster as we go higher. This is undoubtedly the most significant kind of change occurring in the experience of mankind; the history of civilization should be focussed upon it.

At any rate, that is what I have been repeating *ad nauseam* for the last thirty years. May I confess, that without having lost any part of my zeal, I am not as full of confidence today as I was before; I have never been very dogmatic (and therefore am a very poor propagandist), but I am less dogmatic now than I ever was. There are other approaches to the past than mine; there may be better ways (at least for other people) of describing the creativeness of the past and of appreciating our heritage from it—such as the history of religions, the history of arts and crafts, the history of philosophy, the history of education, the history of laws and institutions. Each of those histories is an avenue of approach. Which is the best? And for whom? The history of science has, it is true, a kind of strategic superiority; scientific discoveries are objective to a degree unknown and even inconceivable in other fields; as they are largely independent of racial and national conditions, they are the main instruments of unity and peace; these discoveries are cumulative to such an extent that each scientist can so-to-say begin his task where his predecessors left off (artists and religious men must always begin *da capo* and their labors are Sisyphean); it is only from the point of view of its scientific activities that the comparison of mankind with a single man, growing steadily in experience, is legitimate, and this evidences once more and more emphatically than anything else the unity of mankind; it is only in the field of science that a definite and continuous progress is tangible and indisputable; we can hardly speak of progress in the other fields of human endeavor.

These arguments are plausible and convincing, but I am not naïve enough to believe that their power of conviction is transferable to other people. They convince me, because I know science and love it, but how could they convince other people who do not know it and shrink from it, now perhaps more than ever. They might taunt me and say, "Progress leading to the atomic bomb, what kind of progress is that?" For a man more intensely religious than I am, the history of religion would naturally seem more important than the history of science, and to an artist loving beauty above aught else, would not the history of art be far more interesting than the history of religion or the history of science? Indeed, those other histories would hardly have a meaning for him and he would have little patience with them.

The history of science is not simply what the title implies, a history of our increasing knowledge of the world and of ourselves; it is a story not only of the spreading light but also of the contracting darkness. It might be conceived as a history of the endless struggle against errors, innocent or wilful, against superstitions and spiritual crimes. It is also the history of growing tolerance and freedom of thought. The historian of science must give an example of toleration in admitting the equal claims to other minds than his of the history of art or the history of religion; he should even be ready to admit the anti-historical attitude of the tough-minded technicians.

It is nevertheless his duty as well as his pleasure to explain as well as he can the civilizing and liberating power of science, the humanities of science. He must vindicate science from the crimes which have been committed in its name or under its cloak; he must commemorate the great men of the past especially those which have been deprived of their meed; he must justify the man of science in comparison with the saint, the philosopher, the artist or the statesman. Each of these is playing his part, and it would be foolish to insist that this part or that is more important than the others, for all are necessary and none is sufficient.

❋   ❋   ❋   ❋   ❋

Inasmuch as the development of science is the only development in human experience which is truly cumulative and progressive, tradition acquires a very different meaning in the field of science than in any other. Far from there being any conflict between science and tradition, one might claim that tradition is the very life of science.[7] The tradition

---

[7] This has been beautifully explained by HERBERT DINGLE in his inaugural lecture: "The history of science is inseparable from science itself. Science is essentially a process, stretching through time, in contrast with the instantaneous or eternal character of traditional philosophy. In the first half of the eighteenth century BRADLEY records the positions of a number of stars. In 1818 his reductions are revised by BESSEL, and in 1886 again revised by AUWERS. New observations are made and the results compared, and after 200 years we learn that certain stars have moved in certain directions by a few seconds of arc. Out of such sublime patience scientific knowledge emerges. Science may ignore its history, but if so it

of science is the most rational or the least irrational of all traditions. The gradual unveiling of the truth is the noblest tradition of mankind as well as the clearest, the only one wherein there is nothing to be ashamed of. The humanized man of science, he whom I have called the New Humanist, is of all men the one who is most conscious of his traditions and of the traditions of mankind.

This is true from the humanistic point of view, but it is also true from the purely scientific or philosophic one. For the inveterate and narrow-minded technician the only things worth considering are the latest fruits of science; the tree is "irrelevant." For the philosophically minded scientist, however precious the fruits, the tree itself is infinitely more precious. It is not the results of today that matter most in his eyes, but the curves leading to them and beyond them. For practical, immediate purposes the last points or knots, the last discoveries, may be sufficient; for true understanding the whole curves must be taken into account. This is even more obvious to the historically minded scientist who realizes more keenly the probable imperfection of the latest results and is not so easily taken in by the latest fashion; the immature technician is likely to fancy that he is sitting at the top of the world; he does not know that later technicians will deride him as heartily as he derides his own predecessors. From his parochial angle, the latest results are exceptionally wonderful; from the point of view of eternity they are just points on infinite curves. Men of science (excepting perhaps the astrophysicists) do not indulge in extrapolations, but they know that the curves have reached neither their climax, nor their end; they know that the curves will be continued, though they would be chary of prophesying their direction.

When we contemplate the universe we may adopt one of two points of view—horizontal or vertical, geographical or historical; we may contemplate the side-by-sidedness of things or their one-after-anotherness. It would be misleading to say that the second point of view is exclusive to the historian, and the first to the naturalist. Both assertions would be wrong. In reality, both points of view are necessary and complementary. We need geography and history; we need natural history as well as physical geography and human history as well as human geography.

This remark applies also to science itself. Science is not simply the top of the tree; it is the whole tree growing upward, downward and in every direction; the living tree, alive not only in its periphery but in its whole being. The historian of science appreciates as keenly as other scientists the "marvels" of modern science, but he is more deeply im-

---

fails." And a little further he remarks, "The history of philosophy, in the narrower sense of the word, is the history of philosophy, but the history of science is science. Scientific workers may forget this, and, knowing little or nothing of the ground on which their edifice rests, may add to its structure and reach positions of the highest eminence in their profession, but they are not then educated men. To the true scientist they are as the artificer to the artist, the sleep-walker to the explorer, the instinctive cry to the pregnant phrase. Such a one may achieve much of value, but he is also a potential danger. At the moment he happens to be a profoundly disquieting menace to our civilization" (p. 3-4, London, Lewis, 1947).

pressed by their genesis than by their occurrence. He admires the wonders of science, but the greatest wonder of all, he reflects, is that man revealed them. The infinity of stellar space and the inverse infinity of atomic structure are awe-inspiring, yet less so, than their gradual penetration by the mind of man.

* * * * *

Many men of science have reached a peculiar mid-way stage. They recognize the value (philosophic, scientific, humanistic) of the history of science, but lacking historical training they do not understand the implications. Let me tell you an anecdote first. A very distinguished physicist once told me that physics had become a field of such large size that no man could encompass the whole of it, while history was easy enough to read up. His remark proved that he was more familiar with physics than with history. Both domains being infinite it is foolish to say that one is larger than the other. It is certainly easier to read a book of history than a book of physics; the superficial difference may be enormous, for there is no historical book which would be entirely closed to an educated man, while many a physical book would be as dark to the uninitiated as if it were written in Chinese. The real difference, however, between both cases grows smaller, much smaller, as one's familiarity with them increases. It will be found that the reader will obtain from either book as much knowledge—living, integrated knowledge—as his previous experience justifies, not more. His ability to judge either book will be a function of his knowledge of either subject and of his study of many other books covering more or less the same field.

Reading is but the first stage, the passive stage, of education. If one wishes not simply to study the knowledge obtained by others, but also to extend that knowledge, strict methods must be used. The methods of physical science are pretty well known, the methods of historical research are less well known (at least by men of science); they are not so easy to define and their application is made especially difficult by their subtlety and by the circumstance that human facts are infinitely more complex than physical ones. In both fields the specific methods applying to them must be abided by and the materials used must be sound (it is a part of the method to determine their soundness). Here again beginners (and most scientists who become interested in the history of science are beginners) may have, and generally do have, illusions. They known well enough the difficulties of their own field, but as they ignore or underestimate historical difficulties, they rush in where angels fear to tread; they seem to fancy that historical work is comparable only to the final stage of scientific work, the writing up of the results! They accept uncritically statements published almost anywhere and mix them together. As a wit put it, "When five books have been devoted to a subject, it is easy enough to write a sixth one." True enough, but what is the value of that sixth book? However small the time of writing it, it was a waste of time. We must admit that books produced in that easy way contain much truth, but as the truth is promiscuously mixed with error and not differentiable from it, the whole must be considered erroneous. Historical works written by men of science disregarding historical methods must necessarily lead to a degradation of spiritual energy.[8]

It is curious that most men of science would recognize the difficulties of historical work in other fields than the history of science, say, in the fields of Greek history, or mediaeval history, or even English history. If they be well educated we may assume that they have a good all-around knowledge of the history of their own country, and they may have read considerably on that subject throughout the years, yet they would be the first to disclaim any authority, and they would never venture to publish a book on it. The same modest men might consider themselves fully equipped to teach the history of science, though without any suitable preparation. What is the explanation of that paradox? Simply this that for teaching the history of science the first condition is to know science, to have a first-hand knowledge of it; that condition is so hard to satisfy, in fact, unattainable for anyone who has not received in his youth a scientific training of some kind or another, that it may be thought to be sufficient. It is necessary but not sufficient.

As the importance of the history of science is more generally recognized not only by men of science, but by educated people in general and by "educators"[9] there is an increasing need of trained historians of science. AUGUSTE COMTE had understood that need more than a century ago when he observed that as science is becoming more specialized, there must needs be one more specialty, the study of the generalities of science, the interrelations of its parts, and its wholeness. This new kind of specialist must be a historian of science, for knowledge of the tree of science (which is the very knowledge required) is almost impossible to obtain without knowledge of its genesis and development.

We may thus, or rather we should, intrust that task of unification and communication to the historian of science, but the latter will have other duties, which may be summed up with the words, he shall be the keeper of scientific memories and the defender of tradition.

We shall come back to that presently but first let us remark, that the work of the historian of science is often misunderstood and even resented by the very scientists who need it most, that is, those who are at the same time the most specialized and least educated. Those extreme specialists, who know everything about a tiny little subject and nothing about the rest of the universe, do not like what they might call the Olympian attitude of philosophers and historians. Of course, it cannot be denied that the latter may be sometimes a bit complacent and offen-

---

[8] Non-historians may do occasionally useful work in quoting a definite statement from a good source or a good book, correctly referred to. To know the best source or the best book on a topic is almost as good as to know that topic. Such bibliographical information is not easy to obtain for a great variety of topics and is exceedingly complex; the mastery of it in a large field may require a whole life of study and meditation.

[9] In the United States the title "educator" is assumed not so much by teachers and writers, but rather by administrators, such as presidents and deans of colleges, trustees, directors of educational conferences and projects, etc.

sive, witness WHEWELL of whom it was said that science was his forte, and omniscience his foible.   They should bear in mind, and the historian of science himself should never forget it, that he is simply a specialist like the others, having a special knowledge and special duties and using special methods.   He may be good or not so good, and may have all kinds of virtues and vices like other people, but that is another question. Other scientists must have the grace to admit on their side that investigations which have occupied their whole life and may have entailed numberless sacrifices, may be understood in a relatively short time, and that it may be possible for the historian to explain and discuss them without taking anything away from their merit, but rather the contrary. The historian should not take a superior or dominating attitude and other scientists should not be unduly jealous of him, nor contemptuous. He is a fellow like themselves who may be more or less successful in discovering new things; if he be honest and modest he deserves their respect even when he is out of luck.

The conflict between scientist and historian of science is only one example of the temperamental opposition between creator and critic. That conflict is far better known in other fields such as literature and art.   The artist resents the critic and historian yet he needs them more deeply than he realizes, the public needs them, and the art itself cannot grow without them.[10]   It is very significant but not surprising, that histories of art or of music the writing of which was attempted by great artists have generally been mediocre.   The qualities required for creation and for criticism are not only different but opposite, even mutually exclusive.   This is as true in science as it is in art.

* * * * *

The main duty of the historian of science is the defense of tradition. The traditions of science are not essentially different as traditions, from traditions in other fields, even if we may perhaps flatter ourselves that they are generally better and purer.   These traditions deserve to be known and religiously kept because they are really the best we have; they are all that makes life worth living, they are the nobility and the goodness of life.   Without them we are like animals and without them all the technicians and the "wizards" of the world could not lift us from the mud of our material desires.   We owe gratitude to the benefactors of the past, in particular the great men of science who opened the new paths, and also the lesser men who helped them, for we are standing on their shoulders.   While we express our gratitude we feel that we become worthy of them, worthy to grasp with our own hands the torches which they have brought to us.   We are encouraged to continue their task,

---

[10] Professor DINGLE's lecture, referred to in another footnote, above, was given by him the challenging title "The missing factor in science."   What is the missing factor?   According to him, it is the internal criticism of science, a criticism largely based upon historical knowledge, and without which scientific growth may become stupid and dangerous.   There can be no real understanding of science, that is, there can be no science, without continuous criticism of it.

the main task of mankind, and we know that the work which we are all doing together will not be destroyed by wars and other calamities, and will not be interrupted by the accident of our own death. This revives our faith and joy in our work.

❖   ❖   ❖   ❖   ❖

The fundamental importance of science in human life need not be emphasized; that importance will necessarily increase and therefore the relative importance of science in education will also increase. That is unavoidable and no sensible and rational person would try to deflect the trajectory of man's destiny, the irresistible growth of knowledge, of science, yea, of techniques. Yet such a growth is not without dangers, and it is part of our duty to minimize those dangers and to strengthen our resistance to them.

The Good Society, of which we are dreaming and which each of us is trying in his own feeble way to encompass, will need the constant help of two kinds of servants, the Statistician and the Historian. We have already spoken of the former when we referred to QUETELET. It is his business to keep his finger on the pulse of mankind and give the necessary warnings when things are not going as they should. QUETELET's message was delivered more than a century ago and was long misinterpreted, except by a few people. It is proper to evoke here one of the earliest acceptances of that message, by a great English woman, FLORENCE NIGHTINGALE,

"Her statistics were more than a study, they were indeed her religion. For her, QUETELET was the hero as scientist, and the presentation copy of his *Physique sociale* is annotated by her on every page. FLORENCE NIGHTINGALE believed—and in all the actions of her life acted upon that belief—that the administrator could only be successful if he were guided by statistical knowledge. The legislator—to say nothing of the politician—too often failed for want of this knowledge. Nay, she went further: she held that the universe—including human communities—was evolving in accordance with a divine plan; that it was man's business to endeavour to understand this plan and guide his actions in sympathy with it. But to understand God's thoughts, she held we must study statistics, for these are the measure of his purpose. Thus the study of statistics was for her a religious duty." [11]

Since those days the function of the statistician are better understood, but he has not yet received his full responsibilities. As to the historian, I believe that most educated people understand the need of him for political purposes, but not yet for the higher purposes which I have tried to outline in this lecture—to wit, the deeper interpretation of science, the defense of scientific tradition, the reconciliation of science with the humanities, or as you may prefer to call it, the humanization of science, the consecration of science to the Good Life.

---

[11] KARL PEARSON: The life, letters and labours of FRANCIS GALTON (vol. 2, 414, 1924; Isis, 8, 186; 23, 8).

II. THE TRADITION OF ANCIENT AND MEDIAEVAL SCIENCE

When men of science become interested in the history of science, their interest is generally focussed upon the immediate past, or what we might call "modern" science—however this may be defined. They may choose to begin it with the western reinvention of typography (c. 1450), or with COPERNICUS or VESALIUS (1543), or with KEPLER (1609-19) and GALILEO (1632-38), or with NEWTON (1687), or with VOLTA (1800), or with the introduction of astrophysics, or radioactivity, or later still. Each of these limits can be justified, and one is as good as another. Almost every man of science, whether he be historically minded or not, is obliged to do a certain amount of retrospection, because his own investigations bring him face to face with the work of some predecessor, or because of academic conventions. The historical difficulties of such superficial retrospect are not great, the sources are easily obtainable, the chronological basis is relatively easy to establish. The fundamental questions "When did that happen? where?" are easy to answer. The questions "why?" and "how?" are more difficult of course, yet they are still comparatively easy for late periods. Men of science whose retrospective insight does not go much deeper than the last century have few chronological troubles to speak of [1] and no idea of the vicissitudes of tradition. Consider OERSTED's famous paper of 1820 which is the foundation of electromagnetism; originally written in Latin, it was promptly translated into French, Italian, German, English, and Danish, and within a year every physicist of Europe knew of it and some had already developed new experiments on its basis.[2] Or consider ROENTGEN's paper of 1896 [3] which might well be taken as the opening of the new physics. The message which it contains was almost immediately broadcast all over the civilized world; the necessary apparatus being available in almost every physical laboratory, and the experiments being simple enough they were promptly repeated in a hundred places; more than a thousand books and papers on X-rays were published within the year of their discovery.[4] By the end of that year 1896, a physicist admitting

---

[1] Chronological difficulties are not completely eliminated. For example, see my paper "The discovery of conical refraction by WILLIAM ROWAN HAMILTON and HUMPHREY LLOYD in 1833" (Isis 17, 154-70, 1932).

[2] Facsimile reprints of the original Latin text and of the English translation (Isis, 10, 435-43, 1928).

[3] The redaction of it was completed on Dec. 28, 1895, and it was immediately printed, but it could hardly be distributed before 1896. See facsimile and SARTON's analysis (Isis, 26, 349-69, 1937). E. WEIL (Isis, 29, 362-65, 1938).

[4] List of those 1044 books and papers in OTTO GLASSER: ROENTGEN (p. 422-79, Springfield, Illinois, 1934; Isis, 22, 256-59).

ignorance of those rays would have branded himself as an ass. In our day it is almost impossible for a man who reads but a few journals, to escape the knowledge of a new discovery. The problem of tradition does hardly exist; the transmission of knowledge from one end of the world to the other is almost automatic. Hence the historian of science who restricts himself to "modern" science does not think of tradition, he takes it for granted.[5] Reciprocally, in order to understand the true meaning of scientific tradition and its value one has to look backward more deeply, and this we shall now proceed to do.

Think of Greek science of the sixth and fifth centuries, what we might perhaps call the "Greek miracle," as do people who have HOMER, SOPHOCLES or PHIDIAS in mind. The early blossoming of Greek science is just as miraculous (*i.e.*, as little explainable) as that of Greek art or Greek literature. (Is not each masterpiece a miracle?, you might say. Yes, but that is another story.) For Greek science the difficulty of explanation or the "miracle" if you prefer to use that word, is of a double nature. There is the miracle of creation and the miracle of transmission. We know, of course, that a substantial amount of Greek science is lost, probably forever; the astonishing thing, however, is not that much has been lost, but rather that so much has escaped the vicissitudes of time and reached our very hands.

Take the case of ARCHIMEDES, who was killed at the age of 75 during the siege of Syracuse by the Romans in 212 B.C. Thus his works were written during the period c. 257 (aet. 30) to 212. He was already famous in antiquity, but the earliest commentaries on his works known to us are those of the Palestinian mathematician, EUTOCIOS OF ASCALON (VI-1) and these are restricted to three treatises (the sphere and the cylinder, measurement of the circle, equilibrium of planes). The oldest Greek MS. to which definite reference is made was written during the Byzantine renaissance of the ninth to the tenth century, initiated by LEON OF THESSALONICA (IX-1), probably at the beginning of that period. That MS. contained only seven treatises (the three already mentioned, conoids and spheroids, spirals, sand-reckoner, quadrature of the parabola); it is lost, but the earliest Greek MSS. extant are copies of it made toward the end of the fifteenth century and the beginning of the sixteenth. Another copy of the lost archetype found its way to Baghdād, for we have Arabic translations and commentaries by AL-MĀHĀNĪ, THĀBIT IBN QURRA, YŪSUF AL-KHŪRĪ, ISḤĀQ IBN ḤUNAIN, all of whom flourished in the second half of the ninth century. Another Archimedian treatise, the one on floating bodies in two books, not included in the MS. tradition just referred to, was translated into Latin by the Flemish Dominican, WILLEM OF MOERBEKE, in 1269. His translation of book 1 appeared in

---

[5] His difficulty is rather to account for exceptional failures of transmission. *E.g.*, the "Edison effect" discovered in 1884 which remained unnoticed for many years until it was exploited by JOHN AMBROSE FLEMING (1905) and by LEE DE FOREST in wireless telegraphy.

the Latin edition of TARTAGLIA[6] (Venice 1543)—the first printed ARCHI-
MEDES in any language—; his translation of both books was printed by
TROIANUS CURTIUS (Venice 1565) and by FEDERICO COMMANDINO (Bologna 1565). The Greek text of the "floating bodies" was lost until 1906.
In that year the Danish philologist, J. L. HEIBERG, discovered it in a
Constantinople palimpsest below a twelfth to fourteenth century euchologion.[7] The same palimpsest concealed other Archimedian texts, the
most precious of all being the Method (ἐφόδιον), the existence of which
was known only through a remark of SUIDAS (X-2).[8] That method is
one of the most important books of antiquity. We have it!, but remember that it was preserved only in the most erratic way—as a palimpsest
—, that is, it was preserved in spite of its being deliberately cancelled,
and that its recovery happened only within our own lifetime, in 1906.
An Archimedian monograph on the regular heptagon was preserved in
the Arabic translation of Thābit ibn Qurra (IX-2) and this was discovered in a Cairo MS. and published in 1926 by CARL SCHOY.[9]

In other words, lost treatises of ARCHIMEDES were revealed only in
1906 and 1926. It is possible that other lost treatises may still be discovered, chiefly in the second manner. The Greek palimpsests have
been pretty well examined and there is little hope of repeating HEIBERG'S
stroke of genius and luck, but there is much hope on the contrary of finding Arabic translations of lost Greek scientific books, because many Arabic libraries are still unexplored and many Arabic MSS, undescribed.
Some of the classics of Greek science have been revealed in that way,
notably books V to VII of APOLLONIOS' Conics and various treatises of
GALEN.[10]

---

[6] The Latin tradition of some other Archimedian treatises was different. NICHO-
LAS V (pope from 1447 to 1455), one of the early patrons of humanism, founder
of the Vatican Library, caused an Archimedian MS. to be translated into Latin by
one JACOPO DA S. CASSIANO of Cremona. A copy of that translation was made c.
1461 by REGIOMONTANUS, who added marginal glosses derived from Greek MSS.
REGIOMONTANUS' copy, preserved in Nuremberg, was the source of the Latin version
added to the Greek princeps by THOMAS GECHAUFF (Basel 1544).

[7] A palimpsest is a "rewritten" MS., the first writing having been erased to make
room for the new one. An euchologion is a book of the Orthodox Church containing liturgies, etc. As writing materials (parchment or paper) were expensive
and difficult to obtain, monks would rub off texts of no interest to them to replace
them by the texts which they needed. We would do the same under similar circumstances. Chemical and optical means make it possible to read the erased text.

[8] SUIDAS remarked that THEODOSIOS OF BITHYNIA (I-1 B.C.) wrote a commentary
on the Method. Three propositions are quoted from it in the *Metrica* of HERON
OF ALEXANDRIA, but the *Metrica* itself was discovered only in 1896, in a Constantinople MS., by R. SCHÖNE; it was first published in 1903 by the discoverer's son,
HERMANN SCHÖNE.

[9] CARL SCHOY: Graeco-Arabische Studien (Isis, 8, 21-40, 1926).

[10] The Arabic translation of books V to VII of the Conics by THĀBIT IBN QURRA
(IX-2) was revised by ABŪ'L-FATḤ MAḤMŪD IBN MUḤAMMAD AL-IṢFAHĀNĪ (X-2);
it was first published in Latin version by ABRAHAM ECCHELLENSIS and GIACOMO
ALFONSO BORELLI (Florence 1661), then again in EDMUND HALLEY'S monumental
edition of Apollonios (Oxford 1710). The seven books of GALEN's anatomy were

My account of the Archimedian tradition is incomplete[11] but sufficient to illustrate many features, the various contingencies, riskiness and
at best the complexity of such traditions.   A Greek text is known to us
by a MS. preserving it, or by extracts from it or references to it by later
writers; or by Arabic, Hebrew or Latin versions, commentaries, extracts;
or by references in each (or all) of these languages.   The paradoxical
aspects of tradition are evidenced by the fact that the study of Arabic is
now, all considered, the most promising method to increase our knowledge of Greek science!

*   *   *   *   *

Thoughtful readers may well ask themselves two questions: (1) If
the tradition is so full of risks and adventures, how were any texts preserved, especially mathematical texts which could never interest more
than a few people?   (2) Considering those risks and vicissitudes, how
can we be sure that the texts which have survived are really what they
are claimed to be?

The two questions are pertinent and sufficiently ticklish to be stimulating.   If one bears in mind the number of wars, conflagrations and
other calamities which have occurred in the Mediterranean world since
ARCHIMEDES' death, how did any one of his writings escape destruction
and oblivion?   When ARCHIMEDES composed one of them, say the *Ephodion* or the *Ochumena,* the number of students directly interested in it
must have been exceedingly small and that number remained small
throughout the ages.   It is unlikely that the "first edition" issued by the
Master himself included many copies.   Perhaps a dozen or even less.
Some of those copies found their way to the libraries of Alexandria and
Pergamon, but those libraries were destroyed.   We have relearned quite
recently that the safest libraries are not absolutely safe, and the greater
they are, the greater the loss in case of destruction.   Other copies were
preserved in private libraries, *e.g.,* in the libraries of ARCHIMEDES himself,
of the king of Syracuse HIERON and his son GELON, of ARCHIMEDES'
friends, DOSITHEOS OF PELUSION, CONON OF SAMOS and ERATOSTHENES
OF CYRENE (III-2 B.C.), but how insecure they were!   Did a copy preserved by the tyrant of Syracuse have a great chance of survival?   And
as to ARCHIMEDES himself and his friends, these men were probably poor,
they were certainly not rich, but even if they had been rich enough to
live in palaces, what of it?   Are any of the private palaces of antiquity
extant?   Have their contents come down to us?   How then did the

edited in Arabic and German by MAX SIMON (2 vols. Leipzig 1906).   GALEN on
medical experience was first published in Arabic and English by RICHARD WALZER
(London 1944; Isis, 36, 251-55).

[11] Complete accounts of the tradition of a text are generally given by the modern editors.   Such accounts include a discussion of the relative trust which may be
placed in each MS. of the original text or of its translations, and in the early editions.   The filiation of those MSS is symbolized by a genealogical tree or stemma.
For ARCHIMEDES *see* HEIBERG's edition (2nd ed., 3 vols. Leipzig 1910-15) or the
English translation by T. L. HEATH (Cambridge 1897), with supplement (Cambridge 1912).

Ephodion finally reach us in 1906 after two millennia of hiding? Its survival is almost miraculous, and yet it is not as rare an event as one might think. Though a large part of the Greek scientific literature is lost, what remains constitutes an imposing treasure. How did all those books, none of them popular in any degree, none of them ever "published"[12] in large editions, survive? The only explanation I can think of is this. Though very few people could be directly interested in ARCHI-MEDES' treatises (to return to the example which was our starting point), a great many men, whether educated or not, were concerned with them. These men—and maybe women also—realized that such MSS were precious and deserved every care. They had a kind of superstitious respect for every kind of writing[13] and for such esoteric writing in particular. We should not deride the superstitions of those ignorant people, in the first place because we are benefiting from them, in the second place because similar superstitions are abroad among ourselves to this day. It is a very strange compensation indeed; in proportion as religious superstitions decrease, the superstitions of science (or pseudo-science) seem to increase; advertisers, who trade on men's gullibility, know that well enough.[14] Are men unable to live without superstitions? At any rate, the Greek MSS, even the least comprehensible, those of which the average person could make no use whatsoever, were jealously kept and transmitted from generation to generation, from owner to robber or looter, from looter to new owner, and so on. From time to time they fell into the hands of people who were sufficiently appreciative and enthusiastic to prepare new copies or new editions, or commentaries, translations, commentaries on those translations, amplifications, abbreviations, paraphases, supercommentaries, etc. The Archimedian MSS which have finally reached us have not escaped one catastrophe, but many.

Indeed, the risks have been so numerous that the second question comes naturally enough to our minds. How can we be sure that the treatise on floating bodies which we may read to-day either in the Greek edition of HEIBERG or in the English version of Sir THOMAS HEATH, is really the text of ARCHIMEDES? In this particular case our doubts are excited by a remark of EUTOCIOS to the effect that ARCHIMEDES wrote in the Doric dialect, of which but few traces remain in the Greek text available to-day.[15] EUTOCIOS (who flourished nine centuries after ARCHI-

---

[12] We can speak of the "publication" of books before the age of printing, and even before the age of writing. It occurs when a finished text is made available for reading or recitation and is thus transmitted to the public, "published." SOLOMON GANDZ: The dawn of literature (Osiris 7, 261-522, 1939).

[13] That kind of superstition can still be observed (or could be observed not very long ago) among many Oriental peoples, such as Chinese and Muslims.

[14] They use such words as "vitamins," "radioactivity," or other scientific terms as bait to sell their merchandise.

[15] The Doric characteristics were already beginning to disappear from the Archimedian writings in the time of EUTOCIOS (VI-1). J. L. HEIBERG: Über den Dialekt des ARCHIMEDES, Interpolationen in den Schriften des ARCHIMEDES (Jahrbücher für classische Philologie, Suppt. 13, 543-577, 1884); De dialecto Archi-

MEDES) discovered a fragment which seemed genuine to him, because it
"preserved in part ARCHIMEDES' favorite dialect." [16]   This means that the
original text was emended, but we may assume that the emendations
were purely linguistic.   Mathematical treatises, by the way, are much
more likely than any others to be transmitted in their integrity, because
of their natural clearness and closely knit structure; one is not tempted
to interpolate them, or if interpolations be inserted it is relatively easy
to detect them.   On the contrary, medical books, especially herbals and
pharmacopoeias, invite interpolations and the latter fit in so well that
they can hardly be revealed except by means of a complex philological
analysis.   If the Archimedian tradition tells us that he made hydrostatic
experiments and found the principle which we call by his name, we are
not surprised to read his treatise on floating bodies in the Latin version
of brother WILLIAM OF MOERBEKE.[17]   The text agrees with the tradition
and has an unmistakable Archimedian flavor.   Why should it not be
what it purports to be?   If any doubts were left in our minds they were
removed when the Greek text was discovered in 1906.[18]   Two different
literary traditions confirmed one another; the lacunae and obscurities of
WILLIAM'S version were neatly healed.   A similar thing happened for
the Method discovered in the same palimpsest.   How can we be sure
that is genuine?   Well, according to SUIDAS that treatise had been com-
mented upon by THEODOSIOS, and the propositions extracted from it by
HERON OF ALEXANDRIA tally sufficiently with the Greek text revealed
in 1906.[19]   We cannot speak of absolute certainty, of course, but when
a new found text corresponds with the tradition of it and with the
references to it or extracts from it made at various times, we may be
reasonably sure that it is what it claims to be.   After all who would care
to invent a new text corresponding to the general description of it and
how could that be done without running afoul of references or quotations as yet undisclosed?

I have discussed the case of ARCHIMEDES but similar arguments would
apply to every ancient man of science.   Our knowledge of the text of
each book is almost never due to an isolated tradition, but rather to the
confluence of many.   This does not mean that each text which has
escaped the ravages of time is known to us in its integrity or is accepted
with the same confidence, as we accept, say, ARCHIMEDES' *Ephodion.*

---

medis (Archimedis opera omnia 2, p. x-xviii, 1913); Indices (*ibid.* 3, 330-448,
1915).

[16] T. L. HEATH: The works of ARCHIMEDES (p. xxxvi, Cambridge 1897).

[17] The Archimedian principle is Prop. 5 of book 1 "Any solid lighter than a
fluid will . . . be so far immersed that its weight will be equal to the weight of the
fluid displaced."   It is said that Archimedes thought of that while he was bathing
in Syracuse and was so happy that he ran out of the water shouting εὕρηκα, εὕρηκα
(I have found, I have found).   That story was first told by VITRUVIUS (I-2 B.C.) in
the preface to the ninth book of his *De architectura.*

[18] The Greek and Latin texts can easily be compared in the ARCHIMEDIS *Opera
Omnia,* edited by HEIBERG (2, 317-413, 1913).

[19] First edited by HEIBERG (Hermes, 42, 243-97, 1907), then in German translation with H. G. ZEUTHEN's commentary (BM 7, 321-63, 1907).   New edition of
the Greek text with Latin translation in ARCHIMEDIS *Opera* (2, 425-507, 1913).

There are special difficulties for each of them, obscure passages, contradictions, gaps, the head or the tail may be missing, etc. This is not true only of scientific texts, but also of Biblical and literary ones. The mechanism of tradition is exceedingly complex and capricious, involving many media—word of mouth, parchment, papyrus, ostraca, paper— and generally more than one language; every accident of history may modify the tradition or suppress it altogether. Each case must be judged on its own merits and the conclusions may vary all the way from discredit to reasonable certainty.

The authorship of an ancient (or mediaeval) book may be difficult to ascertain because of the not-uncommon habit of ascribing it to a famous author or to the master of a popular school. There was a great deal of ghostwriting then as now but the principles underlying it were extremely different. At present "important" people have books written under their name by paid underlings in order to obtain credit for them without pains. In the past modest authors would try to pass off their own compositions under the name of an illustrious master of an earlier time; or else editors would ascribe anonymous books to "plausible" authors, a medical book to HIPPOCRATES or GALEN, an astronomical one to PTOLEMY, etc. Hence, the modern critic must always be on his guard; the author named in a MS. may be the real one or not; a true authorship is proved by convergent traditions (as in the Archimedian examples dealt with above); a false authorship is generally proved by chronological inconsistencies. For example, a book which internal criticism shows could have been written only in the late Roman period, could not be ascribed to ARCHIMEDES (unless the references to a later time are interpolations, an eventuality which must be considered). The Hippocratic corpus, e.g., is not the production of a man but of a school which was active for centuries; it even includes books written by outsiders, some of them very late ones. It was gradually established by editors and librarians who were tempted to lump together all the items which seemed to them sufficiently alike; such a corpus has a way of growing by deliberate or furtive additions. It owes its existence to the same impulses which cause the publication today of so many collections of books devoted to this or that subject; each item shares to some extent the credit of the other items and of the whole; each item helps to sell the others. When the time came when knowledge had to be decanted into another linguistic vehicle for further transmission, those collections or bodies drew the attention of translators; each corpus provided a sufficiently large task which could be directed and divided. It was natural enough for the master of a school of translators wishing to transmit, say, the Hippocratic corpus, or the Galenic one, or the "middle books," [20] to distribute various parts to a number of collaborators. Each of them would do his own share under his own name or under the name of his director;

---

[20] The middle books between geometry and astronomy (Kitāb al-mutawassiṭāt bain al-handasa wal-hai'a), collection of mathematical and astronomical books to be studied in addition to the Elements and the Almagest. Introd. (2, 1001f.). W. H. WORRELL: An interesting collection (Scripta mathematica, 9, 195-96, 1943).

indeed the responsibility as well as the work was shared. As all of these scholars were translating texts of the same nature at about the same time in the same milieu and under the same guidance, all the translations made by a single group or school, have naturally the same philological and spiritual characteristics.

In the case of philosophical writings a new kind of difficulty had to be overcome because different traditions coalesced and contaminated one another. Thus the Peripatetic tradition was spoiled by Neoplatonic contaminations of various sorts and later by theological interference. The history of Muslim Aristotelism, and of mediaeval Aristotelism in general, is to a large extent an account of the gradual recovery of the Aristotelian texts in their integrity.[21]

*   *   *   *   *

From the point of view of tradition it is very fortunate that almost all of those mediaeval translators (whether Muslims, Jews or Christians) had one quality in common; they were far more interested in the contents than in the form; their superstitious reverence for the text to be translated was such that their translations were literal and pedantic. This is so true that one can easily spot Hellenisms in the Arabic translations and Arabicisms in the Latin ones; these literary faults are not restricted to words, they extend to phrases and idioms.[22] Some translated phrases are so literal indeed that they cannot be correctly understood without a mental retranslation into the original language, or to look at it from another angle, that peculiarities of the original language can be inferred without doubt.[23]

In short, if accidents did not destroy the MSS. in the course of time, the masterpieces of antiquity were remarkably well preserved because of the slavish faithfulness of oral and written traditions.

In spite of that we still have many doubts, especially concerning the writings of many Greek men of science anterior to PLATO. The only fragment of Hellenic (*i.e.*, pre-Alexandrian) geometry which has come

[21] An initial difficulty was due to the fact that the works of Aristotle were not finished literary productions like those of PLATO but rather in the form of rough lecture notes.

[22] The Arabic (or Latin) word might reproduce a metaphor of the Greek (or Arabic) or when no word existed in Arabic (or Latin) and none could be easily built, the original term might be transliterated into the other language. *E.g.*, the word mater in the terms designating the membranes of the brain (dura mater, pia mater) is a reproduction of the Arabic metaphor umm al-dimāgh. The coccyx was called in Arabic al-ʿuṣʿuṣ and this became in mediaeval Latin alhasos or alhosos (the Arabic article was often incorporated as if it were an integral part of the word); the wisdom teeth al-nājidh, pl., al-nawājidh were called in Latin nuaged, neguegid, etc. In the Qānūn IBN SĪNĀ dealt with love as a mental disease; the Arabic for sexual love, al-ʿishq appeared in the Latin version as ilixi or alhasch. These examples could be multiplied endlessly.

[23] Thus HEIBERG translated book 1 of the *Ochumena* into Greek (Doric) on the basis of the Latin version of WILLIAM OF MOERBEKE. ARCHIMEDIS περὶ ὀχουμένων liber 1 graece restituit JOHAN LUDWIG HEIBERG (Mélanges Graux, 689-709, Paris 1884) It is very interesting to compare his "reconstruction" with the original Greek text which he found some twenty years later in Constantinople. Archimedis opera (2, 317-45, 1913).

down to us in its integrity is the text of HIPPOCRATES OF CHIOS (V B.C.) on the quadratures of lunules; it is really a fragment of the history of geometry of EUDEMOS (IV-2 B.C.), preserved by SIMPLICIOS (VI-1) in the latter's commentary on ARISTOTLE's Physics! [24] Please note the tortuousness of that tradition. Thanks to the industry and sagacity of many scholars, such as the German HERMANN DIELS, the Scot JOHN BURNET, and the Frenchman PAUL TANNERY, the fragments and doxography concerning the early Greek "physiologists" are now gathered in convenient form and can be scrutinized at leisure. Our doubts are restricted to definite fragments or quotations or to definite personalities and hardly affect our conception of the whole, that is, of, let us say, early Greek mathematics or astronomy.

Yet for all that our friends who are investigating Egyptian and Babylonian mathematics have the pleasure of triumphing over the Hellenists. Though the period which attracts their attention may be anterior to the Hellenic period by a thousand years or more, they have the privilege of dealing with original documents (not mediaeval copies) —hieroglyphic papyri or cuneiform tablets. In some cases those documents may be contemporary with their authors or even holographs! In contrast with the sayings of ANAXAGORAS OF CLAZOMENAE (V B.C.) or even with the *Ochumena* of ARCHIMEDES, which we know from MSS. a thousand years posterior to ARCHIMEDES think of the Papyrus Rhind written c. 1650 B.C. (not the text but the papyrus itself) after an older work of say the eighteenth century.[25] That mathematical papyrus is almost as good as an original while the *Ochumena* is a copy many times removed from its source. This would be a cause of despair, but for the faithfulness of ancient and mediaeval traditions which we have explained a moment ago, and let it be added, but for the elaborate methods of external and internal criticism which enable good scholars to make the most of the least documents available to them, and yet restrain them from expressing immoderate claims.

❖　　❖　　❖　　❖　　❖

The transmission or tradition of modern science is insured by so many agencies that it is almost automatic; the individual man of science need make no efforts to obtain news; indeed, he would have to take special pains in order to eschew it, on the contrary the transmission of scientific news in the ancient world and even in the mediaeval one was extremely capricious and uncertain. A scientific book might survive and many did, but many more were lost; it is possible that some never reached anywhere. It is even conceivable that men of science did not trouble to write up their discoveries, because they may have thought

---

[24] Greek and French edition by PAUL TANNERY (Mémoires de la Société des sciences de Bordeaux 5, 217-37, 1883), reprinted in TANNERY's Mémoires (1, 339-70, 1912). Greek and German edition by FERDINAND RUDIO (194 p., Leipzig 1907).

[25] T. ERIC PEET: The Rhind mathematical papyrus (folio 136 p. 24 pl., University Press, Liverpool, 1923; Isis 6, 553-57).

A. B. CHACE, LUDLOW BULL, H. P. MANNING, R. C. ARCHIBALD: The Rhind mathematical papyrus (2 vols. Oberlin, Ohio, 1927-29; Isis, 14, 251-55).

"What is the good of it? Who will read the stuff, and who will preserve it?" Such reticence as opposed to the cacoëthes scribendi which is one of the diseases of our time, was probably one of the causes of the slowness of progress in antiquity. The relationship of PTOLEMY (II-1) to HIPPARCHOS (II-2 B.C.) is like that of a younger contemporary to his senior, yet they were separated by almost three centuries. Much knowledge has failed to reach us because of the silence of the inventors, or of their lost pains if they broke it. After all a discovery hardly counts if it be not published; the tradition of a discovery is second in importance to the discovery itself.

The history of ancient and mediaeval science is very largely a history of traditions. The discoveries and inventions are not many, because the laborers were few as compared with to-day and because the progress of science is naturally an accelerated one (hence if we look backward the acceleration is negative). The enumeration and discussion of those

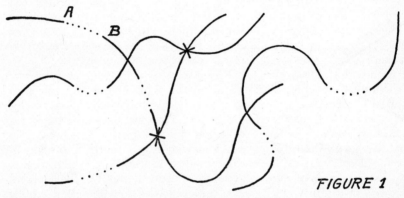

FIGURE 1

discoveries are relatively brief; on the other hand, it is very difficult to explain their tradition (without which they would be as if they had never been) and this requires considerable space. The tradition was oral, written or manual; the last one is the most difficult to deal with in accurate detail. We can only speak of it in general and infer it from the results; it is like an underground river which remains hidden for long stretches, yet we can be reasonably certain that the river emerging from the earth at a point B is the same as disappeared at another point A many miles distant. Much of the knowledge of craftsmen, physicians, alchemists, and perhaps their most valuable knowledge, was transmitted by manual examples to their apprentices. The master would say "Watch me, see what I am doing and how I am doing it, and try to do the same."

We might attempt a graphical representation of these views. The tradition of each single idea or fact might be symbolized by a line, more or less regular, with ups and downs. Some of these lines are interrupted because the tradition has ceased for a time to be visible. Sometimes the lines cross and their intersections may be indifferent or they may correspond to a knot or new discovery (FIG. 1).

Should we wish to represent the whole tradition, not only the development of single ideas or inventions, but the scientific pattern in its totality, the graph would be very different, something like this (FIG. 2). The roots of western science, the graph reminds us, are Egyptian, Mesopotamian, and to a much smaller amount, Iranian and Hindu. The central line represents the Arabic transmission which was for a time, say, from the ninth to the eleventh century, the outstanding stream, and remained until the fourteenth century one of the largest streams of mediaeval thought.

The diagram makes it easier to explain many things. In the first place it shows that the Arabic tradition was a continuation and revivification not only of Greek science but also of Iranian and Hindu ideas. This is still very imperfectly known and will require many more investigations than have hitherto been possible, but we are already well aware that two of the fundamental branches of mediaeval science, the

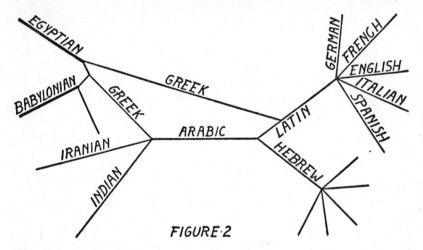

FIGURE·2

new arithmetic and the new trigonometry, were due to the mutual fertilization of two very different streams of thought, the Greek and the Hindu.

This disposes of the criticism often made by people who ignore mediaeval science almost completely, which is bad; or who think that they understand it though they lack adequate information, which is much worse. They will glibly say "The Arabs simply translated Greek writings, they were industrious imitators, and by the way, the translations were not made by themselves but by Christians and Jews . . ." This is not absolutely untrue, but is such a small part of the truth, that when it is allowed to stand alone, it is worse than a lie.

Let us consider first the particles of truth. It is correct that most of the translations were made by non-Arabs, non-Muslims, but how else could it be? The latter were to a large extent monoglot, and few if any ever knew Greek. In order to translate from one language into another one must know very well the two languages involved. The Christians and the Jews living in the Near East, in the Dār al-islām, were generally good linguists, born dragomans; it is clear that if the translations were to be made, they would be the men to make them; the translations could not be completed without their help. Yet they were made for Arabic and Muslim usage, by order of the Muslim rulers. To say that there was no Arabic science is like saying that there is no American science; the truth and untruth of both statements are of the same order. The Arabs were standing on the shoulders of their Greek forerunners just as the Americans are standing on the shoulders of their European ones. There is nothing wrong in that. It is the fundamental law of evolution. We are all the sons and followers, imitators and critics of other men; in most cases we are much smaller than our ancestors, and if we have enough intelligence and grace we feel that we are like dwarfs standing upon the shoulders of giants. Sometimes the descendants are greater than their forefathers. What makes the study of human tradition so deeply moving is just that, the multitude and variousness of accidents and above all, the unpredictable apparition of giants at one time or another, here or there.

Some of the giants of mediaeval times belonged to the Arabic culture, mathematicians and astronomers like AL-KHWĀRIZMĪ (IX-1), AL-FARGHĀNĪ (IX-1), AL-BATTĀNĪ (IX-2), ABŪ-L-WAFĀ' (X-2), 'UMAR KHAYYĀM (XI-1), AL-BĪRŪNĪ (XI-1); philosophers like AL-FĀRĀBĪ (X-1), AL-GHAZZĀLĪ (XI-2), IBN RUSHD (XII-2), IBN KHALDŪN (XIV-2), physicians like AL-RĀZĪ (IX-2), ISHĀQ AL-ISRĀ'ĪLĪ (X-1), 'ALĪ IBN 'ABBĀS (X-2), ABŪ-L-QĀSIM (X-2), IBN SĪNĀ (XI-1), MAIMONIDES (XII-2). This enumeration could be greatly extended. Few of these men were Arabs and not all of them were Muslims, but they all belonged essentially to the same cultural group, and their language was Arabic. This illustrates the absurdity of trying to appraise mediaeval thought on the basis of Latin writings alone. For centuries the Latin scientific books hardly counted; they were out-of-date and outlandish. Arabic was the international language of science to a degree which had never been equalled by another language before (except Greek) and has never been repeated since. It was the language not of one people, one nation, one faith, but of many peoples, many nations, many faiths.

The best Arabic scientists were not satisfied with the Greek and Hindu science which they inherited. They admired and respected the treasures which had fallen into their hands, but they were just as "modern" and greedy as we are, and wanted more. They criticized EUCLID, APOLLONIOS and ARCHIMEDES, discussed PTOLEMY, tried to improve the astronomical tables and to get rid of the causes of error lurking in the accepted theories. They facilitated the evolution of algebra and trigonometry and prepared the way for the European algebraists of the sixteenth century. Occasionally they were able to define new concepts, to state new problems, to tie new knots in the network of earlier traditions.

That network, Oriental-Greek-Arabic, is *our* network. The neglect of Arabic science and the corresponding misunderstanding of our own mediaeval traditions was partly due to the fact that Arabic studies were considered a part of Oriental studies. The Arabists were left alone or else in the company of other orientalists, such as Sanskrit, Chinese or Malay scholars. That was not wrong but highly misleading. It is true the network, our network, included other Oriental elements than the Arabic or Hebrew, such as the Hindu ones to which reference has already been made, but the largest part for centuries was woven with Arabic threads. If all these threads were plucked out, the network would break in the middle.

Much in the field of orientalism is definitely exotic as far as we are concerned, but the religious Hebrew traditions and the scientific Arabic ones are not exotic, they are an integral part of our network today, they are part and parcel of our spiritual existence. The Arabic side of our culture cannot even be called Eastern, for a substantial part of it was definitely Western. The Muslim IBN RUSHD and the Jew MAIMONIDES were born in Cordova within a few years of one another (1126, 1135); AL-IDRĪSĪ (XII-2), born in Ceuta, flourished in Sicily; IBN KHALDŪN (XIV-2), was a Tunisian; IBN BAṬṬŪṬA (XIV-2), a Moroccan. The list of Moorish scientists and scholars is a very long one. Spain is proud of them but without right, for she treated them, like a harsh stepmother, without justice and without mercy.

The Arabic culture[26] is of a singular interest to the student of human traditions in general, to those whose greatest task it seems to them is the rebuilding of human integrity in the face of national and international disasters, because it was, and to some extent still is, a bridge, the main bridge between East and West. It is through that bridge that the Hindu numerals, sines and chess, and the Chinese silk,[27] paper, and porcelain reached Europe. Latin culture was Western, Chinese culture was Eastern, but Arabic culture was both, for it extended all the way from the Maghrib al-aqṣā' to the Mashriq al-aqṣā.[28] Latin culture was Mediterranean and Atlantic, Hindu culture was bathed in the Indian Ocean, Far Eastern culture in the Pacific; the Arabic sailors, however, were as ubiquitous in all the oceans of the Middle Ages as the English are in those of to-day. The Latin and Greek cultures were Christian, Hebrew culture was Jewish, Eastern Asia was Buddhist; the Arabic culture was primarily but not exclusively Islamic; it was stretched out between the Christianism of the West and the Buddhism of the East and touched both.

Christendom was born in the Near East, its cradle being near the cradle of its predecessor, Israel, and not very far from that of their off-

[26] The word "culture" is used here and further on instead of science or knowledge in order to give more generality to my statements, a generality which is not needed for my argument but is too interesting to be abandoned.

[27] Silk was the first Chinese gift to reach Europe (before the Christian era), yet the art of producing silk and of using it was very largely transmitted by the Arabs. T. F. CARTER: Invention of printing (p. 88, New York 1925; Isis, 8, 361-73; 19, 426).

[28] That is, from the Far West to the Far East, both terms having then an absolute meaning which they have lost.

spring, Islām. St. Paul, however, brought it to the West, and it developed mainly as a Western religion. On the contrary, Buddhism, born in India, travelled Eastward. The history of Buddhism is as essential for the understanding of the growth of Far Eastern culture as the history of Christianity for the development of our own culture. In both cases science was carried around the earth upon the wings of religion. The Islamic evangel was a revival of Jewish unitarianism[29] which had been temporarily pushed back by Trinitarian ideals; it was enormously successful and penetrated deeply into the territories of the Christian West and the Buddhist East.

In spite of occasional contacts Hindu culture, and even more so Chinese culture, remained exotic, while the Arabic culture was inextricably mixed up with the Latin one. When we try to explain our own culture we may leave out almost completely Hindu and Chinese developments, but we cannot leave out the Arabic ones without spoiling the whole story and making it unintelligible. Does this mean that we should neglect the study of Hindu and Chinese history? Certainly not, but that is another kind of study, call it exotic or outlandish if you please. The Arabic story helps us to understand our own because it is an intrinsic part of it; the Chinese and Hindu stories help us to understand our own also but in a very different way. They help us to conceive the possibility and reality of different developments, of different patterns. The same fundamental problems (mathematical, astronomical, physical, chemical, biological, medical) had to be solved by them as had been solved by our own ancestors; the Hindus and Chinese are essentially the same kind of beings as we are, having the same needs and similar aspirations, but as their conditions of life were very different from ours, their solutions of those problems were also different (in some respects, not in all respects). It is extremely interesting for the philosopher or the anthropologist to compare those different solutions attained by similar beings under different circumstances. Chinese culture is a "control" for our own; that is very important.[30]

The practical conclusion of all this is that the investigator of medi-

---

[29] The Muslim unitarianism might be considered a Jewish heresy or a Christian one, and this was done by mediaeval writers. Its success was partly caused by Christian disintegration, and especially by the lack of unity on fundamental doctrines, e.g., on Christology. The Monophysites on the one hand and the Nestorians on the other hand had been thrown out of the central Orthodox church to the right and left. In the West (when we speak of Islām, we must always deal with the West as well as with the East), the conquest of Spain was facilitated by the fact that the Visigoths (like all the Goths) had remained Arians; it is true the Visigothic hierarchy was converted to Catholicism in 589 but did the rank and file follow suit? Centuries of Arian tradition could not be blotted out easily. That tradition was to some extent unitarian; it was thus possible for the Muslim invaders to take advantage of anti-Trinitarian prejudices and they did so.

[30] Our remarks concerning the Chinese and Hindu cultures would apply with greater strength to the aboriginal American culture which before 1492 was as separate from our own as if it had developed on another planet; unfortunately, our knowledge of American science is very imperfect because of the scarcity or lack of autochthonous writings.

aeval science should be as well acquainted with Arabic as possible; Arabic is as necessary for him as Greek for the student of antiquity.[31] Mediaeval science and philosophy were written primarily in four languages, Greek, Arabic, Latin, Hebrew, all of which are important, but none more so (at least before the thirteenth century) than Arabic.

The Latin writers of the West had been weaned from the Greek sources, because Europe was cut in two by a wall separating the Catholic world from the Orthodox. The Latins had drifted away from the Greeks since the fifth century, and the separation was already complete and unhealable three centuries later. Their distrust of Greek Christianity was superimposed upon their distrust of Greek paganism; their knowledge of Greek almost vanished and thus they lost all points of contact with the main fountain of science. Instead of being able to continue the work of the ancients and to start from where the latter had left, they had to start as it were from the beginning. That would have been too heavy a task for them, even if they had had more aptitude for scientific study than they had. They had to do again the Greek work without the Greek genius.

It is one of the paradoxes of history that the abyss cloven between the two halves of Christendom was bridged by the Asiatic representatives of another faith, speaking an alien language absolutely unrelated to their own. The Latins would not read Greek, the language of the Orthodox church, but they were finally obliged to read Arabic, the language of Islām. This evolution required some time though less than one would imagine. By the end of the eighth century the Mediterranean Sea had become a Muslim lake and Carolingian power and culture were withdrawing northward. At that time, we should remember, Arabic science had not yet blossomed. Its golden age lasted some three centuries, from the ninth to the eleventh century, and it was only toward the end of that period (a little earlier in Spain) that the Latins became aware of the importance of Arabic science. They were fully aware of course of the material power of Islām, though it took two or three centuries of crusades to convince them of their own military inferiority. A nun of Gandersheim (in the duchy of Brunswick), HROS-VITHA (X-2) spoke of CORDOVA as the ornament of the world.[32]

To appreciate Arabic culture in general was one thing, an easy one, unless one was blinded by religious hatred; to appreciate Arabic science was another, far less obvious, far more difficult. Even as the early

---

[31] The comparison is apposite because the duty is of the same order in both cases, and its limitations are similar. We don't expect the historian of science to be able, let us say, to edit a Greek (or Arabic) text from the MSS; that is a task for the philologist and the edition of a single text may engross the latter's energy for years; but the historian should be able to read those texts or to refer to their main technical points, otherwise he could not properly discuss those points. Some historians of science have edited scientific texts, *e.g.*, TANNERY, Greek ones, JULIUS RUSKA, HENRY ERNEST STAPLETON, ERIC JOHN HOLMYARD, and CARRA DA VAUX, Arabic ones.

[32] Decus orbis, *in* her Passio sancti Pelagii (1.12). KAROLUS STRECKER: HROTSVITHAE Opera (p. 54, Leipzig 1930).

Muslims had realized the need of science, mainly Greek science, in order to establish their own culture and to consolidate their dominion, even so the Latins realized the need of science, Arabic science, in order to be able to fight Islām with equal arms and vindicate their own aspirations. For the most intelligent Spaniards and Englishmen the obligation to know Arabic was as clear as the obligation to know English, French or German for the Japanese of the Meiji era. Science is power. The Muslim rulers knew that from the beginning, the Latin leaders had to learn it, somewhat reluctantly, but they finally did learn it. The prestige of Arabic science began relatively late in the West, say in the twelfth century, and it increased gradually at the time when Arabic science was already degenerating. The two movements, the Arabic progress and the Latin one, were out of phase. This is a general rule of life, by the way, rather than an exception, and it applies to individuals as well as to nations. A man generally does his best in comparative obscurity and becomes famous only when his vigor is diminishing; that is all right as far as he is concerned, for it is clear that solitude and silence are the best conditions of good, enduring, work.

The scientific tradition as it was poured from Arabic vessels into Latin ones was often perverted. The new translators did not have the advantage which the Arabic translators had enjoyed; the latter had been able to see Greek culture in the perspective of a thousand years or more; the Latin translators could not see the Arabic novelties from a sufficient distance, and they could not always choose intelligently between them. As to the Greek classics they came to them with a double prestige, Greek and Arabic. It is as if the Greek treasures, of which Latin scholars were now dimly conscious, were more valuable in their Arabic form; they had certainly become more glamorous. The translation of the Almagest made c. 1175 by Gerard of Cremona (XII-2) from the Arabic, superseded a translation made directly from the Greek in Sicily fifteen years earlier!

To return to the Arabic writings (as distinct from Arabic translations of Greek writings) some of the best were translated such as the works of al-Khwārizmī, al-Rāzī, al-Farghānī, al-Battānī, Ibn Sīnā; others of equal value escaped attention, e.g., some books of 'Umar al-Khayyām, al-Bīrūnī, Nāṣir al-dīn al-Ṭūsī; others still appeared too late to be considered, this is the case of the great Arabic authors of the fourteenth century.[33] By that time Latin science had become independent of the contemporary Arabic writings and contemptuous of them. On the other hand, the Latin (and Hebrew) translations from the Arabic include a shockingly large mass of astrological and alchemical treatises and other rubbish. Some of the astrological and alchemical writings, it should be noted, are valuable or contain valuable materials and are to some extent the forerunners of our own astronomical and chemical literature, but many others are worthless, or rather worse than

---

[33] The only translations taken into account here are those composed in the Middle Ages for actual use, not the translations made by philologists in the seventeenth century or later for archaeological reasons.

worthless, dangerous and subversive. Even so we should not be too severe in judging those aberrations, for we have not yet succeeded in overcoming them and but for the control of scientific societies and academies, the incessant criticism coming from the scientific press and the university chairs, our own civilization would soon be overrun and smothered by superstitions and lies.[34]

❋   ❋   ❋   ❋   ❋

Our judgment of mediaeval science in general must always be tempered by the considerations which have just been offered and by due and profound humility. We may be great scientists (I mean, we modern men), but we are also great barbarians. We know, or seem to know, everything, except the essential. We have thrown religion out of doors but allowed superstitions, prejudices and lies to come in through the windows. We drum our chests in the best gorilla fashion saying (or thinking) "We can do this . . . we can do that . . . yea, we can even blow the world to smithereens," but what of it? Does that prove that we are civilized? Material power can be as dangerous as it is useful; it all depends on the men using it and on their manner of using it. Good or evil are in ourselves; material power does not create it but can multiply it indefinitely.

To return to the Middle Ages it was a long period not of darkness and sterility but of gestation. To call it sterile would be just as foolish as to call a pregnant woman, sterile. Wait and see! It takes nine months of patience in one case and nine centuries in another but time does not matter. Mediaeval developments were undoubtedly slow as compared with our own tempo, but are we not going too fast? Our speed is not necessarily a good thing, nor very admirable; it is largely due to accumulated inertia. It would require unusual wisdom to brake it, and we are short on wisdom.

The essential weakness of mediaeval thought was due to the lack of understanding of the experimental method and of the experimental point of view. Once that "open sesame" had been found, discoveries followed one another, almost automatically in some cases, with increasing speed. Modern science is the fruit of three centuries of that method. Its early development was exceedingly slow. Even the Greeks, so full of genius, had failed to discover it, though some of them had applied it in particular cases.[35] A few Muslim, Christian and Jewish scientists of the Middle Ages applied it too, but with the exception of ROGER BACON (XIII-2), nobody formulated it nor recognized its generality and its astounding potency.[36]

---

[34] *See* review of a new edition of PTOLEMY's *Tetrabiblos* for practical use, Chicago 1936 (Isis, 35, 181).

[35] PTOLEMY (II-1) in his study of refraction, GALEN (II-2) in his experiments to determine the function of the kidneys, and of the cerebrum and spinal chord at different levels.

[36] ROGER BACON's formulation constitutes the sixth part (out of seven) of the *Opus majus* written in 1268. It can easily be read in ROBERT BELLE BURKE's translation (p. 583-634, Philadelphia 1928; Isis, 11, 138-41). The letter on the magnet

After three and a half centuries of additional gestation and many more experiments in various fields, BACON's formulation and vindication of the experimental method was renewed with greater light and strength by his countryman and namesake FRANCIS BACON. In the *Advancement of Learning* (1605) and even more so in the *Novum organum* (1620) the second BACON brought a new charter to the men of science, an invitation to apply the new method of truthseeking to all the problems of science and life. BACON was much less a prophet than an eloquent advocate of the spirit of his time. The experimental method had finally reached maturity. GALILEO's writings were even more influential than BACON's for the latter's were purely rhetorical while GALILEO's were accompanied by great deeds, revolutionary discoveries. BACON preached but GALILEO wrought.

BACON's and GALILEO's ideas were so timely and so readily understood by many eager minds that new societies were created for the very purpose of implementing them. The earliest of those societies were established under GALILEO's influence in Italy, the *Accademia dei Lincei* (1603-30) in Rome and after his death the *Accademia del Cimento* (1657-67) in Florence. Note their titles, the Academy of the lynxes and the Academy of experiment. The first title continued the allegorical habits of earlier academies, but the references to lynxes, animals who see in the dark, was significant; the symbolic meaning was accentuated in the Academy's device, a lynx tearing Cerberus with its claws, the struggle of truth with superstition. The second title was even more significant. The Academy of experiment!; its members gathered for the purpose of experimenting and of discovering the truth by the experimental method.[37]

Both academies were shortlived, for the Italian climate of that time was not favorable to the development of untrammelled truthseeking, but their efforts were continued in exemplary fashion by two other academies established in England and France before the closing of the Accademia del Cimento. The reader knows that I am referring to the *Royal Society* founded in London in 1662, and the *Académie des Sciences* founded in Paris in 1666. These two academies are still functioning to-day but never were their activities more necessary and more pregnant than in their early years. The academies of the seventeenth century marked the triumph of the experimental method and the birth of mod-

which is one of the most remarkable examples of experimental science in the Middle Ages, was written by PETER THE STRANGER (XIII-2) at almost the same time, 1269. It does not speak of the method, except a few lines in chapter 2.

[37] The Accademia del cimento fully justified its title and accomplished its purpose. Its deeds were published by its second and last secretary, LORENZO MAGALOTTI (1637-1712), in a beautiful folio volume Saggi di naturali esperienze (Firenze 1667). This was Englished by RICHARD WALLER (c. 1650-1715) and published by order of the Royal Society, Essayes of natural experiments made in the Academie del Cimento (London 1684). Sixty-four years after the original publication it was translated into Latin by the Dutch physicist, PIETER VAN MUSSCHENBROEK (1692-1761), Tentamina experimentorum naturalium captorum in Academia del Cimento (474 p., 32 pl., Leiden 1731), with additions and a discourse on experimental method by the translator.

ern science; together with other academies established on similar patterns, they remained until the end of the eighteenth century the main agencies of scientific progress; it is impossible to exaggerate their importance.

Yet we should remember two things. First these seventeenth century academicians could not have done what they did but for the long mediaeval gestation. They themselves did not realize that and some of the early academicians were tempted to believe that they were directly continuing the traditions not of the Middle Ages but of Greek antiquity. Their illusion is now exposed without the possibility of doubt. Whenever one investigates carefully the origins of "modern" thought, even in the minds of its most original forerunners (say, LEONARDO DA VINCI, GALILEO, DESCARTES, NEWTON) one finds an abundance of mediaeval roots. The seventeenth century men of science were standing upon the shoulders of mediaeval giants; irrespective of their own sizes they were that much taller.

In the second place, while it is obvious that our scientists have fully understood and exploited the experimental method, this is not true of the great majority of modern men who persist in preferring irrational methods to rational ones (*e.g.*, in the treatment of political and social problems), or else who attach more importance to *a priori* reasoning than to the *a posteriori* reasoning which is the very essence of the experimental spirit. This point deserves elaboration by means of an example.

The discovery of the sexuality of higher plants by CAMERARIUS in 1694 could have been made two thousand years earlier, if the experimental method had been applied to it.[38] It was retarded by non-experimental thinking and by prejudices, and after its publication it was rejected and its general acceptance was delayed for half a century because of the same prejudices. Similar remarks could be offered with regard to almost every fundamental discovery of modern science down to the theory of evolution (1859). Each discovery was delayed by a kind of intellectual inertia, and when it was finally made, its acceptance was delayed by the same inertia, the refusal to experiment (or even to observe) and to abide by the experimental results.

The experimental method is now explained in philosophical courses (one might even say, it is explained nowhere else, for the teachers of science are satisfied to show it in action), but there are many philosophers, even among the greatest, who have never understood it. Moreover, its beneficial value is often minimized and even obliterated by the abuse of purely dialectical methods. Scholasticism (or the abuse of dialectics) is not by any means a mediaeval disease, nor is it a Latin one, as is too readily asserted by people who can think only of Catholic scholasticism, Thomism or neo-Thomism. That is one species of scholasticism, but there are many others and the genus is scattered all over the world. Scholasticism is a mental disease which can be diagnosed in Hindu and Chinese minds, as well as in Latin, Greek, Arabic, or He-

---

[38] G. SARTON: The artificial fertilization of date-palms in the time of ASHUR-NASIR-PAL 885-60 B.C. (Isis, 21, 8-13, 4 pl., 1934).

brew ones.   Few philosophers have been able to shake it off completely.
Scholasticism it should be noted is not at all a denial of the value of
observation and experiment but a tendency to exaggerate deductive
reasoning on a given experimental basis.   The experimental basis of
mediaeval schoolmen was pitifully, ridiculously, small, but the main
point is this, that no matter how large that basis be its fertility and
efficacy are limited.   Deductive reasoning, even of the purest kind as
in mathematical physics, needs periodic checking by experimental
means, or else it may degenerate into fallacies or nonsense.

Many of the discussions of modern astrophysics seem to be based on
an insufficient experimental basis; at any rate, their theoretical constructions are so gigantic that the experimental basis seems infinitesimal.   We
need more than a red-shift [39] of spectral lines to agree to the prodigious
theory of the expanding universe, and more than a beautiful system of
equations to accept as a reality canon GEORGES LEMAÎTRE's ingenious
idea of a cosmic egg.   Everybody who is not an astrophysicist would
require additional evidence, not one set of observations interpreted in
agreement with the theory of relativity, but convergent sets of different
kinds of observation.   The old astronomical theories were not as adventurous; they could be tested in many ways.   The gradual development
of celestial mechanics and the elaboration of appropriate tables made
continual tests possible.   Every observatory was a testing ground and
every eclipse or transit, a new challenge.   Do the astrophysicists not
need cross-examinations?   One would think that they could not rest
until their grandiose ideas had been checked and counterchecked in
every possible manner, yet they proceed cheerfully from one audacious
structure to another which is more audacious still and so on.   Happily,
they restrict their extrapolations to their own field and do not try to legis-
late for the microscopic human world.

Metaphysicians are less restrained and tend to offer their conclusions
in the most general and peremptory form.   In his discussion of PLATO's
Republic the illustrious KANT remarked, "Nothing can be more mischie-
vous and more unworthy a philosopher than the vulgar appeal to what
is called adverse experience, which possibly might never have existed,
if at the proper time institutions had been framed according to those

---

[39] "Red-shift" is short for shift of spectral lines toward the red end of the
spectrum.   According to the Doppler principle such a shift toward the longer wave
length side represents a moving away of the radiating object from the observer.
But is the red-shift really a velocity-shift, or does it bear another interpretation?
For discussion of these puzzling matters *see* ARTHUR EDDINGTON: The expanding
universe (Cambridge University, 1933); EDWIN HUBBLE: The realm of the nebulae
(Yale Press, New Haven 1936); The observational approach to cosmology (Clarendon Press, Oxford 1937).   HARLOW SHAPLEY: Galaxies (Philadelphia 1943).   Both
HUBBLE and SHAPLEY are cautious and uneasy; Sir ARTHUR is more reckless.   My
criticism does not apply to them but only to astronomers who speak too glibly
of the expanding universe.   *See* also the excellent paper of PERCY W. BRIDGMAN:
On the nature and the limitations of cosmical inquiries (Scientific Monthly 37,
385-97, 1933).

ideas, and not according to crude concepts, which, because they were derived from experience only, have marred all good intentions." [40]

Another German philosopher, HEGEL, who was a dictator of European (and American) thought for a good part of the nineteenth century, began his career in a manner which was prophetic of his own unwisdom. His Dissertatio philosophica de orbitis planetarum (1801) was a "philosophical" attack on Newtonian astronomy. HEGEL "proved" that there could not be more than seven planets.[41] That remarkable thesis was published soon after the discovery of Ceres by GIUSEPPE PIAZZI! [42]

Hegelian doctrine and method influenced deeply such men as KARL MARX (1818-83) and FRIEDRICH ENGELS (1820-95) and some of HEGEL's poison penetrated their own philosophy, the dialectical materialism and historical materialism, which in its turn is influencing many men and women of our own times.[43]

This shows that there is always a strong tendency, due no doubt to the intrinsic qualities of the human mind, to add dialectics, enough or too much, in season or out of season, to experience, a perverse desire to transcend experience. Even the greatest men of science are not immune from that weakness, witness one of the best known of our own contemporaries—you have already named him in your own minds—the late ARTHUR STANLEY EDDINGTON. During the last period of his life (1921-44), EDDINGTON developed the astounding doctrine that the structure of the universe can be established on an *a priori* basis because of the structure of our own mind.[44] It is true that the agreement between the value

---

[40] Critique of pure reason. Transcendental dialectic, Book I, section 1, p. 275 in MAX MÜLLER's translation (London 1881).

[41] The duke ERNEST OF SAXONY-GOTHA sent a copy of HEGEL's thesis to the astronomer FRANZ XAVER VON ZACH with the inscription "Monumentum insaniae saeculi decimi noni" (RUDOLF WOLF: Geschichte der Astronomie, p. 685, München 1877). In 1801, HEGEL was no longer a child, he was 31 years old. The text of his Dissertatio "pro licentia docendi" may be found in his Sämtliche Werke, GLOCKNER's edition (vol. 1, 3-29, 1927).

[42] PIAZZI observed Ceres for the first time on the first evening of the nineteenth century, Jan. 1, 1801; the news reached BODE in Berlin only on March 20, but created at once a commotion among astronomers. HEGEL defended his thesis in Jena, on August 27, 1801.

[43] For good illustrations of that sinister influence on men of science, to wit, botanists, see TROFIM DENISOVICH LYSENKO: Heredity and its variability (65 p., New York 1946; Isis 37, 108); P. S. HUDSON and R. H. RICHENS: The new genetics in the Soviet Union (88 p., Cambridge 1946; Isis 37, 106-8); CONWAY ZIRKLE: The death of a science in Russia (334 p., Philadelphia 1949; Isis 41, 238-39). JULIAN HUXLEY: Heredity, East and West (256 p., New York 1949; Isis 41, 239). The words "dialectical materialism" are used so frequently behind the Iron Curtain, that it has been necessary there to coin the abbreviation "diamat."

[44] Sir ARTHUR summarized his views as follows: "An intelligence, unacquainted with our universe, but acquainted with the system of thought by which the human mind interprets to itself the content of its sensory experience, should be able to attain all the knowledge of physics that we have attained by experiment. He would not deduce the particular events and objects of our experience, but he would deduce the generalizations we have based on them. For example, he would infer the existence and properties of radium, but not the dimensions of the Earth." (Nature, 154, 759, 1944).

of observed universal constants and their value found by his "pure reasoning" was impressively close. And yet the undertaking frightens us beyond words.[45]

We must philosophize, but it is safer never to lose sight of experience. We must go back to the concrete and tangible facts as often as possible to keep our strength and our sanity. Like ANTAEOS we are safe only as long as we remain in touch with the good earth. We must not extrapolate too far; in such matters it is safer to imitate the plain terrestrial physicists than the astrophysicists. With the disturbing exception of EDDINGTON, the majority of scientists of our time avoid superrationalism and fantastic extrapolations. It is not that they are wiser than their mediaeval ancestors, but centuries of experimental success and failure have sobered their thoughts. In a curious way EDDINGTON helps us to be more tolerant with mediaeval scholasticism, for he shows us how difficult it is to follow the narrow road between irrationalism and excessive rationalism.

*   *   *   *   *

The mediaeval gestation was necessary; it would have had to occur in one way or another. It might have been faster, but we cannot explain why things happen as they do, and in particular their tempo defies analysis; it is futile to consider imaginary sequences different from the real ones.

Young historians of science, who know only the bare outline as may be read in a short primer, may fancy that the development of science was much simpler than it really was; that it was logical, continuous, straightforward. Nothing is further from the truth. To begin with, the march of science was often thwarted and deflected by general principles or prejudices, not to speak of physical or human calamities (such as earthquakes, epidemics, wars). The notion that the trajectories of planets must be circular retarded KEPLER's discovery for centuries, though APOLLONIOS had prepared the mathematical basis of it. That is the classical example of inertia due to prejudice, but there are plenty of others. Each great discovery of the past has been retarded by a similar inertia. In a particular case that spiritual inertia is still blocking the way. I am referring to the metric system. One of its two fundamental ideas[46]— that the system of weights, measures and moneys should be built on the same basis as our number system—was hit upon by Sumerian mathematicians more than five thousand years ago. It was reasserted very clearly by the Flemish mathematician, SIMON STEVIN in 1585. The metric system was established in 1795.[47] It has since been accepted by the majority of civilized nations, but not by England nor America.

---

[45] For further discussion of this, see MAX BORN: Experiment and theory in physics (44 p., Cambridge University Press, 1943; Isis 35, 261, 263) and DINGLE's inaugural lecture (1947).

[46] The other one concerns the choice of units; the independent units should be as few and as universal as possible.

[47] SARTON: The first explanation of decimal fractions and measures, together with a history of the decimal idea (Isis, 23, 153-244, 1935).

Leaving out of account calamities and prejudices, how could one expect the path between one discovery and the following to be the shortest one? How could one determine the shortest distance from A to B as long as B is unknown (Fig. 3)? What happens, of course, is that men of science having reached the point A are wondering what to do next; they feel their way around A and after more or less beating about the bush, after many circumvolutions, hesitations, retrogradations, one of them may finally discover B. When B has been sufficiently reconnoitred and its coordinates are known but not before, it is easy to determine the shortest distance to it. After that the shortest distance from A to B will be the way from A to B and investigators will be carried as rapidly as possible to this new outpost and be prepared to continue their exploration further on. There are thus always at least two roads from A to B, the long "historical" one which leads to the discovery of B, and the "dogmatic" one which leads from A to B in the simplest and quickest manner. Any discovery is a new outpost and a new starting point; nobody can tell what may still be discovered beyond it; it may be little or nothing or else a new world may be hidden behind it. This is espe-

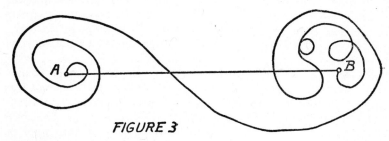

FIGURE 3

cially tangible when the discovery is a new instrument, multiplying the sensitiveness of our senses or perhaps creating new ones, but it is equally true when it is simply an idea, for a scientific idea is like a scientific instrument, a new means of exploration.

One might claim that CHRISTOPHER COLUMBUS did not discover America because he never thought of a new world but remained convinced until the end of his life that he had simply found a westward road to the Far East. Our language perpetuates that illusion of his, for we still call the aboriginal Americans "Indians" and the Islands off the western American coast "West Indies." To me that claim seems a bit pedantic, and if applied to COLUMBUS one might apply it just as well to many other discoverers, who could not possibly know their Americas. They discovered some islands off the coast but as they were not prophets, they could not possibly guess where the mainland lay or what it really was. In a strict sense they could discover only what they saw, they could not discover the things as yet unseen to which they had opened a path; they were the masters of to-day, not of to-morrow. If COLUMBUS did not discover America, then FARADAY is not the father of electrotechnics nor GALOIS, the father of the theory of groups. Should we credit a man with the whole of his posterity or only with his immediate children?

The logical investigation of science has tempted many scholars[48] and the more optimistic, such as the physico-chemist, WILHELM OSTWALD (1853-1932),[49] believed that it might facilitate new discoveries. It is true that an experienced investigator may obtain stimulating "hints" from the reading of ancient memoirs, but he might obtain similar "hints" in many other ways. The most unexpected and bizarre occurrence may excite a mind which is on the alert, sensitive and vigorous. The deeper methods of discovery are not more patient of analysis than the methods of artistic creation. Or to put it otherwise we may analyze them as much as we please, the essential is bound to escape us. It does not follow that the analysis is useless but simply that its usefulness is uncertain, unpredictable and at best small.

The historian of science is not satisfied with such a statement as "BECQUEREL discovered the radioactivity of uranium in 1896." He wants to know much more "How did that happen? Why did it happen in 1896 and not before? What caused or occasioned the discovery? Who was BECQUEREL and why was he following that particular track? . . ." The answers to such questions are not likely to reveal secrets of discovery; their heuristic value is negligible; they reveal something less practical and less pregnant but perhaps more interesting and more moving—the human sources and contingencies of scientific development. The word "reveal" is not excessive; if men of science are properly attuned to it this kind of knowledge comes to them as a revelation of something they could hardly have imagined. Indeed, as long as we study science in the treatises (and we must begin that way) or in technical monographs we have an entirely false view of it as a growing thing, in its genesis and becoming. The treatise gives us the scientific knowledge we need and it gives it in the simplest and most direct manner, without unnecessary detours and digressions; it is unavoidably dogmatic and anti-historical; it has to put in the first place not the oldest notions but the most fundamental, and these are likely to be the latest or at least very recent. In fact the discovery of a new fundamental notion invites the redaction of a new treatise properly focussed upon that very notion.

A complete body of science, or one that seems to be complete, we might say, one that is sufficiently complete, as is offered to us in a well written treatise, such a body is beautiful to look at, so beautiful that it may excite the enthusiasm of a neophyte and determine his career. It is very abstract, almost superhuman or inhuman, but it is in reality—implicitly—very human. The neophyte, if he has imagination and sensibility, feels that even as he would feel a living faith in spite of rite and ceremonial.

After all a discovery, even the most abstract, let us say, a mathematical or physical theorem, is abstract only in its final shape. Was it not

        [48] E.g., FREDERICK BARRY: The scientific habit of thought (372 p., New York 1927; Isis, 14, 265-68); various others are enumerated in SARTON: The study of the history of science (56-57, Cambridge, Mass., 1936), and in chapter 7 in the bibliography below.
        [49] Isis (1, 27).

due to the observations and meditations of a living individual, a being as limited and imperfect as ourselves? However abstract from the outside, it is very concrete from the inside.

The hard-boiled physicist may retort that he is interested only in the results, the technical results, and not at all in the men who obtained them, nor in the contingencies of discovery. His historical curiosity, if he has any, is restricted to the sequences of technical points, as were enumerated by HOPPE,[50] or for that matter by anyone who is charged to relate past events in the briefest time and space; the inventors are named, barely named, and possibly a few dates are hooked to the names; that is all. The names might almost be replaced by mute symbols, for without further explanation they are meaningless. One reads, "In 1828 NICOL invented a prism enabling one to obtain a single pencil of white polarized light." Who was NICOL? NICOL is the man who invented the Nicol prism. Not very helpful. Such historical outlines are almost as abstract as the ideas which they list, but this is due only to their incompleteness. If one empties all the humanities from a story, that story is pretty inhuman, but it is not a real story, only the ghost of one.

The humanist on the contrary is not satisfied unless he be able not only to set forth the discoveries in their chronological sequence, but also to explain the long travail and maybe the sufferings which led to each of them, the mistakes which were made, the false tracks which were followed, the misunderstandings, the quarrels, the victories and the failures; he rejoices in the gradual unveiling of all the contingencies and hazards which constitute the warp and woof of living science. He loves the abstractions of science, the final or latest results, to be sure, but he loves also the human elements mixed with them. He loves science, but he loves men more and men of science, best. He is full of gratitude and wonder, but his wonder occurs as it were on three different levels, first, the wonders of nature, second, the wonders of science, and third, best of all, the wonders of scientific discovery—the wonder that such wonders have been discovered by men, men like ourselves.[51] Therefore, he often takes more interest in the process of discovery or in the discoverer than in the thing discovered. The latter in many cases, whether it be the temperature of a star or the behavior of a louse's louse, leaves him cold. Looked at from that angle, the history of science is a part and perhaps the best part, of the divine comedy, or the human comedy, in which we all participate. We love the truth in itself and for itself. Yet we are eager to know how we reached whatever we reached of it, and thus be able to direct our gratitude to the seekers, the rebels, the fighters, all those who helped us to obtain our main treasures.

The account of these spiritual conquests and of our gradual liberation from errors, doubts, superstitions and fears, fills the best pages in the

---

[50] EDMUND HOPPE (1854-1928): Geschichte der Physik (Braunschweig 1926; Isis, 9, 571; 13, 45-50).

[51] For example, the nebulae themselves are wonderful; stellar astronomy is more wonderful, but most wonderful of all is the fact that that astronomy has been discovered and described by infinitesimal creatures.

archives of mankind.   We are happy and proud to be able to write a
few of those pages, and we love to read the pages which others have
already written;—to read them quietly and thoroughly with all the footnotes.   Those pages touch our hearts, not simply our brains; they represent our noblest tradition, the best that is in us.   Some of those traditions
take us back to ancient or mediaeval times, others date from yesterday,
but whether old or young, they give us pride in the past and faith in the
future.   They help us to be better men, wiser, kinder and humbler, even
more cheerful.

The historian of science in Antiquity and the Middle Ages is better
able to appreciate tradition because the latter takes of necessity as much
place in his account as the discoveries and the inventions; the historian
of modern science takes tradition for granted, yet it exists and is as fundamental as ever.   Discoveries would be useless if they were not transmitted to others, and eventually to the whole of mankind.   When we
study the distant past every document is important because only a few
have survived, and it is our duty to make the most of them.   Historians
who will be charged to write the history of, say, twentieth century science will face difficulties of a very different kind.   They will be as it
were buried under an avalanche of documents, far more than they could
possibly examine, let alone read or study.   Therefore, they will have to
select as well as possible relatively few documents out of the enormous
mass and focus their attention upon these few.   In the case of ancient and
mediaeval science, that preparation has been done by Father Time with
splendid indifference and arbitrariness.   Future historians will have to
replace that random selection by one as rational, impartial and careful
as possible.   That will require an elaborate division of labor between
them, a matter which cannot be explained here and now.[52]

The tradition of experience and knowledge takes another form in
modern times than it did in the past, but it loses nothing of its importance
and necessity.   It is the best part today of our inheritance and tomorrow
of our legacy, and we must be worthy of it.

Appendix

MONUMENTAL AND ICONOGRAPHIC TRADITION
VS. LITERARY TRADITION

Scientific ideas and remembrances are transmitted not only by literary texts but
also by monuments, such as buildings, tombstones, instruments and objects of many
kinds.   In a sense all the ancient buildings and monuments, irrespective of their
original purpose, are witnesses of the ancient men's knowledge as well as of their

[52] *See* preliminary views in the author's Remarks concerning the history of
twentieth century science (Isis, 26, 53-62, 1936).

arts and crafts. The historian of science cannot examine the Parthenon, Hagia Sophia, or the cathedral of Chartres without deep emotion and without the opportunity of learning much concerning the science of their builders.

Instruments and other small objects may be found in the museums and especially in the museums of science such as exist in Haarlem and Leiden, Paris, South Kensington, Oxford and Cambridge, Munich, Washington and Chicago, etc. The authenticity of each item requires a special demonstration but for the purpose of study or teaching, copies of duly accredited items are generally as good as the originals.

Iconographic documents are pictures or images representing the original items. When those items are extant, the pictures of them are comparable to other copies, and have almost as much documentary value as the originals. When the items are lost, the reliability of each image must be appraised separately. Some drawings or printed images are themselves original documents, *e.g.*, the engineering sketches of LEONARDO DA VINCI or the printed placards of ancient universities.

The most attractive of the monuments are statues, busts, or painted portraits; the most attractive of the iconographic documents are drawn, engraved or printed portraits. The tradition of portraits anterior to the fifteenth century is exceedingly difficult to establish. It is precarious at best, for it can hardly bear any solution of continuity between the living man at one end and the document in our hand at the other. Even in the case of modern men of science their iconographic tradition can be easily broken or jeopardized (*e.g.*, when the legends of two portraits are accidentally interchanged in an article or a book).

There is no reason whatsoever to believe in the genuineness of any bust or statue of any ancient man of science. The busts bearing such names as PLATO, EUCLID, etc., are impostures. Mediaeval likenesses of contemporary men of science are almost equally unreliable, except in the case of a few illuminated MSS. When a limner was asked to illustrate and illuminate a given text he sometimes added the portrait of the author (*e.g.*, the author offering his book to his patron, a kind of iconographic dedication). It is possible that some of these portraits are real portraits, yet it is almost impossible to prove their genuineness.

Statues of modern men of science have generally no value as iconographic evidence, and should not be reproduced as portraits, except faute de mieux. Indeed, most statues are posthumous, hence second hand, and a statue derived from a two dimensional portrait may be very far removed from reality.

Similar remarks apply to medals; almost every portrait in medallic form is posthumous and second-hand or *n*-th hand. Such medals are valuable witnesses of a man's fame, of memorial ceremonies or other events.

Historians of science should always deal with the available monuments as well as with the texts, and they should never neglect the iconographic traditions. They should bear in mind, however, the fragility of such traditions and be extremely cautious.

For additional information on this topic *see* SARTON: Iconographic honesty (Isis, 30, 222-35, 1939); Portraits of ancient men of science (Lychnos, 249-56, 1 fig., Uppsala 1945). PAUL SCHRECKER (Isis, 32, 126).

III. IS IT POSSIBLE TO TEACH
THE HISTORY OF SCIENCE?

The first two lectures have considered the question "Is it worthwhile to teach the history of science?", and I trust have prompted you to answer it in the affirmative. The writer is not naïve enough to imagine that such a decision will be universal, or even general. Much hostility or inertia will stop our advance or slow it up. Let me briefly reiterate the main sources of opposition and indifference.

There are, in the first place, those who would reject the whole past. The past is finished, irremediable, permanent; there is nothing we can do about it, and hence it is better not to worry about it. In the second place, some men of science will admit interest in history and realize its importance and difficulties, but they are not interested in the history of science. Science, they would say, need not concern itself with its own past; artists may study the history of art, because the art of the past is, or may be, as up-to-date, as new, as their own; the science of the past, on the contrary, is definitely inferior to our own and has been superseded by it. Our new scientific books contain all that is worthwhile in the old, less the rubbish. The very perfectibility of science causes its past efforts to be negligible.

There is no hope of overcoming the animosity of these two groups; they are historically blind. Let us now introduce a third group, not of enemies but of ignorant and dangerous friends. You may remember VOLTAIRE's saying "God help me against my friends. I can take care of my enemies." That "cri du coeur" has often been repeated, I am sure, with less impertinence but with equal poignancy. There is a large group of men of science, perhaps a majority, who are interested in the history of science, nay, enthusiastic about it, but hardly see the necessity of studying it. "It is all so simple and so easy, hardly a man's job." They know well enough scientific [their own] difficulties but have no idea whatsoever of historical methods and pitfalls. History is easy to read, but it does not follow that it is easy to write. Indeed, it is very difficult to find the truth in historical matters, and having found it, to express it clearly. How difficult is it? Is it more difficult than, say, the theory of functions or spectral analysis? Is it more difficult to walk on a tight rope than to play the violin? Foolish questions all. Each of these things is not only difficult but impossible for those who are not sufficiently prepared for it by nature and training. Historical investigations remain difficult even for those who have received the best preparation; the absence of difficulties is apparent only to those who are unprepared and ignorant. Many of our friends, distinguished men of science, well-meaning but injudicious when the past is concerned, love the history of science so much that they accept as good any book on the subject without criticism of any kind, and thus instead of helping us they hasten the disintegration of our studies,—the spiritual degradation to which I referred before—or a least they make the upbuilding more difficult.

These dangerous friends would have no hesitation in answering the second question "Is it possible to teach the history of science?" It is not only possible, they would say, but very easy, too easy,—a task to be left to second-rate or third-rate minds.

There is no time for me to explain here and now the difficulties of the historical method in general or of the history of science in particular. That cannot be done even in a course in the history of science in which the instructor has hardly time enough to describe the main results of research, but certainly none to explain how those results were obtained. A few difficulties have been indicated, however, in the two previous lectures and for the others I must ask your indulgence and your confidence. The great men to whom we owe a good part of our knowledge, MORITZ CANTOR, KARL SUDHOFF, PAUL TANNERY, PIERRE DUHEM, Sir THOMAS HEATH, LIPPMANN, RUSKA, and *tutti quanti*, spent their lives working with zeal and patience, grappling with one problem after another, clearing up riddles and obscurities, and sometimes they ventured to compose a synthesis of all the knowledge they had managed to unravel and to put in order, making it possible for their successors to continue their task and to improve it; would you say they wrestled with shadows?

History as an art is as old as medicine, which is but another way of saying that it is extremely old. Some of the earliest writings of every cultural group are historical in purpose. Moreover there were great historians in ancient and mediaeval times. I need not mention their names for you know them; nevertheless, historical methods were not established much before the last century and that century has seen the birth of historical science as well as of medical science. At first, history was primarily concerned with political and military matters, the history of dynasties, kings and generals. Then the field was gradually expanded as well as diversified; we were invited to study or to consider economic history, social history, the history of the people, of the common man, the history of agriculture and of commerce, the history of literatures, etc. Among these many branches of the historical tree, three deserve to arrest our attention: our own, the history of science, and two others sufficiently close to it to incite comparison, the history of religion and the history of art. The two last-named are (in their modern form) very young but not quite as young as the history of science, and hence they may help to guide the development of the latter.

Writing in 1905, the distinguished French art historian, ANDRÉ MICHEL, declared,[53] "The history of art has been the last of the historical sciences to be constituted, and as such it can now claim a share in their methods and take its place in their company. The nature and complexity of facts that it is its duty to analyze and to classify would suffice to explain the slowness of its ascension." He then refers to the fantasies

---

[53] In his preface to the *Histoire de l'art* of which he had assumed direction (Paris 1905 ff.).

of HEGEL and to the meditations of TAINE and explains that in order to
reach maturity the history of art like every other historical science required the slow and painful elaboration of a large number of special
investigations.   You can hardly speak of science before a system or synthesis has been created, and on the other hand, the synthesis will hardly
be possible before the monographs have been completed.   Does this
mean that the synthesis must be postponed until the Greek calends?
Surely not.   Tentative syntheses must be prepared from time to time
to make possible further advances; no synthesis is premature which is
effected without extravagant claims, humbly and honestly.   Each such
synthesis is like an encampment in a long, endless march, the march
toward truth.   Last century, the critical methods of the historian of art
were still unknown to the educated public and to the administrators of
our colleges, and a man might be called to teach that history on the
strength of his familiarity with the great museums and of his "good taste"
and his ability to express generalities in the manner of WALTER PATER
or in the manner of TAINE.   That time is past.   Good taste and good
letters are still essential but no longer sufficient.   The departments of
the history of art of our universities are now manned by well-trained
scholars.   Their task is admittedly so considerable that it is divided
between them—some are experts on early oriental art or Greek art or
they deal only with the Renaissance, Baroque, Rococo, or Dada period
(the last-named being, I regret to say, our own).   The field is too large
for one man, although one cannot help hoping that there will appear
from time to time a man big enough and bold enough to encompass the
whole of it.

The task of those new historians was facilitated by their friendly ri-
valry and their keen emulation.   Each one of them might conceive a new
method or a new approach, he might discover a lost masterpiece or bring
to light forgotten documents.   The fruits of their efforts appeared in their
publications and they were discussed in seminaries with their students, in
colloquia with their rivals, in academic meetings and national and international congresses.   To speak only of the latter, for the smaller gather-
ings are too numerous to be recalled, the first international congress
for the history of art was called to order in Vienna in 1873.   Judging
from its proceedings, published in the following year, it was a very modest undertaking but the first of a long series.   The fifteenth congress took
place in London, in July 1939, just before the outbreak of the second
World War.   In these assemblies, historians of art belonging to many
countries exhibit their latest discoveries, ventilate their theories, present
and compare their results and their methods.   Each participant returns
to his home and study a little richer in knowledge, surer in his grasp,
clearer in his mind, more conscious of the general aim and work, and
of his own share in it; sometimes, his education is of a different kind, for
his convictions are shaken by the arguments of colleagues who see things
in a different light; sometimes, his immature convictions are replaced by
doubts, certainties are disturbed by new convictions or new enigmas;
that is just as good if not better.   In any case, the discipline to which

he and the others have devoted their lives is shaping itself with greater clearness and rigor. During the last half century, the history of art has become gradually a solid body of knowledge much more severe than it was but also more rewarding and altogether more pleasant. Many problems have been solved but many more have been evoked, and the historian of art has been kept very busy, learning and unlearning, searching for better knowledge and a deeper understanding of his own position or of the whole field. That field is larger and richer. There is more truth in it than before and more beauty.

*   *   *   *   *

The history of religion reached its period of adolescence at about the same time as the history of art, say, about the last quarter of the century. The main historical difficulties seem to have lain in the correct definition of the field. This was more difficult than for the history of art which shaped itself naturally. Take the history of painting or the history of music. We start with a collection of masterpieces—paintings or partitions. These are concrete, dated or datable objects; it is not too difficult to put them, or most of them, in a chronological sequence, and there you have the skeleton of your history. The history of religion, on the other hand, is a history of emotions and of ideas, the origin of which may be extremely difficult to perceive or to date. It is a history of creeds and beliefs, of rites and institutions, and much of that is difficult to analyze and describe, because it does not happen once but flows and continues. The scholars who undertook those studies spent much time in discussing religion, various religions, the comparativeness of religions, the science of religion, the birth and development of religious institutions, etc. The subject was so full of controversies and so widely open to prejudice that it took them a relatively long time to realize the value of purely historical investigations conducted as other historical investigations are, without parti pris or without desire of either apologetics or disparagement. The history of that discipline is well known, because of the methodical writings of many scholars[54] and of the lectures delivered at the international congresses of the history of religion.

The first of these congresses took place in Paris, in 1900,[55] and the latest one in Amsterdam, in 1950. These congresses were more important than the art congresses, because they attracted the attention of more scholars, indeed, there are far more men professionally concerned with religion and its past than there are concerned with the history of art. Moreover, every religious man is obliged to think historically, if only because he is always obliged to look back to the origin of his religion, while creative artists are more exclusively concerned with their own

---

[54] E.g., the Belgian, Count GOBLET D'ALVIELLA (1846-1925) in his collected essays, *Croyances, rites, institutions* (3 vols., Paris 1911); in vols. 2 and 3.

[55] An earlier congress "The world's first parliament of religions," had been held in Chicago in 1893, but that was something very different in purpose and in realization, a noble appeal to religious toleration rather than to impartial scholarship. The Chicago Congress was philanthropic rather than scientific.

creations and with their own ideas rather than earlier ideas. Every theologian is a scholar *ipso facto,* while very few artists are scholarly minded.

This is the second time that I mention international congresses, because these played a great part in the organization of science and especially in the definition of new disciplines and the formulation of their methods. Such congresses are very useful but not sufficient. The new discipline will scarcely flourish, unless the scholars devoting themselves to it are given opportunities to do their work, to earn a living, and to train apprentices. That condition was fulfilled, both for the history of art and the history of religion. Professors were appointed to teach the history of religion in the four Dutch universities in 1877 and very soon afterwards in Switzerland, Belgium and France. A special chair was established at the Collège de France in 1879. Before the end of the last century, there were a good number of professors of the history of religion or of the science of comparative religion, etc., in the leading universities of the world. The situation was even more favorable to the history of art, for, in addition to professorships in the leading universities, the museums needing curators and experts offered tempting positions to hundreds of scholars.

The third discipline, the history of science, was not so fortunate. It is true, international congresses were organized as early as 1900, but they enjoyed neither the importance nor the popularity of the congresses of the history of art and the history of religion, and their desiderata were not implemented by the creation of professorships.[56] What is even more tragic, when a professorship was finally created at the Collège de France in 1892, the history of science was so badly understood that the professorship was awarded to incompetent persons and did more harm than good.[57] Even today, more than half a century later, the number of professorships in the history of science is still exceedingly small. This suggests that my queries are pertinent. "Is it worthwhile and possible to teach the history of science?" If the general answer of administrators and educators had been yes, the number of professorships would be much greater than it is. How shall we account for the fact that there is, at least, one professor of the history of art and one professor of the history of religion in almost every university and a professor of the history of science in almost none.

*   *   *   *   *

To begin with, let us clear up a misunderstanding, the confusion between the history of science and the history of particular sciences. That confusion is ancient. If we leave out of account various histories written in the 18th century which are too superficial and discursive and

---

[56] For congresses on the history of science, *see* Guide below, Chapter 24.
[57] That story is told with some detail in my article PAUL, JULES and MARIE TANNERY (Isis 38, 33-51, 1947).

even MONTUCLA's history of mathematics (which was in reality a history of mathematical and physical sciences),[58] the first modern history is the history of the inductive sciences by the Reverend WILLIAM WHEWELL (3 vols., London 1837), a book which maintained the dignity of a classic in English libraries and colleges during the whole of the Victorian age and even beyond.[59]   Now this work was curiously built, and it is instructive to examine its structure.   It is divided into 18 books.   The first 5, constituting volume 1, deal respectively with: (1) Greek philosophy; (2) Greek physics; (3) Greek astronomy (the final section of which is entitled Arabic Astronomy, or From Ptolemy to Copernicus; all that in 10 pages); (4) Mediaeval Physics; (5) Formal astronomy after the stationary period, or From Copernicus to Kepler.   Volume 2 bearing the subtitle "mechanical sciences" is also divided into 5 chapters, that is (6) Mechanics; (7) Astronomy; (8) Acoustics; (9) Optics; (10) Thermotics and atmology, i.e., the study of heat and vapors.   The subdivision of volume 3 is more complicated.   That volume deals with 8 sciences, divided into 6 groups.   The subdivision will appear more clearly, if we begin a new paragraph for each group.

The mechanico-chemical sciences: (11) Electricity; (12) Magnetism; (13) Galvanism or Voltaic electricity (last pages 98-101, transition to chemical science).

The analytical science: (14) Chemistry.

The analytico-classificatory science: (15) Mineralogy and crystallography.

Classificatory sciences: (16) Systematic botany and zoology.

Organical sciences: (17) Physiology and comparative anatomy.

The palaetiological sciences: (18) Geology.

There would be much more to say about WHEWELL's cumbrous and artificial classification, but that would lead us too far afield.   It will suffice to remark that WHEWELL's purpose was philosophical rather than historical.   The master of Trinity was following in the footsteps of FRANCIS BACON and was dreaming of "a renovation of sound philosophy directed by the light which the history of science sheds" (his own Preface,

---

[58] GEORGE SARTON: MONTUCLA (Osiris 1, 519-67, 12 figs., 1936).

[59] WHEWELL's History was published in the very year of the Queen's accession. Its influence was considerable in the English world, much less so, I think, on the Continent.   It is true it was translated into German (by the astronomer, J. J. v. LITTROW, Stuttgart 1840-41) but not into French.   I seldom noticed references to it in Continental books.   Though I bought a copy of it as early as 1911 (I have just examined it), I must confess that I have never read it, or much of it.   Indeed, when I began my own studies, better books were available.   I owe a debt to WHEWELL's book, however, the telling of which may amuse the reader.   My first opportunity for teaching the history of science in the United States occurred in 1915 when I was invited to lecture at the summer school of the University of Illinois in Urbana.   That invitation was extended to me thanks to the Carnegie Endowment for International Peace and to the personal interest of Mr. EDMUND JANES JAMES (1855-1925), who was then president of that University.   Mr. JAMES showed much kindness to me, which I remember with gratitude.   He had been trained as an economist; he told me that his interest in the history of science, and indirectly in me, was due to his reading WHEWELL's book, which by that time I myself had almost forgotten.

p. ix). He was influenced also by the "Preliminary discourse on the study of natural philosophy" which his friend, Sir JOHN HERSCHEL, had published a few years previously (1830, 1831).[60] For such philosophical and pedagogical tendencies a classification was necessary. The result of it, irrespective of its value, was that his work was not an integrated history of science but a collection of separate histories printed under one cover. Each of the chapters, 6 to 18, deals with a branch of science from the beginning of the seventeenth century to his own time. WHEWELL's work was not historically up-to-date at the time of its first publication; it is at present almost entirely out-of-date. It is a dangerous book for young students of the history of science, but it has itself become a document of great value enabling us to recapture the scientific outlook of a hundred years ago. Nothing illustrates better the backwardness of our studies than the fact that WHEWELL's book was still commanding the respect of many thoughtful readers at the beginning of this century.

If the French readers of last century were immune to WHEWELL's teaching, they were submitted to that of FERDINAND HOEFER (1811-78), a German exile who spent the best part of his life in Paris and published a series of books dealing each of them with the history of a particular science or group of sciences.[61] The best of them was his history of chemistry which continued an old German tradition. It first appeared in 1842-43 and devoted 1046 pages to that history as against the 80 pages of chapter 14 in WHEWELL's treatise. It was reprinted with a new final chapter (1868-69). Instead of improving his knowledge of the history of chemistry, a field in which he might have become a master comparable to his great rival, HERRMANN KOPP,[62] he allowed himself to become a bookseller's hack and published in quick succession a history of physics and chemistry (1872), a history of botany, mineralogy and geology (1872), a history of zoology (1872), a history of astronomy (1873), a history of mathematics (1874). These books became standard books in the French world, were frequently reprinted, and are found to this day on the reference shelves of French libraries. Their influence was not good.

It is curious to note that the Whewellian-Hoeferian method of dealing with each branch of science separately, instead of attempting to take them all together in a straight chronological order, is still followed today to some extent by ABRAHAM WOLF, sometime professor in the University of London.[63]

---

[60] HERSCHEL's book was philosophical and methodological rather than historical in purpose; yet it included a number of historical remarks. It was far more popular on the Continent than WHEWELL's, for it was translated into French (1834) and Italian (1840). WHEWELL's work was dedicated to HERSCHEL, who was working at that time at the Observatory of Feldhausen near Cape Town.

[61] SARTON: HOEFER and CHEVREUL (Bulletin of the History of Medicine, 8, 419-45, Baltimore, 1940).

[62] MAX SPETER: Vater KOPP (Osiris, 5, 392-460, 1938).

[63] ABRAHAM WOLF: History of science, technology and philosophy in the sixteenth and seventeenth centuries. With the cooperation of F. DANNEMANN and A. ARMITAGE (720 p., 316 ill., London 1935; Isis, 24, 164-67); History of science, tech-

The first satisfactory textbook dealing with the history of science as a whole was the German work issued in 4 volumes by the late FRIEDRICH DANNEMANN.[64] The term satisfactory should be understood in a relative sense; that textbook was sufficiently comprehensive when it appeared, and much of it was based on original documents. Indeed, it was composed partly to serve as a kind of framework to the *Klassiker der exakten Wissenschaften,* edited by the German physico-chemist, WILHELM OSTWALD.[65] Brief as it is, even sketchy in many parts and incomplete, it is, nevertheless, the most elaborate work of its kind in any language. This statement is less a praise of DANNEMANN's achievement than a proof of the infancy of our studies and of the immense amount of work which remains to be done.

DANNEMANN's main merit lies in the fact that he really tried to explain, as the title put it, "science in its evolution and 'hanging together' (wholeness)." Instead of dividing the subject into large scientific groups (mechanics, astronomy, physics, etc.) as WHEWELL and HOEFER had done, and as WOLF continued to do, he divided it into short chapters each of them dealing with a scientific topic, and as he avoided putting all the mechanical topics together or all the astronomical ones and so on but arranged his chapters in the rough chronological order of their centers of gravity, he managed to give his readers a deep impression of unity.

That is very important. The history of science is much more than the juxtaposition of all the histories of the special sciences, for its main purpose is to explain the interrelation of all the sciences, their cooperative efforts, and their common aims and methods. The division of science into sciences is to a large extent artificial and apparent only in concrete cases. It is clear that a collector of butterflies need not study thermodynamics, and that an observer of meteors can do very well without botany or palaeontology. It is also clear that the great mass of our scientists and technicians are so deeply specialized that they can no longer see the wood for the trees, or the tree for the twigs. They are like birds standing upon peripheral twigs who fancy their twig is the thing, and nothing else matters.

These facts explain the difficulty of making the history of science acceptable to men of science and also the very necessity and urgency of doing so. Can there be a more natural way of opposing excessive spe-

---

nology and philosophy in the eighteenth century (814 p., 345 ill., London 1938; Isis, 31, 450).

[64] FRIEDRICH DANNEMANN (1859-1936): Die Naturwissenschaften in ihrer Entwicklung und in ihrem Zusammenhange (4 vols., 1910-13; Isis, 2, 218-22; second edition, 4 vols., 1920-23; Isis, 4, 110, 563; 6, 115-16).

[65] The *Klassiker der exakten Wissenschaften* were founded and edited by WILHELM OSTWALD (1853-1932), and their publication was begun by W. ENGELMANN in Leipzig, 1899 (Isis, 1, 99, 706; 2, 153). It is the largest collection of original scientific texts ever published; the texts are published in German translation with commentaries by specialists. More than 200 volumes have appeared; the latest was, I think, the one devoted to MAX VON LAUE (no. 204, 1923; Isis, 5, 526). As DANNEMANN's history was largely based upon the *Klassiker,* it tended to ignore or minimize the discoveries omitted in that collection, *e.g.,* those of CLAUDE BERNARD!

cialization than by showing that all those twigs belong to the same tree, the old tree of knowledge, which stood in the garden of Eden? And how best can we show that than by describing the growth of the tree?— Now the growth of that tree, that is the history of science.

We remarked that that history is much more than the sum of special histories; it is also much less. The special histories are, of necessity, far more technical, while in the general history, the humanistic and social elements are much stronger; for that history deals not only with every branch of science and with their various interrelations and mutual repercussions but also with the impact of all the social and philosophical influences to which they are all submitted. Every great discovery overflows its original field in many ways. The history of instruments implies the history of physics and chemistry, irrespective of their uses. The microscope is built by physicists and used by biologists, physicians, crystallographers, chemists, etc. The chemical revolution was also a physiological revolution. The development of thermodynamics did not simply affect the physical sciences, it influenced deeply our philosophy. The theory of evolution dominates the whole of modern thought. The development of, say, photographic or statistical methods concerns all the sciences. This list might be extended endlessly. There are, it is true, discoveries which are so small that they cause no stir outside of their own little field; they may be abandoned to the historian of that field; such discoveries do not affect the tree but only a few twigs; the historian of science may safely overlook them.

From this point of view there are interesting resemblances and differences between the history of science, on the one hand, and the history of religion, on the other. The last-named discipline was unsectarian from the beginning; in fact, its purpose was more often anti-sectarian than pro-sectarian. The first historians of religion were anxious to study religion per se as a general attribute and desire of the human spirit always and everywhere. This led naturally to the study of what was called comparative religion, and for the most scholarly minded it led also to impartial history. On the other hand, each religion developed very much within its own field; Buddhism was not influenced by Christianity, nor Parseeism by Islām. The situation is very different from that of science, for every science may influence willy-nilly all the others, and the synthesis is unavoidable. Visit the great laboratories and observatories, and you will find scientists of many kinds working together, needing one another. In a modern observatory, there are, of course, astronomers but also mathematicians, physicists, chemists, and sometimes biologists and geologists are called in consultation.

The arts grow together, too, but they are not bound together as closely as the sciences. Their integration is tangible enough in a cathedral the building of which required the collaboration of architects, sculptors, painters, and decorators, while fulfillment of the offices and rites called for musicians and stage managers. In spite of that, the arts developed, to a large extent, independently and each is autonomous. Hence, one may study the past of one of them very profitably, say, the history of painting or the history of music. Each of these histories is much more complete and much more revealing, not only of the whole artistic but also of the whole social life, than the history of any particular science could possibly be. Moreover, art is so deeply connected with sentiments and feelings that it is much more justified to study its national development than to study the national development of any science. A history of Russian or Italian science would be somewhat artificial; while the histories of Russian music or Italian painting are relatively self-contained.

The history of special sciences is very useful for many purposes, technical and philosophical, but totally insufficient, if our purpose is to explain the development of mankind or the organization of knowledge.

※   ※   ※   ※   ※

The main objection that one can make to the history of science is that it is far too big a subject. Think of it! The history of all knowledge everywhere and throughout the ages. Is it possible to encompass such a field?, ask the sceptics. Their doubts are fully justified. It is not yet possible, or it is possible only in a first approximation, but this does not mean that it is worthless to try. Moreover, many scientists resent the preposterous ambition of the historians—to know the whole of science plus the whole of history. How could anybody do it? Historians may seem to be soaring high up in the clouds "au dessus de la mêlée." What do they really know?, would the scientist ask. What do they know down to brass tacks? What could they do with their knowledge? Could they use this instrument and make correct measurements with it? Could they solve this particular problem? The historian might answer that he does not try to know things "down to brass tacks"—but down to the roots which is very different; he does not try to know for the sake of solving individual problems but rather for the sake of understanding the general situation; he does not try to apply his knowledge to practical and immediate purposes, but he tries to understand the relationship of ideas as deeply as possible. Of course, his way of doing this may be offensive; his own knowledge (however he may define it) may be inadequate and superficial; he may be conceited and too easily satisfied with insufficient surveys. We are not dealing here, however, with the shortcomings of historians of science which are as varied and numerous as the shortcomings of other men. Our concern is different: is it possible to have a general knowledge of science and history, that is, of nature and of man? Is it possible to unravel the spiritual vicissitudes of the men of every age and climate who faced nature, tried to solve its riddles, to understand its mysteries and take advantage of them, to grasp its wholeness, to guess its purpose, and to adapt themselves to it? I believe it is possible and my faith is strengthened by the successful efforts of many great scholars.

General knowledge, it should be noted, is not the same as universal knowledge. The latter is beyond human reach, the former not. When I read a scientific or learned journal, I am always impressed by the large

number of facts with which I am unfamiliar; yet, I do not feel disqualified
from understanding a subject, because I do not know every detail of it.
Let us take a simple example.   Consider two teachers of geography, the
former teaches the geography of England and the second the geography
of the world.   The former could make fun of the latter saying, "I have
spent my life studying the geography of England, and in spite of that,
I am still learning new facts every day.   Think of my colleague who
presumes to teach the geography of the whole world.   He has seen only
a small part of it, and as you know, there are some parts which no scholar
has ever seen."   His fallacy lies in believing that the geography of the
world is a larger subject than the geography of England.   It is not.
Both subjects are equally inexhaustible; they are equal in infinitude.
All that we can say is that the two subjects are very different.   It is
probable that both instructors teach in the same time the same number
of facts; their two collections of facts are different but about equal.   Not
only does the world geographer abandon many of the facts of the English geographer, but he would give proof of ignorance and stupidity if
he introduced them in his own survey.

   This example is perhaps too simple to be convincing; yet, it suffices
to illustrate the general truth.   One may know a general field without
knowing every detail of it.   Such knowledge may be almost worthless
for practical work in that very field, but it is sufficient to realize the nature and peculiarities of that field and its relationship to other fields.
One thing is certain: our two geographers must know the basic facts of
geography.   They cannot know them too well; in the same way, the
historian of science must know the general facts and theories of science,
he must be as familiar as possible with at least one branch of it or he
will remain unable to understand anything clearly.   We shall come back
to that presently.   After all, is that situation different from any other
in education?   Can one expect the man who teaches chemistry to have
a first-hand knowledge of the whole of chemistry?   Of course not, but
why should he?   All that we claim is that he should have a first-hand
knowledge of a part of his field.

                    *   *   *   *   *

   As our studies are still in the pioneer stage, they must necessarily suffer from pioneer imperfections and crudities.   If it be your lot to live
on the frontier, you must do without many conveniences; but that should
not prevent you from living a well integrated life.   As the laborers are
few, historians of science are, more often than not, alone in their university, and this obliges them to be like the frontiersmen, jacks of all
trades.   When we bear in mind the specialization of tasks in our history
departments (ancient history, classical antiquity, middle ages, Renaissance, colonial history), each jealously guarded against trespassers, it
seems foolish to expect one scholar to be equally familiar with every
period of history plus the whole of science.   It cannot be done.   It is
absurd, quoth the sceptic.   And yet in this pioneer stage, it must be
done, and it can be done.

Let me give you an example. I trust you will allow me to relate the results of my own experience. I do not choose it because it is my own, but simply because it is the one which I know by far the best. It has been my privilege to teach the history of science in Harvard University for many years, more than thirty, a lifetime. In the course of that long period, I have lectured on almost every aspect and problem of science; I have delivered many hundreds of different lectures. Some subjects are so important that I have come back to them repeatedly; yet, as at least two years would elapse before I could come back to the same topic and as I was attentive to every novelty concerning it and never stopped gathering new ideas, asking myself new questions, evoking new doubts or solving old ones, when I finally came back to that topic, both the topic and myself were somewhat different; the canvas of my lecture remained perhaps the same, but it was not filled in exactly in the same way. The accent was not put on the same details nor the emphasis in the same places. I am not expressing here vague generalities. As I have generally preserved old lecture notes, I could reconstruct, if it were worthwhile, which it is not, the evolution of my views on every important subject, say, FARADAY, DARWIN, or PASTEUR, the discovery of analytical geometry, or of the calculus, the circulation of the blood, or the periodic system. Between one lecture on any one of those subjects and the next, many things might occur, and some of them did occur, for example, the publication of unknown documents, or of a new biography, or a new discovery throwing new light upon the old one, contradicting it, or on the contrary, justifying it, or amplifying it, putting it altogether in a new perspective. It has been truly said of political history that even the best books have no finality; for, on the one hand, new facts are constantly exhumed which may modify our knowledge of the past, even of the most distant past,[66] and on the other hand, we see the past in a different light as our experience increases. The past, as we know it, is not irremediable and final. It could be so only in the eyes of an omniscient god, knowing not only the whole past but the whole future as well. If that be true of political history, it is even more true of the history of science. Think of the theories of light. At the end of last century, the wave theory seemed to be established forever. Crucial experiments had proved its correctness; the electro-magnetic theory had brought a beautiful confirmation. The judgment of any historian writing at that time would have been different from our own. A similar remark would apply to the history of the periodic system; the introduction of the idea of atomic numbers threw an entirely new light on it. And to take an earlier example, GALILEO's discussion showing that the number of square numbers is as large as the number of positive integers was intriguing,[67] but it did not assume its full interest until the theory of infinite aggregates had been

---

[66] Indeed, our knowledge of pre-Hellenic times in the Near East has been deeply modified within our own days. Much of it was entirely unknown before, and the rest is almost entirely renewed or reinterpreted.

[67] Discorsi e dimostrazioni matematiche intorno à due nuoue scienze (p. 78, Leida 1638).

completed by GEORG CANTOR (1845-1918).   It is always the same thing.
We only see what we already know, hence our appreciation of the past
changes as the future unrolls.   Scholars of the seventeenth century who
were more familiar with the Greek language than we are could not understand Greek science as well as we do, but our knowledge of it is
not by any means completed.   As to mediaeval science, we are only
beginning to appreciate its true value without exaggeration of praise or
disparagement.   The darkness of the Dark Ages of which uneducated
scientists speak so glibly is partly the darkness of their own ignorance
and unwisdom.

Now to return to my own experience.   After many tentatives in various directions, such as an attempt to review the whole field in a single
course (of, say, thirty-five lectures) or of dealing within the same orbit
with a relatively brief period (say, the Renaissance) or with a single
branch of science (say, mathematics or physics), I have come to the conclusion that the needs of honest students in a good college are satisfied
best with the following arrangement.   My general course on the history
of science is a combination of four courses of about thirty-five lectures
each, dealing respectively with (1) antiquity, (2) Middle Ages, (3) the
fifteenth, sixteenth and seventeenth centuries, (4) the eighteenth and
nineteenth centuries with glimpses of the twentieth.   These courses are
independent.   Few students attend the four of them, and fewer still are
able to take them in the proper order.   Classical students may take only
the first, mediaevalists only the second, scientific students only the third
and fourth or only the fourth.   I offer only two such courses each year,
never more, but sometimes less.   Hence, two years at least will elapse
before I come back to the same subject.[68]   This interval is long enough
to make possible a partial renewal not only of that subject but of myself.

To be sure, each of these courses is a summary, but it is perhaps of
sufficient length to satisfy the majority of the students and to encourage
a few of them to go ahead and seek more knowledge either with my help
or without.   Consider the case of ancient science.   I doubt whether it
would be possible to give a fair idea of its richness and diversity and to
place it clearly in its cultural background in much less than thirty or
thirty-five lectures.   One must devote one lecture to the pre-historic
beginnings, two or three more to Egyptian and Babylonian antiquities.
(This is running at full speed.)   There remain then some thirty lectures,
or less, for the whole of Hellenic, Hellenistic and Roman culture, from
HOMER down to PROCLOS, a stretch of at least fourteen centuries.   During those centuries, not only did science develop in many directions but
the cultural, philosophical, social, and religious background was constantly modified.   Whenever I try to explain such momentous changes
in thirty lectures, I cannot help feeling that my speed is dangerous.   A
little more speed and everything would vanish.   The survey would become almost meaningless.   This is the more true, because a great num-

---

[68] Not necessarily to every subject, for the contents of each course varies somewhat
from each offering to the next one.   As the total of lectures is fixed, it is not possible
to introduce a new subject without dropping an old one.

ber of my students have no classical education whatsoever, and except when they are of Greek descent, have no knowledge of Greek. My course on ancient science is sometimes their classical initiation; in such cases, it is utterly insufficient, yet I hope that even then it may possibly awaken a dormant interest, not only in science but also in ancient wisdom.

I need not discuss mediaeval science, because I have already spoken of it in my second lecture, but it is worthwhile to insist once more upon my attitude concerning oriental science. Arabic science must be dealt with some fulness, because it is an intrinsic·part of our own traditions. As to Hindu and Chinese science, important as they undoubtedly are, there is no time to discuss them in the usual courses, for any such discussion would be a digression taking us too far away from the main tracks. It is well, however, to speak sometimes of India and China, if only by way of contrast and comparison and to make the students realize the coexistence of scientific efforts which, insofar as they reached a part of the truth, converged with the western efforts. The men of science of India and China were trying to solve problems which were essentially the same as ours; their solutions were sometimes the same as ours, sometimes curiously different; the differences are as instructive as the resemblances. I only wish such comparisons might be made more often and more thoroughly, but then our courses would be incomplete in other respects or altogether disjointed.

It all comes down to this, that even a course like mine extending to 140 lectures is barely sufficient to give the student a bird's-eye view of science. And yet, I am told that many teachers are expected to cover the whole field in half that time, or even in a third or a quarter of it. What happens then?

We shall come back to that presently, but I must first complete the account of my experience with a sad confession. I have never given a lecture which satisfied me, because I have hardly ever had that feeling of security and happiness, which is a scholar's best reward when he has finally succeeded in checking every statement down to its ultimate sources. This failure is due to the fact that I had to deal not with one separate subject which I would have leisure to study thoroughly but with hundreds of subjects jostling each other. It was also due to the immaturity of our studies. The situation is vastly different in older fields, such as English history, or English literature, in which elaborate monographs are available for every point of importance. On the contrary, if an expert opens any "history of science," wherein everything seems to be neatly explained, he recognizes unwarranted statements on almost every page. If he be honest, he will do his best to trace those statements to their sources, to prove them or disprove them, and finally to present a new statement nearer to the truth. He can do that to his satisfaction in some instances, but if he be a teacher of the history of science in general, he is soon obliged to move on. In other words, thousands of investigations remain to be made, and the writing of the history of science will improve gradually in proportion as those investigations are carried through.   No one scholar is competent or has time enough to make them all.   For every period, for every science or branch of science, for every country or cultural group, there is plenty of work left for many generations of scholars.   This does not matter so much as long as we are fully aware of the imperfections of our knowledge; more work for our successors means also more joy for them.

✿   ✿   ✿   ✿   ✿

It is hard and tantalizing to cover the whole field in, say, a series of 130 to 150 lectures.   What would be the fate of a teacher who was expected to cover it in 60 lectures or 40 or even less?   There is a way out, however, and that is simply not to attempt to cover the whole of it. After all, if any teacher finds that the subject is too vast, he can always, to some extent, restrict it.   As the most interesting part of the history of science for young men of science of today is naturally modern science, a teacher could hardly leave that out; he could focus his lectures on modern science or rather on particular topics to which the very progress of science is giving a new significance.

Indeed, the history of nineteenth and twentieth century science is so enormous that it can only be dealt with in a given course in one of two ways.   Either the instructor may attempt to cover the whole of it, and that will oblige him to give a catalogue of facts so bare as to lose meaning,[69] or he will select only a few examples and treat them as fully as possible.[70]   The second solution is undoubtedly the better one, and it implies the teacher's salvation.   The samples should be selected in different parts of the field in order to give of it as comprehensive a view as possible.   Yet the teacher will be guided, to some extent, by his own merits and shortcomings.   It would be fair for himself and the students to select the subjects which he knows best, and, which is more important, to leave out the subjects that he does not feel competent to deal with.   The main thing is that the students be made to realize the complexity and wealth, the diversity of methods, the social implications of modern science.

As to the more distant past (however you define that), it may possibly be sacrificed.   It is, in fact, what most teachers do.   They either leave it completely out or reach the sixteenth century in a few gigantic jumps.   That is deplorable, but if the teacher is assigned the task of

---

[69] A good example of highly compressed history is that given by SIEGMUND GÜNTHER (1848-1923): Geschichte der Naturwissenschaften (2nd ed., 2 little vols. of the Philipp Reclams Universal-Bibliothek which were selling at 20 Pf. each, 136 p., 290 p., ill., Leipzig 1909).   The limit in that direction was attained in the Handbuch zur Geschichte der Naturwissenschaften und der Technik, edited by LUDWIG DARMSTAEDTER (1846-1927) (2nd edition, 1273 p., Berlin 1908); this is simply a list of discoveries and inventions in chronological order from 3500 B.C. to 1908 A.D., a very useful work which ought to be improved and continued (Isis 26, 56-58, 1936).

[70] This was done very well by JAMES B. CONANT: On understanding science.   An historical approach (162 p., 10 figs., Terry Lectures, New Haven, Yale Press 1947; Isis 38, 125-27).

teaching the history of science in, say, 60 lectures and is warned to give due importance to modern science, what else can he do? He will probably devote 40 to 50 lessons to modern science and the small remainder to the whole past. This is bad, but not as terrible as it might seem. The main point is to teach well what he teaches, and always to warn the students that much, very much, is unavoidably left out.

If the whole of science is considered as a continuous living body, which it is, moving with us toward the future, head forward, of course, and the tail trailing back to the beginnings, and if we have no time to study the whole beast, then we must concentrate our attention on the head rather than the tail. If we must let something go, let it be the past, the more distant past. Yet, it is a pity, a thousand pities.

As a historian of ancient and mediaeval science, I may be suspected of prejudice in their favor, yet I have made many investigations concerning modern science and devoted many more lectures to it, hundreds of them, than to the rest. I can assure you that the history of ancient and mediaeval science is not only very interesting, even from the most modern point of view, but that it can be used to fulfill the main purpose of our teaching, to wit, to explain the meaning of science, its function, its methods, its logical, psychological and social implications, its deep humanity, its importance for the purification of thought and the integration of our culture.[71]

The problems of ancient and mediaeval science have this advantage over those of modern science that they are on the whole simpler, more free of disturbing technicalities and easier to discuss before a nontechnical audience; yet many of those problems are fundamental.

*   *   *   *   *

In the selection of professors in charge of a new discipline, the most important factor to be considered is the man himself and his singular gifts. Of course, one whose knowledge is too special and esoteric could hardly be selected except as a second man, another being responsible for the main teaching; but barring extreme cases, it would be easier to adapt the program to the man rather than do the opposite. The best candidate might be a physician, more familiar with medical and biological matters than with the mathematical sciences. That would be regrettable, yet might be better than to take a poorer candidate who knows mathematics. The teaching of the former might be excellent within its limitations. The professor of the history of science in small universities, where there can be only one, might be a physician at one time and be succeeded by an astronomer and the latter by a chemist. The teaching would thus vary from man to man, yet if they were good men, each would be able to teach the outstanding messages of science and tradition, knowledge and humanity.

Or the apostolic succession might imply other difficulties. At one

---

[71] It is noteworthy that my courses on ancient and mediaeval science are as well attended as my other courses, in spite of the fact that the majority of my students are scientific or premedical.

time, the teacher might be a student of technology, primarily interested in the technical wonders of our age; his successor might be a classical scholar more at home in the Greek writings; the third might be a mediaevalist, etc.

The Hellenist and the mediaevalist would not be as much out of step as one might think, because every teacher would have to satisfy one indispensable requirement. He should be deeply familiar with at least one branch of today's science and he should have a more superficial acquaintance with various other branches. By deep familiarity is meant work at the front, experimental work in the laboratory or observational work in the observatory or in the field. If he met that requirement, his other learning, whether classical, mediaeval or oriental would not tend to sidetrack him completely. He would remain, first of all, not a historian or a philologist but a historian of science. His scientific training and experience would guarantee his adequate treatment of scientific subjects and would give him the needed authority to talk about them in the presence of young scientists. Nothing can be worse in the teaching of the history of science than learned discussion of topics of which the instructor has no inward knowledge; the more learned, the worse it is.

Just how detailed should the discussion of a scientific topic be? It is not possible to give a general answer to this question. Each topic will require separate treatment. This much can be said, the students must be given a feeling of concreteness and genuineness which implies a certain amount of detail. Why is precise knowledge always desirable? Simply because we can never be sure of anything unless we know it as exactly as possible. The procedure of our criminal courts is very instructive in that respect. A man cannot be convicted of a murder unless the circumstances of that murder have been minutely described. The same procedure must be followed in the discovery of truth. A general statement may be right or wrong: the necessary checking is possible only if we come to well defined facts. The history of science is a good means of illustrating that point of view not only for its own sake but also for the strengthening of knowledge and for the unification of mankind. Whatever be the utility of mystical ideas in religion, mankind cannot be unified on a mystical basis but only on tangible facts, objective, impartial, and controllable knowledge. Darkness covers too many crimes and opens too many opportunities to trouble-makers; truthfulness and light are the first conditions of social health.

The teaching of the history of science should be as concrete and clear as possible rather than philosophical and foggy. Its concreteness will be easier to attain if the instructor is given facilities to make a few simple experiments and to illustrate his course with maps, charts and other exhibits. E.g., he should be able to show the students some of the old instruments and demonstrate their use.[72] Such equipment

---

[72] It is difficult to explain simple problems, let us say, of mathematical geography or astronomy without models. I have always been embarrassed by the lack of models when I discussed the ancient theories of homocentric spheres, of eccentrics and epicycles. The necessary models should be easily available to the instructor.

might be borrowed from a technical museum or else the old instruments might be replaced by new copies, less impressive perhaps than the originals but just as good for the sake of demonstration.

The main qualification of a teacher, it is worthwhile repeating it, is a sufficient familiarity with the scientific problems and methods of today, a familiarity which no one can acquire except in the laboratory, the observatory or the hospital. The necessity of that qualification is obvious enough when the teacher must deal with modern or contemporary science, which is the general case, but it exists in every case. A good and broad scientific training is needed to explain properly the history not only of modern science but also of ancient and mediaeval science.

That qualification is necessary but far from sufficient. The time is past when courses on the history or philosophy of science were organized to satisfy the historical dilettantism of a distinguished man of science. The teacher should be historically minded and should have a sufficient grasp of historical methods. He should be philosophically minded and sufficiently polyglot. Moreover, his value, like that of any other teacher, is partly measured by his own investigations and his ability to train other investigators (not the ability of a parrot to train other parrots). It becomes clear that a professor of the history of science should be selected on the same basis as, say, a professor of Greek or a professor of botany. Their qualifications are proved by their publications in their respective fields. There are, of course, many ways of distinguishing oneself as a botanist but the prospective teacher must have distinguished himself in at least one of these ways. No other kind of distinction will be acceptable as a substitute. His main qualifications are his botanical publications and his ability to advance botanical knowledge and to inspire and guide his students.

Impromptu lectures on the basis of one or a few incomplete textbooks, there are no others, will not do any longer. The scholar who is privileged to teach the history of science must be prepared to speak from the abundance of his knowledge and experience. His teaching must be a kind of overflow or otherwise it is not worth having. He is obliged to simplify a great deal, because the subject is so large, the time so short, and the students have many other things to study. I believe his teaching should be as simple as possible, but a simplification without an adequate knowledge of a multitude of unmentioned details is spurious and misleading. Teaching is like paper money which is worth nothing without a gold reserve or other guarantee, hidden but substantial.

It may be objected that the qualifications which have been enumerated are so heavy that few candidates will be found. There will be few candidates at the beginning, but the jobs are equally few; as these increase in number, more candidates will have obtained the necessary training and will become available. With regard to the purely scientific qualifications, I would say that as the technicalities of science increase there will be more and more men whose technical ability and interest will not be equal to their love of science and to whom the work and meditation of a historian will appeal more strongly than research in a laboratory. It is highly probable that laboratory work will be organized more and more on a group basis and such work will not be agreeable to some individuals or will be made disagreeable by rude officers. Thus, some individuals will lose interest in laboratories without therefore losing interest in science or their knowledge of it. The more time they will have spent in the laboratory before abandoning it the better it will be for their teaching. Dislike of laboratory work may bring back scientists to the humanities but is not a quality in itself. Those deserters will not be welcome in our camp unless they meet other requirements. Two fundamental ones, historical interest and philosophical interest, are really qualities with which a man is born and which grow with him. If a man have them, they will take care of themselves; if he lacks them, he is out.

A sufficient linguistic ability, let us say, the ability to read Latin and the outstanding languages of today is also a gift, yet it may be acquired, and can be greatly increased. The main difficulty is the lack or the weakness of Latin. We are beginning to suffer for our neglect of Latin in high schools and in colleges. Short-sighted administrators or educators who are driving Latin out do not realize that they are burning behind us the ships that brought us where we are.

The teacher of the history of science in the larger universities must be prepared to face a paradoxical situation. As his students are recruited from every department, the largest common denominator of scientific knowledge is necessarily low, and he must avoid technicalities; on the other hand, some of the students may be taking very advanced scientific courses and will prick their ears whenever he approaches their own field. He must be prepared to meet their questions and will not retain their confidence unless he can answer most of them. If he be well prepared those advanced students will stimulate him and actually help him to give better lectures and to write better books. The cooperation thus obtained is of the highest value but he must deserve it.

*   *   *   *   *

The following anecdote will illustrate the point which has just been made. When I am lecturing on Euclid, I seldom fail to quote his very ingenious proof of the theorem that there are an infinite number of prime numbers. As I like to connect ancient knowledge with the new, even with the very newest (the past explains the present and *vice versa*), I could not resist the temptation in one of my Euclidean lectures to refer to prime pairs not mentioned by Euclid (*i.e.*, prime numbers of the form $2n + 1, 2n + 3$ like 11 and 13, 17 and 19, 41 and 43). Like the primes themselves, the prime pairs have the peculiarity of becoming rarer and rarer as one passes from smaller numbers to larger ones; the prime pairs become exceedingly rare indeed. In spite of that, we have the feeling that there are an infinite number of them. I proceeded to say that this proposition had remained uncertain until recently when Dr. Charles N. Moore, professor at the University of Cincinnati, had presented an involved but convincing proof of it.[73] After my lecture, one of the students came to me and told me very gently that I was mistaken and that the infinity of prime pairs had not yet been proved. I bade him to come to my study to discuss the matter. The upshot of our discussion was that the proof by Professor MOORE had been shown to be imperfect; arguments used in the theory of numbers are often very subtle and tricky. I had read in *Science* the announcement of MOORE's discovery, but the disproof of it had not been registered in *Science* or I had failed to notice it. The student who gave me that valuable information was a graduate student who had been studying prime pairs for the last two years and knew more about them than anyone else in the university.

This is the most striking example in my experience of the cooperation which may exist, and should exist, between the teacher and some, at least, of his students. In this case, the student knew very well the topic discussed; in the majority of cases, however, the student does not, but if he be intelligent his queries and his doubts may be very stimulating and oblige the teacher to consider the subject from a new angle. Many of my lectures have been modified because of such queries. Moreover, whenever a student has evoked a point requiring additional explanation or emphasis, I have given the necessary explanation to the whole class,[74] being careful to name and to thank the student who had prompted me.

❀   ❀   ❀   ❀   ❀

Courses on the history of science have often been intrusted to professors whose main function was to teach other subjects. Readers who have followed me thus far will realize the utter unwisdom of that practice. The teaching of the history of science is far too important and too difficult to be treated that way. The very fact that it is not yet standardized as is the case for older disciplines (say, political and diplomatic history, or Greek literature) increases its difficulty. The teacher cannot depend, as many of his colleagues do, on excellent textbooks, each of which is the fruit of a long evolution and of continued selection and correction.

It is generally understood by the administrators of universities that a professor is expected to give about half of his time to teaching and complementary activities, and the other half to research. In this new field, where so much remains to be done and where the work is often slowed up by the absence or the inadequacy of tools, it would be a good policy to allow more than half the time to research. In any case, research would be a very important part of the man's work. It should be realized that the work done by honest historians is difficult and slow;[75]

---

[73] The proof was presented at the Wellesley meeting of the American Mathematical Association in the summer of 1944.

[74] Except, of course, when the point was not significant enough to be explained publicly or when it was too technical to be explained in the available time. Queries the scope of which is too narrow are generally answered by me in writing.

[75] This statement may seem commonplace to historians; I am making it here for the scientific readers who appreciate well enough scientific difficulties, but not at all historical ones

it is thus expensive in time and money. Such honest work brings us nearer to the goal—slowly, very slowly, "pedetemptim"; careless, dishonest work is much faster but it leads nowhere; it is apparently cheap, yet wasteful. It leads downward, not upward. The results of it (books or articles) are hopeless mixtures of good and evil, truth and error, wherein the good and true can no longer be separated from the wrong.

Though I have spent thirty-five years of my life doing naught but studying the history of science, I am only beginning to know it. Studying and teaching the history of science is a full-time job. If administrators cannot afford to intrust the teaching to specialists and to give the latter full-time for it, it would be better for all concerned to abandon it. No teaching at all is much cheaper and far less dangerous than bad teaching.

❖   ❖   ❖   ❖   ❖

Whom will the teacher reach? Who will come to him? Most of my students are scientific or pre-medical students, but a few are attracted from the other departments. As always happens, many will select such courses with little reason and without profit, but to others, a very small minority, these lectures will remain a source of inspiration, perhaps the deepest of their college life. The profession of historian of science hardly exists, and hence it would not be fair to encourage students, except a very few, to prepare themselves for it. However, the study of the history of science will help to qualify good men or women for many other para-scientific professions. I mean by that, the literary, historical, philosophical, or even administrative, professions connected with scientific investigations or with scientific teaching, scientific libraries and museums, the editing of scientific periodicals or the writing of scientific books. These para-scientific professions are already numerous, and they require every day more men and better men.

❖   ❖   ❖   ❖   ❖

The responsibilities of the historian of science are greater than they appear on the surface. To write or teach a good account of the development of science is necessary but not sufficient, or rather it is only a means to an end. The end is to help the integration of scientific teaching in all its forms and the integration of our spiritual life.

The teacher of the history of science has the opportunity of showing the interrelation of the branches of science, the profound unity of science behind its infinite variety. In particular, he may show bewildered students how all the courses which they have taken are related to each other and all the things they have learned hang together; such teaching may be for them the best viaticum, a reassurance; the feeling of the unity of science will strengthen their own integrity.

His opportunity, or call it his duty, is even greater, for he must teach the unity not only of science but also of mankind. Men are united by their highest purposes, such as the search for truth. There obtains, therefore, between them a profound unity, in spite of endless differences and disagreements, in spite of greed for power and money among the most rapacious, in spite of the natural hatreds of some men for other men, in spite of intolerance, superstition and cruelty, in spite of wars and revolutions. That underlying unity must be revealed by the teacher as frequently and as fully as possible. Within his own immediate milieu, it is his duty to provide links between a whole gamut of leaders, from the technical barbarians at the extreme left to the well-meaning but ignorant and inefficient humanists at the extreme right. He should help to integrate our spiritual life, on the one hand, by explaining scientific facts and points of view and methods to the humanists, politicians, administrators, and on the other hand, by humanizing the men of science and engineers and reminding them always of the traditions without which our lives, however efficient, remain ugly and meaningless.

His main business is to build bridges—to build bridges between the nations and what is equally important, within each nation, between life, the good life, and technology, between the humanities and science.

*   *   *   *   *

The main value of the history of science to the philosophically minded scientist, the scientist who wishes to understand the indebtedness of his knowledge, lies in its moderating influence. Retrospective views enable him to keep his balance between dogmatism on the one hand, and scepticism and discouragement on the other. They help him to be patient in the words of ROBERT E. LEE:

"The march of Providence is so slow, and our desires so impatient, the work of progress is so immense, and our means of aiding it so feeble, the life of humanity is so long, and that of the individual so brief, that we often see only the ebb of the advancing wave, and are thus discouraged. It is history that teaches us to hope." [76]

That statement is curious in the mouth of a general, especially of a defeated one. It is more applicable to scientific than to political and military matters. One might sometimes despair of political progress, but there is no reason for good men ever to despair or to be ashamed of science.

Above all, the history of science teaches humility. Some of our inventors and technicians may boast as much as they please. By so

---

[76] These beautiful words are quoted by THOMAS BARBOUR: Naturalist at large (p. 287, 1943; Isis, 35, 343). I tried to trace them in LEE's works but failed. I then applied to LEE's foremost biographer, DOUGLAS SOUTHALL FREEMAN: R. E. LEE (4 vols., New York, 1934-35), who kindly wrote to me from Richmond, Virginia, 27 March, 1947:

"If I could answer the question in your letter of March 17th I would be very happy. The quotation from General Lee first was published in an address delivered by Colonel CHARLES MARSHALL at the laying of the cornerstone of the Lee Monument in Richmond, about 1887. Presumably the paragraph was one of those that General LEE had written down, according to a practice of his, during the war. I have always wondered whether he wrote it or found it somewhere and copied it, but I never have been able to answer that question. You will find it quoted at length in my 'R. E. Lee,' Volume IV, page 484."

doing they only reveal their ignorance and arrogance. Men of science have a better right to be proud of the growth of science, but the greatest of them are singularly humble, for they realize that much as has been done, much more remains to be done. The universe is infinitely mysterious. Light and charity are increasing in some places, but there is still an abundance of darkness, injustice, and suffering. Great wars are not only material calamities, they are fantastic retrogressions. Every good scientist is so far from boasting that he would rather walk in sackcloth and ashes. Though he may say to himself that the inventor of new tools cannot be held responsible for the misuses of them by men of prey, he is not quite convinced of that. He is, perhaps, more guilty than he thinks, and in any case he prefers to assume more guilt rather than less.

It is certain that whatever spiritual progress we may be privileged to enjoy, it is due less to our own efforts than to the accumulated efforts of our ancestors. Should we forget that and become too pleased with ourselves, we would soon fall into scepticism and cynicism. Indeed, we are never so much in danger of losing our spiritual freedom as when we boast too much of it. Nobody can teach men of science better than the historian of science the need of reverence for the past, humility for the present, confidence in the future; nobody can give him more strength to follow his path honestly and courageously, to bear evil and suffering, to do his best to alleviate them, to find and publish the truth.

Part II

A FIRST GUIDE *for the* STUDY *of the* HISTORY *of* SCIENCE

PRELIMINARY REMARKS

1) The select bibliography which follows is a great amplification of the one which was published in an appendix to the author's Study of the History of Science (p. 53-70, Cambridge, Massachusetts, 1936). In spite of the fact that it is considerably larger than the list of 1936, it is still very short when one takes into account the immensity of the field.

It is based primarily upon the author's own library and that is not only a cause of strength but also of weakness. No library is perfect and one which like my own is used not only by myself but by many colleagues and students is bound to have lacunas. A not unimportant book may have escaped my attention, because it was "out" when I examined the shelf where it ought to have been or because it has been mislaid by a careless scholar. Moreover, important books sent to me by the author or publishers are given to collaborators for review in *Isis*. Sometimes, I have replaced the book by buying a new copy of it, sometimes not, when I had no particular need of it. In that case, there is no witness left of its existence, except the review (if the reviewer was faithful). I am thus bound to rediscover it, because this bibliography is built secondarily upon *Isis*. This will give the reader an idea of its condensation. For the items published in the seventy-five Critical Bibliographies must number at least seventy-five thousand.[77]

2) The Bibliography is divided into four parts, and each of these parts into 6-8 chapters (*see* Table of Contents). The chapters are not mutually exclusive and parts of their areas overlap. It must thus happen that an item listed in one chapter is listed again in another chapter or might have been listed. In some cases, duplication seemed more expedient than cross-reference.

3) As this book is written in English and will be used mainly by English-reading students, their needs were given priority. More English books are listed than non-English; when a non-English book was translated into English, the English translation is listed, but the other translations (if any) are not; if the non-English book was not translated into English but, say, into French or German, that translation is listed for the sake of readers more familiar with French (or German) than with the original language.

Many books originally published in England are also published in

---

[77] Moreover, these 75,000 notes refer to books or papers published within the last forty years, while the "First Guide" refers to the main publications irrespective of time.

America (and *vice versa*). I have listed the edition available to me
which was sometimes the English edition, sometimes the American.
When the place quoted is New York or Boston, the experienced reader
knows that it might as well be London.

Sometimes the same book has different titles in the English and
American editions. The fact has been mentioned whenever I was aware
of it.

Some authors will entitle their book, say "*The* history of biology."
Others seem to think that it is more modest to phrase the title "A history
of biology." Either article is superfluous and it has generally been left
out. It is quite enough to write "History of biology."

I have tried to give an idea of the size of each item, because it makes
a great difference to the student whether an item covers a hundred pages
or a thousand, but it suffices to indicate that size *grosso modo*. *E.g.*, if
a book has iv + 256 p. it is simply stated 260 p. That indication is but
an approximation. For what matters is the length (or capacity) of a
book, and that length is very incompletely measured by the number of
pages.

4) It was tempting to add critical remarks to each item, and thus to
help the reader to select one book among twenty devoted, say, to the
history of physics. It was not possible to indulge that temptation to any
extent, because it is very difficult to compare twenty books dealing with
the same subject, without unfairness. To begin with, they seldom deal
with the self-same subject. Even when their subject is defined by the
same title "History of mathematics," the areas covered by each author
are not the same; they may overlap considerably but are never identical.

The author has examined almost every book listed by him, but he
did not examine them at the same time. He may have read the one
thirty years ago and the other yesterday; under those conditions it is
clear that comparisons between them would be adventurous and unreliable. The best that he could do was to refer to reviews or shorter
notices in *Isis*, whenever possible. References to the Critical Bibliographies of *Isis* have the additional advantage of bringing the reader in
touch not only with the item he is particularly interested in but also with
many others. It is like hunting for a book in a library where the books
are well classified by subjects: sometimes one does not find the book one
is hunting for, but one may find a better one, that is, one better adapted
to his immediate purpose.

5) The choice of books dealing with a large subject, say, the history
of mathematics is difficult, because the best books generally do not deal
with the whole subject but only with a part of it, and because the subject may be (and is actually) divided and subdivided in many ways
which do not tally. For example, one book is devoted to the history of
trigonometry, another to the history of mathematics in Germany, a third
one to the history of algebra in Italy, a fourth to the history of trigonometry in the sixteenth century, a fifth to the history of reckoning in
England during the Middle Ages.

Some books are too special to be listed; yet, those books may be the most valuable of all in their own field. Nothing is more instructive than a good biography, and when a good biography is not available, the scholar should be ready to use one which is less good yet will answer his need. It was impossible to mention biographies, because a sufficient list of them would require considerable labor and space. Moreover, that is not necessary. It must suffice to warn the reader, that when he is exploring any field (defined by topic, place and time), he should make for himself a list of the great men dominating it and then try to find biographies of them. Some of those biographies might be his best tools.

A general bibliography like this one, a first guide, cannot do more than facilitate for every scholar the preparation of his own. Every investigation must begin with a bibliography, and it must end with a better bibliography.

6) Even within its modest scope, this first guide cannot be as good as it might be, because in spite of every effort the author is bound to overlook some items or (and this is equally bad if not worse) to include items which it would have been better to leave out. Every bibliography contains errors by omission or commission and at best it is bound to be vitiated by an irreducible minimum of accidental arbitrariness. Critics should bear in mind that they are subject to similar accidents. A man had spent many years in France and travelled considerably about the country. He thought that he knew it pretty well, but a friend said to him "Have you been to Rocamadour? " The man admitted that he had not. His friend exclaimed "What a shame! If you have not seen Rocamadour, you have missed the essential, you do not really know France . . ." I can only hope that my own critics will not reproach me for having forgotten Rocamadour and condemn my book on that basis.

I remember with pain that a colleague of mine became unfriendly to me, because I had forgotten to mention a book of his, and he assumed that my omission of it was deliberate. What a mean and unjust supposition! If I had an enemy and he wrote a good book, I would be anxious to mention it; I would mention it with special emphasis, and nothing could please me more than the opportunity of praising it.

7) Many chapters of this bibliography, especially chapter 20, dealing with Journals and Serials on the History (and Philosophy) of Science, were much enriched thanks to the collaboration of Dr. CLAUDIUS F. MAYER of Washington, D.C. My gratitude is expressed to him here and again with more precision, in the preface to that particular chapter.

Various additions to the Bibliography have been kindly suggested by Prof. I. BERNARD COHEN, who is my colleague in Harvard University.

A. HISTORY

1. HISTORICAL METHODS

The best known of general treatises on historical methods are those of BERNHEIM and LANGLOIS-SEIGNOBOS:

ERNST BERNHEIM (1850-   ). **Lehrbuch der historischen Methode** (Leipzig 1889). Second edition 1894; third and fourth, 1903; fifth and sixth 1908. Photographic reprint 1914. I have used the fifth edition entitled Lehrbuch der historischen Methode und der Geschichtsphilosophie. Mit Nachweis der wichtigsten Quellen und Hilfsmittel zum Studium der Geschichte (852 p., Leipzig, Duncker & Humblot, 1908). The book is divided into six parts: (1) Concept and essence of historiography, (2) Methodology, (3) Knowledge of sources (heuristic), (4) criticism, (5) Interpretation (Auffassung), (6) Representation (Darstellung), that is, the final redaction.

CHARLES VICTOR LANGLOIS (1863-1929) and CHARLES SEIGNOBOS (1854-1942): **Introduction aux études historiques** (Preface dated August 1897; first edition, Paris 1898). Second edition 1899, third 1905. I have before me an edition called the fifth, undated, 1913 (?). English translation entitled Introduction to the study of history, by G. G. BERRY. First published, London 1898, reprinted 1907, 1912, 1925, 1926, 1932.

The work is divided into three books. *I.* Preliminary studies (search for documents, auxiliary sciences), *II.* Analytical operations (external and internal criticism), *III.* Synthetic operations (construction, exposition). Two appendices concern the teaching of history in the French high schools and universities.

CH. V. LANGLOIS: **Manuel de bibliographie historique.** In two parts. The first part was first published in Paris 1896, then again in 1901; the second part was first published in 1904. The second edition of the first part and the first of the second form a volume of 634 p. (Paris 1901-4).

The first part deals with bibliographical tools, the second with the history and organization of historical studies in various countries from the Renaissance to the end of the nineteenth century.

Note that the three works mentioned above cover two fields, and even three fields, which are separate yet related in various ways (A) Historical methods and philosophy of history, (B) Historical tools, (C) History of historiography. BERNHEIM covers A and B, LANGLOIS and SEIGNOBOS A, LANGLOIS B and C.

GILBERT JOSEPH GARRAGHAN (S.J.): (1871-   ): **A guide to historical method,** edited by JEAN DELANGLEZ (S.J.) (546 p., Fordham University, New York 1946; Isis 41, 139-43). Bound with it by the publisher is LIVIA APPEL: Bibliographical citation in the social sciences. A handbook of style (30 p., University of Wisconsin, Madison). The book of Father GARRAGHAN and DELANGLEZ is well documented and full of examples; p. 427-31 contain a bibliography of historical method to 1939. Miss APPEL's supplement deals with "style," mechanical details of writing and printing. These details are important but the less one fusses about them the better; each student should learn them by himself, and nobody should bother to teach him, certainly not in college; he ought to know them just as he ought to know how to spell and how to blow his nose.

Mlle LOUISE NOËLLE MALCLÈS is preparing a new bibliographic guide, **Les**

sources du travail bibliographique. Vol. 1, Bibliographies générales has appeared (384 p., Genève 1950); vol. 2 will list special bibliographies relative to Sciences humaines and to Sciences exactes et techniques.

There are many other works answering the general purpose of the books already mentioned, but it would take too long to enumerate them. There are also books of the same kind but of a less general scope. The following three examples may suffice.

GIUSEPPE GABRIELI (1872-1943): **Manuale di bibliografia musulmana.** Parte prima. Bibliografia generale (501 p., Roma 1916; Isis 5, 449-50). Bibliography concerned with Islamic studies. Part 1 was the only part published.

LOUIS JOHN PAETOW (1880-1928): **A guide to the student of medieval history** (Berkeley 1917). Revised edition prepared by the Medieval Academy of America (660 p., New York 1931).

GINO LORIA: **Guida allo studio della storia delle matematiche. Generalità, didattica, bibliografia.** Appendice: Questioni storiche concernenti le scienze esatte. Seconda edizione rifusa ed aumentata (416 p., Milano 1946; Isis 37, 254). First edition, Milano 1916 (Isis 3, 142). This brings us very close to our own field, the history of science, of which the history of mathematics is an essential part. In the absence of a manual for the special use of the historian of science, LORIA's Guida is indispensable to the latter. It is divided into two books plus the four appendices cited in the title:

Book I: Preparation for research in the history of mathematics. (1) Generalities, historical method. (2) Principal works concerning the history of mathematics. (3) Periodicals and societies.
Book II: Auxiliary tools. (1) Generalities. (2) MSS, especially oriental. (3) Greek and Roman mathematics. (4) Mathematics of ancient non-European nations. (5) Bibliography and biographical collections relative to modern times. (6) Other biographical sources. (7) Complete works and letters. (8) Catalogues and bibliographies, general and mathematical. (9) Reviews and critics of mathematical writings. (10) Various kinds of historical writings.

Epilogue: Evolution of mathematical historiography. Appendices: (1) What is the history of science? (2) The history of mathematics as a branch of teaching in universities. (3) Has mathematical teaching developed in a regular way? (4) Unity of mathematics.

GEORGE SARTON: **The history of science and the new humanism** (New York 1931; reprinted with additions, 216 p., Harvard University, Cambridge 1937); **The study of the history of mathematics** (114 p., Harvard University 1936); **The study of the history of science** (76 p., Harvard University, 1936). The purpose of these three volumes is largely methodological, but the two last named are followed by select bibliographies. The mathematical bibliography is of course much smaller than LORIA's.

Many nations of Europe and America have encouraged the publication of guides for the study of their national history in all its ramifications. Some of these guides are extremely elaborate and historians of science will be well advised to consult them. If they have to investigate a French item, they should consult AUGUSTE MOLINIER (1851-1904) and others: **Les sources de l'histoire de France des origines jusqu'en 1815** (17 vols., Paris 1901-34); if a German one, DAHLMANN-WAITZ: **Quellenkunde der deutschen Geschichte.** First edition by FRIEDRICH CHRISTOPH DAHLMANN (1785-1860) (70 p., Göttingen 1830), 3rd ed. by GEORG WAITZ (242 p., Göttingen 1869), 8th ed. by PAUL HERRE (1310 p., Leipzig 1912; Isis 1, 537, 9th ed. by HERMANN HAERING (1332 p., Leipzig 1931-32). Critical lists of such national bibliographies will be found in BERNHEIM, LANGLOIS, PAETOW, LORIA.

Historical methods can be learned only by personal experience in their use. Books like those of BERNHEIM and LANGLOIS are useful, however, because they attract the reader's attention to various possibilities of error, of which he might be unaware. It is well to study or to read one of those guides from time to time, as one's experience and caution increase. Experience is necessary but insufficient. One's critical sense should be periodically resharpened. Moreover, one's knowledge of valuable tools is never complete, not only because new tools are published almost every year, but also because no matter how diligent a scholar may be there are always some ancient tools which he managed to overlook. I have realized this more than once to my mortification.

2. HISTORICAL TABLES AND SUMMARIES

Many historical tables have been compiled from time to time and for various purposes. Historical books often include synchronic tables, which serve as summaries and index.

I have often referred to the **Time table of modern history** A.D. 400-1870, compiled and arranged by M. MORISON (*2nd* ed., album 31 × 38 cm., London 1908). First ed. 1901.

The best summary known to me is the **Encyclopaedia of world history.** A revised and modernized version of PLOETZ's Epitome. Compiled and edited by WILLIAM L. LANGER (1250 p., Boston 1940; Isis 33, 164; revised edition 1948).

A. M. H. J. STOKVIS: **Manuel d'histoire, de généalogie et de chronologie de tous les états du globe** (3 vols., Leiden 1888, 1889, 1893). On STOKVIS *see* Isis (39, 237).

The student of special areas or periods should compile his own tables *ad hoc* and always be ready to revise them and keep them up-to-date. Those tables would become one of his best tools.

3. HISTORICAL ATLASES

WILLIAM R. SHEPHERD: **Historical atlas** (Seventh edition revised and enlarged, New York 1929). This is an unpretentious school atlas, first published in 1911, which I have been using profitably for many years. It is partly derived from the atlas of FRIEDRICH WILHELM PUTZGER (1849-), very popular in Germany (first ed., Bielefeld 1878; 50*th* ed. 1931).

There are many other atlases, many more detailed, but SHEPHERD's will answer the average queries. The historian interested in a definite country or period should consult the special atlases devoted to them. Indeed, each civilized country has published its own atlases (geographical, historical, economic, etc.). If his needs are very special, he should prepare his own maps and keep them within sight or within immediate reach.

REGINALD FRANCIS TREHARNE (1901-): **Bibliography of historical atlases and hand-maps for use in schools** (24 p., Historical Association, London 1939); **Handlist of historical wall-maps** (72 p., Historical Association, London 1945).

One should also consult plain geographical atlases for a better understanding of the past; indeed, administrative boundaries have changed but geographical realities have remained pretty much the same. There are many general atlases covering the whole world and others covering only (or chiefly) definite countries. The general atlases devote more attention to their own country of origin and its dependencies than to the other countries. For the study of a French topic it is naturally better to consult a French atlas, and so on.

The maps and notices published in guide books such as Baedekers and Blue Guides often contain information not available elsewhere.

Historical students should never deal with any event without ascertaining as exactly as possible its location in space and time. They should try to realize also contemporary events and contiguous places. If they are not able to visit those places, they should try to obtain as good a knowledge of them as possible by means of maps, photographs and descriptions.

4. GAZETTEERS

The problem of gazetteers is as complex for the historian of science as the problem of encyclopaedias. In both cases, he cannot be satisfied with up-to-date information, he needs information relative to lower chronological levels.

GEORGE GOUDIE CHISHOLM (1850-1930): **Longmans' Gazetteer of the world** (1800 p., London 1895). New impressions 1899, 1902, 1906, 1920.

Ritters geographisch-statistisches Lexikon (9th ed., 2 vols., Leipzig 1905-6). Third ed. 1847. The first editions were compiled by KARL RITTER (1779-1859).

GOTTARDO GAROLLO (1850-1917): **Dizionario geografico universale** (5th ed., 2 vols., 2204 p., Milano, Hoepli 1929-32).

Lippincott's Complete pronouncing gazetteer (2116 p., Philadelphia 1931), first published in 1855. Originally edited by JOSEPH THOMAS and THOMAS BALDWIN. Many editions under slightly different titles.

For older times, *see* the encyclopaedias such as PAULY-WISSOWA, the Encyclopaedia of Islam, the Jewish Encyclopaedia, etc.

JOHANN G. TH. GRAESSE: **Orbis latinus oder Verzeichnis der wichtigsten lateinischen Orts- und Ländernamen** (3rd ed., 348 p., Berlin 1922). First ed., 1860; 2nd, 1909. Contains only the Latin names with German equivalent and brief identification.

FILIPPO FERRARI (d. 1626): **Novum lexicon geographicum.** New edition by MICHAEL ANTONIUS BAUDRAND (1633-1700) (2 vols., folio, Padua 1695-97). FERRARI's work was first published in Milano 1627, later in Paris 1670. The FERRARI-BAUDRAND gazetteer is one of my standard reference books; it is always near to my hand. Yet, I am not sure that it is really the best book of its class and time, because I have not been able to make the necessary comparisons. A reassessment of early gazetteers would be worthwhile.

ANTOINE AUGUSTIN BRUZEN DE LA MARTINIÈRE (1683-1749): **Grand dictionnaire géographique, historique et critique** (6 vols. folio, Paris 1768). First edition 9 vols., La Haye 1726-36.

For more details it may be necessary to refer to national, provincial or local gazetteers, whose number is considerable. Reference to guide-books, such as Baedekers and Blue Guides, is convenient and often rewarding. Some of the Baedekers were compiled with extraordinary care.

Oriental gazetteers are not mentioned here, because the various kinds of orientalists know which reference books are available to them, and such information is of no use to people without sufficient philological preparation. We may just remark that gazetteers occupy a considerable place in Chinese literature and are very numerous. For more details, *ad hoc, see* my Introd. (3, 204).

The latest gazetteer, the **Webster Geographical Dictionary: A dictionary of names of places with geographical and historical information and pronounciation,** was published by the Merriam Co. of Springfield, Mass. at the end of 1949 (1325 p., 40,000 entries, 177 maps). This is truly an excellent work, the best of its size at present available. The standards of admission in it of a place were lower for the United States and Canada than they were for the rest of the world, but every gazetteer favors in a similar way the country where it was produced. Therefore, for information concerning places one should always refer to a special gazetteer of the country involved or to a general gazetteer published in that country.

5. ENCYCLOPAEDIAS

It is wise to refer to encyclopaedias for first guidance; it is priggish to disregard them; it is foolish to depend too much on them. Information obtained from encyclopaedias, even from the best, should always be controlled, and should not be stated as such except when the responsible author of the article referred to can be named. The leading modern encyclopaedias are able to enlist the services of outstanding scholars, but it does not follow that every one of their articles is written by an authority. On the contrary, it must necessarily happen that many articles remain undistributed and must be composed somehow by the office staff. The very articles written by "authorities" do not escape editorial revision, and that revision is not always skilful; some good articles are shortened and the shortening, however necessary, may be done badly; the proofreading may be insufficient. It would be easy to quote examples of such accidents in the latest editions of the Encyclopaedia Britannica in spite of their relative goodness.

The student of ancient science should consult first of all PAULY-WISSOWA,[78] then indices, such as LITTRÉ's index to the Hippocratic corpus (1861), the Aristotelian indexes,—HERMANN BONITZ' Index aristotelicus (1870), the indices to the Oxford Aristotle in English, TROY WILSON ORGAN: Index to Aristotle (Princeton 1949; Isis 40, 357), indices to PLINY's Natural History or to other classics. For mediaeval science up to 1400, SARTON's Introduction will probably be the first guide. A number of encyclopaedias or encyclopaedic treatises were published during the Middle Ages and later, but there is no place to enumerate them here.

Modern encyclopaedias, generally arranged in alphabetical order of topics, may be said to begin in the eighteenth century. At any rate, it is not worthwhile here to mention earlier ones,[79] except the two "fin de siècle" ones which follow.

Before speaking of the main eighteenth century encyclopaedias, it is well to mention two first published in the preceding century but whose influence was great in the eighteenth century and were frequently reprinted with additions and corrections during that century. Both are restricted to history, religion, philosophy and the humanities; they are equally poor on scientific topics, yet the historian of science may find it profitable to consult them.

LOUIS MORÉRI (1613-80) compiled the first encyclopaedia of the pure alphabetical type, the **Grand dictionnaire historique, ou Mélange curieux de l'histoire sacrée et profane** (1 vol., Lyon 1674). Twentieth and last edition (10 vols., Paris, 1759), Spanish translation (8 vols. in 10, Paris 1753). MORÉRI's erudition was copious but uncritical; he made many errors, even in his treatment of topics (pagan ones) to which his prejudices did not apply.

The **Dictionnaire historique et critique** of PIERRE BAYLE (1647-1706) appeared when the success of MORÉRI's Grand dictionnaire was already well established by seven editions; its publication (2 vols., Rotterdam 1697) was largely determined by the existence of MORÉRI's work and the need of a reaction against it. MORÉRI defended in everything Catholic orthodoxy, tradition and prejudice; BAYLE's point of view was liberal, tolerant, skeptical, sometimes cynical. His Dictionnaire was an anticipation of the eighteenth century rationalism. Its success was even greater than MORÉRI's, and it lasted much longer. The 11th ed. in 16 vols. appeared in Paris as late as 1820-24. English translations of it were published in 1709, 1710,

---

[78] PAULY-WISSOWA (1894-   ). **Pauly's Real-Encyclopädie der classischen Altertumswissenschaft.** Neue Bearbeitung herausgegeben von GEORG WISSOWA. Metzler, Stuttgart. 1894-1938. First series, 38 half volumes, Aal to Philon. 1914-39. Second series, 13 half volumes, Ra to M. Tullius Cicero. 1903-35. Supplement 6 vols. Abbr. PW.

[79] A student of, say, the seventeenth century, should establish for himself a list of encyclopaedias or encyclopaedic treatises published during that century, as well as a list of the works and correspondence of the leading men of science of that period. If possible, he should work in close neighborhood of a collection of these books; or keep always a list of them before his eyes.

1734-41, 1734-38 (that is a different edition from the previous one). Though BAYLE died at the beginning of the eighteenth century (in 1706) he influenced very deeply the whole of that century.[60]

Let us now consider the encyclopaedias born in the eighteenth century, dealing with them in the chronological order of their first editions.

The first is EPHRAIM CHAMBERS (d. 1740): **Cyclopaedia, or An universal dictionary of arts and sciences** (2 vols. London 1728). Second edition (1738). Italian translation (Venice 1748-49). Seventh edition (2 vols. 1751-52), with supplement by GEORGE LEWIS SCOTT (2 vols. 1753). Eighth edition of the text, supplement, and a great many additions arranged in one alphabet, by ABRAHAM REES (4 vols. London 1778-88), a fifth volume was added in 1788. We may say that CHAMBERS' dictionary was used from 1728 to the end of the century. We remember it today, however, less for its own virtues than because it was the indirect cause of the Encyclopédie.

The Encyclopédie was preceded by a German work, remarkable because of its gigantic size, the **Grosses vollständiges Universal Lexicon** (64 vols. folio, Halle 1732-50), Nöthige Supplemente (4 vols., A-Caq, Leipzig 1751-54), edited or published by JOHANN HEINRICH ZEDLER of Breslau (1706-63).

Young DENIS DIDEROT (1713-84) having undertaken to translate CHAMBERS' Cyclopaedia for a Paris publisher realized that something much better could be done and should be attempted. The result was **L'Encyclopédie, ou Dictionnaire raisonné des sciences, des arts et des métiers, par une société de gens de lettres. Mis en ordre et publié par M. DIDEROT . . . et quant à la partie mathématique par M. D'ALEMBERT** (17 vols. Paris 1751-65), Supplément (4 vols. Amsterdam 1776-77), Recueil de planches sur les sciences, les arts libéraux et les arts méchaniques avec leur explication (11 vols. of plates, Paris 1762-72), Suite du recueil de planches (Paris, Panckoucke 1777). Table analytique et raisonnée des matières contenues dans les XXXIII volumes in folio du Dictionnaire etc. (2 vols. Paris, Panckoucke 1780). Note the accent on science in the title. The Encyclopédie was perhaps the most powerful intellectual force of the century, not only from the social or political point of view but also from our point of view, the interpretation and diffusion of science.

Various reprints of this or that volume or of whole sets were made in different localities; the bibliography of that is difficult and not necessary here. Mention must be made however of the **Encyclopédie méthodique** undertaken in 1781 by the bookseller CHARLES JOSEPH PANCKOUCKE (1736-98) of Paris, who had taken part in the diffusion of the old Encyclopédie itself (see above). The Encyclopédie méthodique was an enormous undertaking; begun in 1781, it was not yet completed half a century later (1832) when it was stopped; 166 volumes had already appeared and the work was still unfinished. Some articles mostly by DIDEROT and D'ALEMBERT were borrowed from the old Encyclopédie, but very much was added. PANCKOUCKE'S main idea was to divide the work into a series of partial encyclopaedias each dealing with a branch of knowledge or technology (e.g., agriculture, 7 vols.; anatomy, 4 vols.; botany, 11 vols.; chemistry, 4 vols.). This idea was interesting, and has been frequently imitated even in our own time. To my mind it is a perversion of the encyclopaedic purpose. An alphabetic encyclopaedia is exceedingly useful in every age for quick reference. Partial encyclopaedias are less useful, for the equivalent is found in systematic treatises dealing with the same subjects; the indices of those treatises serve the same purpose as the alphabetical arrangement of the partial encyclopaedias and the explanations available in the treatises are more satisfying and more complete because each is placed in its proper logical context.

The **Encyclopaedia Metropolitana** (29 vols., London 1845; 2nd ed. 40 vols. 1848-58) went a step further than the Encyclopédie méthodique in trying to explain all the arts and sciences in a single natural sequence. The plan had been proposed by the poet SAMUEL TAYLOR COLERIDGE (1772-1834) whose essay on method was published in the first volume as a general introduction. It was divided into four main

---

[60] SARTON: BOYLE and BAYLE. The Sceptical Chemist and the Sceptical Historian (Chymia 3, 155-89, 11 fig., 1950). See also Isis 31, 442-44.

parts. I. Pure science, II. Mixed and applied sciences, III. History and biography, IV. Miscellaneous. Part I and II include many authoritative articles which still deserve the attention of historians of science.

The most popular and useful of all encyclopaedias, and we might perhaps say, the best for general purposes, the **Encyclopaedia Britannica**, is also a child of the eighteenth century. Its first edition began to appear in serial form (6d. per number!) in 1768 and was completed in 1771. Let us list here the following editions: 2nd in 1778-83, 3rd in 1788-97; 4th in 1801-10; 5th in 1815-24; 6th in 1823; 7th in 1830-42; 8th in 1853-61; 9th in 1875-89 (reprinted in 1898); 10th in 1902; 11th in 1910-11; 12th in 1922; 13th in 1926; 14th in 1929,[81] later Chicago editions 1943 ff.

The most ambitious encyclopaedic effort of the nineteenth century was made by JOHANN SAMUEL ERSCH (1766-1828) and JOHANN GOTTFRIED GRUBER (1774-1851). Their **Allgemeine Encyclopädie der Wissenschaften und Künste** began to appear in Leipzig in 1818; by 1889, 167 volumes had been published and the work was stopped before being completed. In order to hasten its publication, it was divided into three series A-G, H-N, O-Z. Only the first A-G was completed (99 vols., 1818-82); the second H-N, stopped at the entry 'ligature' (43 vols. 1827-89), the third stopped at the entry 'Phyxios' (1830-50). Some articles were monographs of considerable size. E.g., vol. 27 of the second series included an "article" by MORITZ STEINSCHNEIDER on Jewish literature (printed 1850). That article was Englished by the mathematician and physicist, WILLIAM SPOTTISWOODE (1825-83), revised by the author and published in book form "Jewish literature from the eighth to the eighteenth century" (414 p., London 1857); an index to the 1600 Jewish writers dealt with was published much later (52 p., Frankfurt a. M., 1893). The ERSCH and GRUBER purpose was defeated by its own magnitude, and that immense work is almost forgotten today, at least outside of German lands.

A briefer enumeration of the nineteenth and twentieth century encyclopaedias will suffice as the reader is familiar with them. Instead of dealing with them in straight chronological order, it is simpler to divide them into four linguistic groups, German, French, Spanish, Italian.

The first "new" encyclopaedia of importance in the German world was established by the firm Brockhaus of Leipzig, the founder of which was FRIEDRICH ARNOLD BROCKHAUS (1772-1823), and the first edition of the **Brockhaus' Konversations-Lexikon** (as different from an older Lexikon, dating back to 1796-1808, out of which it developed) is the one dated 1809-11, second edition 1812-19. 15th ed., called **Der Grosse Brockhaus** (20 vols. Leipzig 1928-35, supt. vol. 21, 1935); revision (20 vols., plus atlas, Leipzig 1939).

Meyers Grosses Konversations-Lexikon was first published in 46 vols. (Leipzig 1840-55), seventh edition (12 vols. Leipzig 1924-30, supp. vols. 13-15, 1931-33; atlas 1933, gazetteer 1935).

Herders Konversations-Lexikon was first published in 5 vols. (Freiburg im Breisgau 1853-57). Third edition (8 vols., 1902-07; supt. 1, 1910, supt. 2, 1921-22).

After the German debacle a new Lexikon, to be completed in 7 volumes, was undertaken in Switzerland. (7 vols., **Schweizer Lexikon** Zurich 1945-48).

The leader of encyclopaedic endeavor in France was the grammarian, PIERRE LAROUSSE (1817-75), whose family name has almost become a common name wherever French language is used. The main work edited or published by him was **Le grand dictionnaire universel du XIXe siècle** (15 very large vols., Paris 1866-76; suppt. 2 vols., 1878-90). This is the combination of a French dictionary with an encyclopaedia. **Nouveau Larousse illustré**, edited by CLAUDE AUGÉ (8 vols., Paris 1897-1904; Supplément et Complément 1906-7). **Larousse du XXe**

---

[81] Some of these editions were not completely new but constituted by the volumes of the preceding editions plus supplementary volumes; annual supplements were also published from time to time, like the Britannica Year-Book of 1913 (Isis 1, 290-92) but these things do not matter much in retrospect. The main point is that there are 15 editions of the Encyclopaedia Britannica, 3 of these in the eighteenth century, 6 in the nineteenth, 6 in the twentieth. There is no other "encyclopaedic" record comparable to that, that is, if size, authoritativeness and frequency of publication are all taken into account.

siècle, edited by PAUL AUGÉ (6 vols., 1928-33). The Larousse house has also published many special encyclopaedias (agriculture, medicine, etc.).

Grande Encyclopédie (31 vols., Paris 1886-1902). Some of the signed articles are excellent. Many articles on the history of science contributed by PAUL TANNERY are reprinted in his Mémoires scientifiques.

The most ambitious of French undertakings as well as the most recent is the Encyclopédie française conceived in 1932, edited by LUCIEN FEBVRE, the publication of which began in Paris in 1935 and is still very incomplete. Out of 21 volumes only 11 have appeared (1, 4-8, 10, 15-18). The general idea was to avoid the highly arbitrary alphabetical order and explain the whole of knowledge in logical order. For ex., vol. I entitled "L'outillage mental" deals with the evolution of thought (A. primitive, B. logical), language and mathematics. II-III. Matter, energy, astronomy, IV-V. Life and the living world, VI-VII. Anthropology, VIII-IX. History, X-XI. Government, XII-XIII. Economics, XIV-XV. Games, sports, recreations, XVI-XVII. Arts and literatures, XVIII. Religion and philosophies, XIX-XX. Technology, XXI. Conclusions (or Introduction). Each volume includes a brief alphabetical table of topics. Beginning with 1937 quarterly supplements provided additional pages or new pages to replace the original ones (a tempting but dangerous method).[82] The undertaking was too ambitious and to my mind superfluous. Textbooks are meant to give accounts of the knowledge available in this or that field and to integrate that knowledge as well as possible. The Encyclopédie française implied an excess of integration, defeating its own purpose. The articles of an ordinary encyclopaedia will retain their practical and theoretical value much longer than an integrated whole. In spite of the insertion of additional or substituted leaves, each part of the Encyclopédie française is bound to be replaced sooner or later by a new textbook.

The idea of an integrated or logical (vs. alphabetical) encyclopaedia has been realized more modestly in such books as the Grand Memento Encyclopédique Larousse, edited by PAUL AUGÉ (2 vols., Paris 1936-37), and by many other works of the same kind, summaries of knowledge arranged in a definite order.

The Encyclopédie française reminds us of other efforts made for the integration of knowledge. Various collections of books have been planned upon an encyclopaedic pattern. E.g., the Encyclopédie scientifique, published by Doin, Paris; chief editor EDOUARD TOULOUSE. It is divided into 40 sections and will include about a thousand volumes. An even more ambitious project was Die Kultur der Gegenwart, begun c. 1906, published by Teubner, Leipzig; chief editor, P. HINNEBERG. Such collections are not essentially different from the other collections published, less systematically, by the largest publishing houses. An alphabetic encyclopaedia is an indivisible whole, all the volumes of which however numerous are kept on the same shelves. On the other hand, the volumes of such collections as Die Kultur der Gegenwart and the Encyclopédie scientifique are often bought separately; even when they are bought together by a continuous subscription, the volumes are soon separated and placed upon different shelves. The integration exists only in the mind of the chief editor.

On the other hand, the philosophical integration may be stressed even more deeply than is the case of the Encyclopédie française. This occurred in the Encyclopädie der philosophischen Wissenschaften, edited by WILHELM WINDELBAND (1848-1910) and ARNOLD RUGE, begun in 1912 (Isis 2, 284). Only one volume appeared dealing with logic (Tübingen 1912) and including contributions by WINDELBAND, JOSIAH ROYCE, LOUIS COUTURAT, BENEDETTO CROCE, FEDERIGO ENRIQUES and NICOLAJ LOSSKIJ. A more ambitious attempt of the same kind was begun by OTTO NEURATH, International encyclopaedia of unified science, the publication of which began in Chicago in 1938 (Isis 32, 340-44; 33, 721-23; 37, 104).

Spanish encyclopaedia.—Enciclopedia universal ilustrada europeo-americana (70 vols., Madrid 1912-30; appendix, 10 vols. 1930-33; annual suppts., 7 vols. 1934-48).

---

[82] The inserted page is convenient for the regular and careful subscriber, but how can readers in a public library know when and where leaves have been inserted or should have been inserted?

Italian encyclopaedias.—**Nuova enciclopedia italiana** (14 vols. 1841-51). Revised 6th edition (30 vols. 1875-99). One of the greatest achievements of the Fascist regime was the preparation and rapid completion of the **Enciclopedia italiana di scienze, lettere ed arti** (37 vols., Rome 1929-39; 2 vol. suppt. 1948). The philosopher, GIOVANNI GENTILE (1875-   ), was chief editor. That encyclopaedia is less important than the Britannica but very full, well documented and admirably illustrated.

There are many other encyclopaedias in other languages, Russian, Dutch, Danish, Norwegian, Swedish, Portuguese, Greek, Hebrew, Arabic, Japanese, etc., partly because the publication of an encyclopaedia has become an essential element of the national aspirations of each country and of the linguistic aspirations of each linguistic group. Some of these encyclopaedias are excellent, but there is no need of mentioning them here, because they are of no use except to readers understanding their particular language, and those readers are fully aware of their existence.

However impartial the editors of encyclopaedias may be, they are bound to give more importance to the topics concerning their own national or linguistic area and that is all right if that natural partiality is not carried too far. The encyclopaedias written in "small" [83] languages are particularly valuable for what concerns their area which may be somewhat neglected in the encyclopaedias published in other, larger, areas.

In addition to the encyclopaedias already quoted, which however international they may be, have a natural predilection for a national or linguistic area, there are other encyclopaedias of which the area is primarily religious; that is, they are also international or supranational, but in a different way. Here are a few which I am using constantly:

Encyclopaedia of religion and ethics (13 vols., New York 1908-27).

Catholic.—**Dictionnaire de théologie catholique** (15 vols., to "théologie," Paris 1903-43). **Catholic encyclopaedia** (16 vols., New York 1907-13).

Jewish.—**Jewish encyclopaedia** (12 vols., New York 1901-6). **Encyclopaedia judaica** (10 vols, to "Lyra," Berlin 1928-34) in German, interrupted because of German anti-Semitism. There is also an edition in Hebrew.

Muslim.—**Encyclopaedia of Islam** (4 vols., suppt. 1 vol., Leiden 1908-38). Editions in English, German, French; also in Arabic and Turkish.

Buddhist.—**Hōbōgirin** (Tōkyō 1929 etc.), interrupted by the war (Introd. 3, p. 1889).

For classical antiquity, *see* PAULY-WISSOWA mentioned at the beginning of this chapter.

The indications given above on encyclopaedias are rudimentary, but amply sufficient for ordinary usage. A scholar should never be ashamed to consult encyclopaedias but he should do so carefully. Such consultation is very often the best way to begin an investigation. If one has to deal with a topic having national or linguistic implications, it is well to consult in the first place an encyclopaedia covering particularly that national or linguistic area, but then to consult also encyclopaedias covering other areas, rival areas. This gives one a preliminary view of that topic, which is many-sided and sufficiently objective.

A complete bibliography of encyclopaedias would be very long and difficult, and not useful for our purpose. Even the exact and complete bibliography of a single encyclopaedia, such as the Britannica or Brockhaus, would require much labor and space. Most encyclopaedias contain articles on "encyclopaedias" and generally a history of their own endeavor. There is a good unsigned article in the Britannica (8, 424-31, 1929).

Up-to-date encyclopaedias are of very great service to scientists and scholars of every kind for first aid on many subjects (chiefly on subjects with which they are not familiar). Historians of science need not only the latest encyclopaedias but also the old ones, as such offer one of the simplest means of recapturing the educated

---

[83] The word "small' is not used here in a bad sense. We call "small" languages those which are used only by a relatively small population, and have no international currency. They may be, and often are, "great" languages in other respects. SARTON: The tower of Babel (Isis 39, 3-15, 1948).

opinion of earlier times. Unfortunately, the old encyclopaedias are difficult to consult, because even when they are available as they are in the larger libraries, they are generally hidden away on the theory that they are obsolete and superseded and that nobody will ever want to consult them.[84] That practice is certainly wrong as far as the historian of science is concerned. Indeed, encyclopaedias are not available except when they are completely available on open shelves. When the historian wishes to consult them to investigate the evolution of ideas (say, on the speed of light), he will generally wish to consult not one of them but a whole series, and in many cases he will not know which particular volume to ask for (the information *ad hoc* might be given under light, or optics, or speed of light, or even elsewhere). It would be impracticable to borrow every one of those bulky series, each time that a similar investigation had to be made.

An Institute for the history of science should include an "encyclopaedia room" where all the new as well as the old encyclopaedias could be easily consulted. For example, there ought to be a full set of all the Britannicas. The same room might contain also (if space permitted) other reference books such as the biographical collections (to be described presently), gazetteers, dictionaries and grammars.

---

[84] Many of the old encyclopaedias owned by the Harvard Library are stored away in the Deposit Library across the river, and cannot be consulted except after their return from Deposit to Widener; this may take a few days.

Brugnet

6. BIOGRAPHICAL COLLECTIONS

The older encyclopaedias did not always include biographies, because a distinction was made between encyclopaedias dealing with scientific topics of various kinds on the one hand and historical dictionaries (like MORERI's and BAYLE's) on the other. The first edition of the Britannica (1768-71) did not include biographies, but the second (1778-83) and all the following did. At present, every alphabetical encyclopaedia includes biographies, but on account of the competition for space of many other items, those biographies are brief and relatively few in number.

There is thus a need in addition to the encyclopaedias for biographical collections.

First aid is obtainable in such books as GOTTARDO GAROLLO (1850-1917): Dizionario biografico universale (2 vols., 2126 p., Milano, Hoepli 1907); the Universal pronouncing dictionary of biography and mythology by JOSEPH THOMAS (1811-91). New 4th ed. revised (2550 p., London and Philadelphia 1915), the first edition had appeared in 1870; Webster's Biographical dictionary (1733 p., Springfield, Mass., 1943).

Of the earlier biographical collections only one must be quoted here, the one begun by CHRISTIAN GOTTLIEB JÖCHER (1694-1758), born in Leipzig, professor in the university of that city and director of its library, Allgemeines Gelehrten-Lexicon (11 vols., Leipzig 1750-1819, 1897). The first four volumes, covering the whole alphabet, are JÖCHER's work (1750-51), the following six volumes (1784-1819) are supplements provided by JOHANN CHRISTOPH ADELUNG (1732-1806) to the letter J, and for the rest by HEINRICH WILHELM ROTERMUND (1761-1848). A final supplement edited by OTTO GÜNTHER appeared much later (1897). These volumes are still worth consulting, especially for personalities of the seventeenth and eighteenth centuries.

Two very large biographical collections appeared last century, both in France. JOSEPH MICHAUD (1767-1839) and LOUIS GABRIEL MICHAUD (1773-1858): Biographie universelle (85 vols., Paris 1811-62). Italian translation with additions, Biografia universale (65 vols., Venezia 1822-31).

The second and better is the one begun forty years later by FERDINAND HOEFER (1811-78):[85] Nouvelle biographie générale (46 vols., Paris 1855-66).

The historical standards of the national collections are generally higher than those of the universal collections, because their scope is less ambitious, they are more homogeneous, the collaborators use to some extent the same sources and to a large extent the same methods. The best known of those national biographies are:

Allgemeine deutsche Biographie (55 vols., Leipzig 1871-1910). Abbreviated ADB. Vol. 56 published in 1912 is a general index, very convenient. This bibliography is periodically continued by the Biographisches Jahrbuch und deutscher Nekrolog (18 vols. for 1896 to 1913, published in Berlin 1897-1917) and then by the Deutsches biographisches Jahrbuch herausgegeben vom Verbande der deutschen Akademien (vol. 1, for 1914-16, published in 1925; vol. 11 for 1929, published in 1932).

The ADB contains biographies not only of Germans but of many other people, Dutchmen, Belgians, Swiss, Poles, whom the editors saw fit to annex. E.g., it contains elaborate biographies of REMBRANDT, VESALIUS, JACOB STEINER and COPERNICUS.

The Dictionary of National Biography (DNB) contains biographies of people born in Great Britain, Ireland, the British Commonwealth and colonies, and of Englishmen born abroad. It was begun in 1885 and the last (63 d.) volume appeared in 1900. It was reprinted in 22 volumes. Various supplements cover the period 1901-40; they include biographies of people who died before 1941. A "concise dictionary," wherein the articles are reduced to one-fourteenth of their original length

---

[85] SARTON, HOEFER and CHEVREUL (Bulletin of the history of medicine, 8, 419-45, 1940).

was published in 1917 and the supplements have been or will be abbreviated in the same manner.

The **Dictionary of American Biography** (DAB) began to appear in 1928, and was completed in 20 vols. in 1936. Index to vols. 1-20, 1937. Supplement including biographies of men who died before 1935 (1944). Some articles of DAB relative to the colonial period duplicate articles of DNB, but are posterior to them, and hence presumably better.

The French biography, **Dictionnaire de biographie française,** is still too far from completion to be very useful. Vol. 1 is dated 1933; vol. 3, published in 1939, stops at Aubermesnil. Latest part seen, fasc. 27 to Bassot (Paris 1950).

Biographie nationale de Belgique. 27 vols. (Bruxelles 1866-1938). Vol. 28, General Table (1944).

Dictionnaire historique et biographique de la Suisse (7 vols., Neuchatel 1921-33; suppt. 1934).

Splendid biographical collections have been published in the Netherlands and in Scandinavia, but as they are printed in Dutch, Swedish, etc. they are not generally available to foreign scholars.

Bibliography of biographical dictionaries classified by countries in the Enciclopedia italiana (7, 47-49, 1930).

The two most important collections of scientific biographies are

JOHANN CHRISTIAN POGGENDORFF (1796-1877): **Biographisch-literarisches Handwörterbuch zur Geschichte der exacten Wissenschaften** (2 vols., Leipzig 1863). Supplements: vol. 3, for 1858-83 (1898); vol. 4, for 1883-1903 (1904); vol. 5, for 1904-22 (1926); vol. 6, for 1923-1931 (1936-40). Facsimile reprint of the whole set in 10 vols. (Ann Arbor, Mich., 1945). The biographical information given in these volumes is very brief, the purpose being rather to give the complete bibliography of each author.

ERNST GURLT, AGATHON WERNICH and AUGUST HIRSCH: **Biographisches Lexikon der hervorragenden Aerzte aller Zeiten und Völker** (6 vols., Wien 1884-88). Revised edition by WILHELM HABERLING, FRANZ HÜBOTTER and HERMANN VIERORDT (5 vols., Berlin 1929-34; Suppt. 1935). Though this collection is restricted to physicians, it is more general; indeed, a great many men of science of the past, especially the naturalists, practiced medicine or at least had a medical degree.

JAMES BRITTEN and GEORGE S. BOULGER: **Biographical index of deceased British and Irish botanists** (2nd ed., 364 p., London 1931; Isis 36, 229).

Some of the most valuable biographies of men of science are to be found in academic publications, but a list of these would involve too long a digression. It is hoped that a bibliography of all of these academic biographies will eventually be compiled and then kept up to date in periodical supplements.

THOMAS JAMES HIGGINS: The function of biography in engineering education (Journal of engineering education 32, 82-92, 1941); Biographies and collected works of mathematicians (American mathematical monthly 51, 433-45, 1944); Book-length biographies of chemists (School science and mathematics 650-65, 1944); Book-length biographies of physicists and astronomers (American Journal of physics 12, 234-36, 1944); Book-length biographies of engineers, metallurgists and industrialists (14 p., reprinted from Bulletin of Bibliography, vols. 18-19, 1946-47); Biographies of engineers and scientists (Research Publ. of Ill. Inst. Tech., vol. 7, no. 1, 62 p., 1949); Biographies and collected works of mathematicians (Am. math. mly. 56, 310-12, 1949).

B. SCIENCE

7. SCIENTIFIC METHODS AND PHILOSOPHY OF SCIENCE

It is generally difficult to separate books dealing with scientific methods from those dealing with the philosophy of science. The difference is one between means and purpose, but means and purpose are as closely related as the obverse and the reverse of a medal. It is "means," one might say, if you look from the left, and "purpose" if you look from the right. It is only when one has a purpose in mind that one can conceive means of attaining it, and if means are used, a purpose is implied.

The only way to study scientific methods thoroughly is to work in a special field of science, and to carry on as many experiments and investigations as possible. Book knowledge cannot possibly replace the experimental knowledge obtained in the laboratory. Of course this is true also of historical methods, which can only be mastered by long practice.

However, for the historian of science, the experimental knowledge, indispensable as it is, is not sufficient. He must be more fully aware of the methods which scientists are applying to their purpose, and be able to analyze them.

It is noteworthy that scientific methods are not taught systematically in scientific courses but rather in philosophical courses. Teachers of science may refer to them but generally take them for granted and are satisfied to insist upon the rules and precautions of definite experiments. After having completed a cycle of, say, physical experiments, students are aware of general methods (in addition to the special ones), but their awareness may remain largely unconscious or unformulated.

There are a great many books dealing with the philosophy and methods of science, and I could not tell which are the best, as I have read only a few. A good part of the subject is already standardized and explained sufficiently well in every book. Each author throws emphasis on certain aspects of the subject; a comparison between their books would imply a comparison of these aspects the relative importance of which cannot be weighed, except in a few cases.

Early nineteenth century writers like BADEN POWELL, WHEWELL [86] and HERSCHEL have been mentioned in the text above and many more might easily be, such as COMTE, COURNOT and SPENCER, but that would lead us too far. There are three men of science of the second half of the nineteenth century who stand out above the others for the present purpose, BERNARD, MACH, and PEARSON.

The Introduction à l'étude de la médecine expérimentale (Paris 1865) by CLAUDE BERNARD (1813-78) is still the most important book ever written by a man of science to explain the genesis and development of his own methods of investigation. English translation, An introduction to the study of experimental medicine, by HENRY COPLEY GREENE (250 p., New York 1927; reprinted 1949).

BERNARD was a physiologist; MACH, a physicist deeply concerned for philosophical problems and realizing that such problems could not be solved without historical investigations. One cannot understand the meaning of a concept if one does not know its origin and development.

The main works of ERNST MACH (1838-1916) are Die Mechanik in ihrer Entwicklung historisch-kritisch dargestellt (Leipzig 1883; 7th ed., 1912), Englished under the title The science of mechanics (Chicago 1893; 3rd ed., Chicago 1907; supplement by PHILIP E. B. JOURDAIN, Chicago 1915; 4th ed. Chicago 1914, 5th, La Salle, Ill., 1942).

---

[86] In addition to his History of the inductive sciences (3 vols., London 1837), WHEWELL published a few years later The philosophy of the inductive sciences founded upon their history (2 vols., London 1840; revised ed. 1847). History of scientific ideas. Being the first part of The philosophy of the inductive sciences. Third ed. (2 vols., London 1858).

Die Analyse der Empfindungen und das Verhältniss des Physischen zum Psychischen (1st ed.?; 2nd, Jena 1900; 6th, 1911); Analysis of sensations and the relation of the physical to the psychical (Chicago 1897; revised 1914; Isis 3, 369).
Erkenntnis und Irrtum. Skizzen zur Psychologie der Forschung (Leipzig 1905, 5th ed. 1926).
As to the third one, KARL PEARSON (1857-1936), he was a mathematician, but one with very broad scientific interests, and one of the first to try to apply mathematical methods to biology (Biometrika 1901-35). His Grammar of science was first published in London 1892; increased editions in 1900, 1911. A somewhat reduced edition was included in Everyman's library in 1937.
The books published in the twentieth century will be listed in the alphabetical order of the authors' names. Such an order is logical disorder, but any kind of logical order would introduce superfluous difficulties. Books on the methods and philosophy of science cover a very long range, the whole gamut extending from philosophy (epistemology, logic, metaphysics) on one end to technicalities at the other; moreover, their philosophical points of view vary greatly, to the point of mutual contradiction.
Many of the books listed below seem to be restricted to physics, but the scope of physics is so broad that such books are really concerned with the philosophy of science, or, at any rate, with the philosophy of inorganic sciences.

Abro, A. d':
1927: The evolution of scientific thought from Newton to Einstein (revised ed. New York 1950; Isis 42, 70).
1939: The decline of mechanism in modern physics (988 p., New York; Isis 32, 380-82).

Bachelard, Gaston (1884-   ):
1927: Essai sur la connaissance approchée (312 p., Paris; Isis 11, 522).
1932: Le pluralisme cohérent de la chimie moderne (Paris; Isis 19, 233-35).
1933: Les intuitions atomistiques (162 p., Paris; Isis 21, 443).
1934: Le nouvel esprit scientifique (180 p., Paris).—Reprinted 1937.
1938: La formation de l'esprit scientifique, contribution à une psychoanalyse de la connaissance objective (256 p., Paris; Isis 40, 283-85).—Reprinted 1947.
1940: La philosophie du non, essai d'une philosophie du nouvel esprit scientifique (145 p., Paris).
BACHELARD is professor of the history and philosophy of science at the Sorbonne.

Barry, Frederick (1876-1943):
1927: The scientific habit of thought. An informal discussion of the source and character of dependable knowledge (371 p., New York; Isis 14, 265-68; 34, 339-40).
The author was trained as a chemist and taught the history of science in Columbia University.

Bavink, Bernhard (1879-1947):
1932: The natural sciences. An introduction to the scientific philosophy of to-day. Translated from the 4th German edition with additional notes (696 p., 87 ill., New York; Isis 26, 565).
The original German text was first published in 1914; 2nd ed. 1921, 5th ed. 1933, 8th ed. 1945, 9th ed. (822 p., Zürich 1948), posthumously edited by M. FIERZ.

Benjamin, A. Cornelius:
1936: The logical structure of science (344 p., London; Isis 29, 461-64).
1937: Introduction to the philosophy of science (485 p., New York; Isis 29, 464-69).
The author is professor of philosophy in the University of Chicago.

Born, Max (1882-   ):
1943: Experiment and theory in physics (48 p., Cambridge; Isis 35, 261, 263).
1949: Natural philosophy of cause and change (224 p., London).
The author is a German physicist.

Bridgman, Percy Williams (Isis 37, 128-31, portr.):
  1922: Dimensional analysis (New Haven).
  1927: Logic of modern physics (New York).
  1936: Nature of physical theory (Princeton).
  1941: Nature of thermodynamics (Cambridge, Massachusetts).
  The author is an American physicist.

Brown, Guy Burniston:
  1950: Science. Its method and its philosophy (190 p., 8 pl., London).
  The author is an English physicist.

Brunschvicg, Léon (1869-1944):
  1922: L'expérience humaine et la causalité physique (691 p., Paris; Isis 5,
  479-83).
  The author is a French philosopher.

Caldin, E. F.:
  1949: The power and limits of science. A philosophical study (205 p., London).

Campbell, Norman Robert (1880-1949):
  1928: An account of the principles of measurement and calculation (304 p.,
  London).
  The author was a physicist, engaged in industrial research.

Cannon, Walter Bradford (1871-1945):
  1945: The way of an investigator. A scientist's experiences in medical research
  (229 p., New York; Isis 36, 259 p., portrait).
  CANNON, professor of physiology in Harvard, was naturally influenced by BER-
  NARD in many ways and particularly in the writing of these autiobiographical remi-
  niscences. I would advise every student who has read BERNARD's Introduction, to
  read also CANNON's book.
  This book suggests that many other biographies and autobiographies of men of
  science contain valuable information concerning not only the history of science (that
  is obvious) but also its philosophy and methodology. The best of those biographies
  enable one to study various methods in action. A critical list of such biographies
  would be very helpful but cannot be provided here and now.

Carmichael, Robert Daniel (1879-   ):
  1930: The logic of discovery (290 p., Chicago; Isis 15, 373-76).
  The author is an American mathematician.

Cohen, Moris Raphael (1880-1947) and **Nagel, Ernest:**
  1934: Introduction to logic and scientific method (479 p., New York; Isis 23,
  284-87).
  Both authors are philosophers and logicians.

Davis, Harold Thayer:
  1931: Philosophy and modern science (350 p., Bloomington, Indiana; Isis 18,
  204-6).
  DAVIS is a mathematician, statistician, econometrist.

Dingle, Herbert
  1931: Science and human experience (141 p., London).
  1937: Through science to philosophy (New York; Isis 29, 160-63).
  DINGLE is an astrophysicist, now professor of the history of science in University
  College, London (Isis 37, 77).

Dingler, Hugo (1881-   ):
  1921: Physik und Hypothese (211 p., Berlin 1921; Isis 4, 385).
  1923: Die Grundlagen der Physik (350 p., Berlin; Isis 6, 572-73).
  1924: Die Grundgedanken der Machschen Philosophie mit Erstveröffentlichungen

aus seinen wissenschaftlichen Tagebüchern (106 p., Leipzig; Isis 7, 603, 339).
1926: Der Zusammenbruch der Wissenschaft und das Primat der Philosophie (400 p., München).
1928: Das Experiment. Sein Wesen und seine Geschichte (272 p., München).
1931: Philosophie der Logik und Arithmetik (198 p., München).
1932: Geschichte der Naturphilosophie (174 p., Berlin; Isis 22, 284-85).
1938: Die Methode der Physik (422 p., München; Isis 32, 203-5).

Duhem, Pierre (1861-1916):
1908: Essai sur la notion de théorie physique de PLATON à GALILÉE (Annales de philosophie chrétienne; reprint of 144 p., Paris).
1905-6: Origines de la statique (2 vols., Paris).
1906-13: Etudes sur LÉONARD DE VINCI (3 vols., Paris).
1913-17: Le système du monde (5 vols., Paris; Isis 2, 203; 3, 125; 26, 302-3).
The author was a physico-chemist, and wrote very important studies on the history of science. Biographies of him have been published by PIERRE HUMBERT (Paris 1932; Isis 21, 399) and by his daughter, HÉLÈNE PIERRE-DUHEM (Paris 1936; Isis 27, 161).

Eddington, Arthur Stanley (1882-1944):
1928: The nature of the physical world (380 p., Cambridge).
1933: The expanding universe (190 p., New York; Isis 21, 322-26).
1935: New pathways in science (348 p., 4 pls., Cambridge).
1939: The philosophy of physicial science (239 p., Cambridge; Isis 33, 79-80).
1946: Fundamental theory (300 p., Cambridge).
English Astrophysicist and philosopher.

Einstein, Albert (1879-   ):
1922: The meaning of relativity (128 p., Princeton; enlarged ed. 135 p., Princeton 1945; Isis 37, 154).
1934: The world as I see it (325 p., London; Isis 23, 277-80).
1938: (with LEOPOLD INFELD). The evolution of physics, the growth of ideas from early concepts to relativity and quanta (330 p., New York; Isis 30, 124-25).
1950: Out of my later years (300 p., New York).
Mathematician and physicist, discoverer of the theories of relativity.

Enriques, Federigo (1871-1946):
1906: Problemi della scienza (Bologna) English translation by KATHERINE ROYCE with preface by JOSIAH ROYCE, Problems of science (408 p., Chicago 1914; Isis 3, 368).
1922: Per la storia della logica, i principii e l'ordine della scienza nel concetto dei pensatori matematici (302 p., Bologna; Isis 5, 469-70).
1938: Le matematiche nella storia e nella cultura (340 p., 22 pl., Bologna; Isis 31, 108-9).
ENRIQUES was a mathematician and director of the institute for the history of science attached to the University of Rome.

Frank, Philipp:
1932: Das Kausalgesetz und seine Grenzen (323 p., 4 fig., Wien).
1941: Between physics and philosophy (238 p., Cambridge, Massachusetts; Isis 34, 180).
1946: Foundations of physics (84 p., Chicago; Isis 37, 104).
1949: Modern science and its philosophy (338 p., Harvard, Cambridge, Mass.).
FRANK is a mathematician and physicist.

Friend, Julius Weis and Feibleman, James:
1933: Science and the spirit of man, a new ordering of experience (336 p., London).
1937: What science really means. An explanation of the history and empirical method of general science (222 p., London; Isis 31, 105-8).

George, William Herbert:
1936: The scientist in action, a scientific study of his methods (364 p., London; Isis 29, 159).

Gonseth, Ferdinand (1890-   ):
194?: Déterminisme et libre arbitre. Entretiens présidés par GONSETH, recueillis et rédigés par H. S. GAGNEBIN (185 p., Neuchâtel).

Hartmann, Max (1876-   ):
1948: Die philosophischen Grundlagen der Naturwissenschaften, Erkenntnistheorie und Methodologie (250 p., Jena).

Howells, Thomas H.:
1940: Hunger for wholiness (307 p., Denver 1940; Isis 33, 288-89).
Psychologist.

Jeans, Sir James Hopwood (1877-1946):
1928: Astronomy and cosmogony (430 p., Cambridge).
1929: The universe around us (362 p., 24 pl., Cambridge; 4th ed., 1944).
1930: The mysterious universe (163 p., 2 pl., Cambridge).
1931: The stars in their courses (200 p., 47 pl., Cambridge).
1933: The new background of science (309 p., New York; Isis 21, 326-28).
1934: Through space and time (238 p., 53 pl., Cambridge).
1942: Physics and philosophy (229 p., Cambridge).
English astronomer, physicist, philosopher.

Jevons, William Stanley (1835-1882):
1874: The principles of science, a treatise on logic and scientific method (2 vols., London).—Stereotyped ed., 830 p., London 1883. Often reprinted.
English economist and logician.

Joad, Cyril Edwin Mitchinson (1891-   ):
1928: The future of life, a theory of vitalism (London).
1932: Philosophical aspects of modern science (London; reprinted 1934; 344 p., 1943; Isis 40, 77).
The author is a philosopher and publicist.

Johnson, Martin Christopher (1896-   ):
1944: Art and scientific thought, historical studies toward a modern revision of their antagonism (200 p., London; Isis 37, 122).—Reprinted New York, Columbia University 1949 (Isis 37, 122; 41, 85).
1945: Time, knowledge and the nebulae, an introduction to the meaning of time in physics, astronomy and philosophy, and the relativities of EINSTEIN and MILNE (180 p., London).
1946: Science and the meaning of truth (180 p., London; Isis 38, 129).

Lamouche, André:
1924: La méthode générale des sciences pures et appliquées (298 p., Paris).
The author is an engineer in the French army.

Le Châtelier, Henri (1850-1936):
1936: De la méthode dans les sciences expérimentales (319 p., Paris; Isis 27, 519-22).
Industrial chemist, discoverer of LE CHÂTELIER's law. Some of his views are obsolete (e.g., against relativity or quanta). He edited some classics of physics and chemistry (1913, 1914; Isis 1, 770; 2, 277; 4, 156).

Lecomte du Nouÿ, Pierre (1883-1947):
1936: Le temps et la vie (267 p., Paris); translation entitled Biological time (New York 1936).
1939: L'homme devant la science (Paris).
1941: L'avenir de l'esprit (Paris).

1944: La dignité humaine (332 p., New York); translation entitled: Human destiny (New York, 1947).
Biologist, chemist, philosopher.

Lenzen, Victor Fritz:
1931: The nature of physical theory, a study in the theory of knowledge (314 p., New York; Isis 20, 488-91).
1938: Procedures of empirical science (62 p., International encyclopedia of unified science 1 no. 5, Chicago).
LENZEN is professor of physics at the University of California and author of many reviews of books on the philosophy of science in Isis.

Lévy, H.:
1933: The universe of science (238 p., London: Isis 21, 328-30).

Margenau, Henry:
1950: The nature of physical reality. A philosophy of modern physics (486 p., 13 fig., New York; Isis 42, 69).

Metzger-Brühl, Hélène (1889-1944):
1926: Les concepts scientifiques (195 p., Paris; Isis 9, 467-70).
Student of mineralogy, chemistry, and general science, chiefly in the seventeenth and eighteenth centuries (Isis 36, 133).

Meyerson, Emile (1859-1933):
1908: Identité et réalité (3rd ed., Paris, 1926; Isis 9, 470-72).—English translation (London 1930).
1921: De l'explication dans les sciences (2 vols., 852 p., Paris; Isis 4, 382-85).
1925: La déduction relativiste (412 p., Paris; Isis 7, 517-20).
1931: Du cheminement de la pensée (3 vols., 1064 p., Paris; Isis 17, 444-45).
1936: Essais (272 p., Paris). Posthumous publication.
MEYERSON had studied the history of chemistry under HERMANN KOPP and he remained deeply interested in the history of science, but he was primarily a philosopher.

Neurath, Otto (editor):
1938f: International encyclopaedia of unified science (University of Chicago, Isis 33, 721-23; 37, 104; etc.).

Nicolle, Charles (1866-1936):
1932: Biologie de l'invention (178 p., Paris; Isis 19, 301).
1934: La nature, conception et morale biologique (134 p., Paris).
1936: La destinée humaine (106 p., Paris).
Bacteriologist.

Nippoldt, Alfred (1874-1936):
1923: Anleitung zu wissenschaftlichen Denken (3rd ed., 222 p., Potsdam).—66th-75th ed., 232 p., Potsdam 1943.
The author is a German student of terrestrial magnetism.

Northrop, Filmer Stuart Cuckow (1893-   ):
1931: Science and first principles (314 p., New York; Isis 17, 273-77).
American philosopher and educator.

Pelseneer, Jean:
1947: L'évolution de la notion de phénomène physique, des primitifs à BOHR et LOUIS DE BROGLIE (177 p., Bruxelles; Isis 39, 194-96).
The author teaches the history of science at the University of Brussels, and was for some years attached to the history of science section of UNESCO.

Planck, Max (1858-1947):
1922: Physikalische Rundblicke (168 p., Leipzig), essays dealing with the

philosophy of science.—Englished under the title: A survey of physics (191 p., London 1925).—Expanded edition entitled: Wege zur physikalischen Erkenntnis (2nd ed., 1934; 4th, Leipzig 1944).

1931: The universe in the light of modern physics (110 p., London).—Increased ed. (140 p., London 1937).

1932: Where is science going? (222 p., New York).

1936: The philosophy of physics (128 p., London).

PLANCK was the discoverer of the quanta theory; one of the founders of modern physics. Portrait in Isis (38, facing p. 135).

Poincaré, Henri (1854-1912):
1908: La science et l'hypothèse (Paris).
1909: La valeur de la science (Paris).
1909: Science et méthode (Paris).

English translation of the three volumes by GEORGE BRUCE HALSTED, with special preface by POINCARÉ and introduction by JOSEPH ROYCE (one vol. with index, 566 p., New York 1913), reprinted 1921, 1929.

Ramsperger, Albert Gustav:
1942: Philosophies of science (315 p., New York; Isis 34, 270).
The author is a philosopher.

Reichenbach, Hans (1891-   ):
1928: Philosophie der Raum-Zeit-Lehre (386 p., Berlin).
1932: Atoms and cosmos, the world of modern physics (300 p., London). German original, Berlin 1930.
1938: Experience and prediction, an analysis of the foundations and the structure of knowledge (420 p., Chicago University).—Reprinted 1949.
1942: From COPERNICUS to EINSTEIN (123 p., New York).—German original, Berlin 1927.
1944: Philosophic foundations of quantum-mechanics (192 p., Berkeley, Calif.).

Rey, Abel (1873-1940):
1907: La théorie de la physique chez les physiciens contemporains (Paris; 2nd revised ed., 1923, Isis 5, 484-85; 3rd ed., 1930).
1927: Le retour éternel et la philosophie de la physique (320 p., Paris 1927; Isis 9, 477-79).

The author is a philosopher who was director of the institute for the history of science at the University of Paris; he was succeeded by BACHELARD, listed above.

Ritchie, Arthur David:
1923: Scientific method. An inquiry into the character and validity of natural laws (London).
The author is a chemical physiologist.

Russell, Bertrand (1872-   ):
1948: Human knowledge: its scope and limits (540 p., London).
English mathematician and philosopher.

Schrödinger, Erwin (1887-   ):
1935: Science and the human temperament (154 p., London).
1945: What is life? (100 p., Cambridge; Isis 36, 229).
The author is a mathematician and physicist.

Smuts, Jan Christiaan (1870-1950):
1926: Holism and evolution (300 p., London).
South African soldier, statesman, philosopher.

Weizsäcker, Carl Friedrich von:
1949: The history of nature (198 p., University of Chicago; Isis 41, 393).—First published in German: Die Geschichte der Natur (170 p., Zürich 1948).

Werkmeister, William Henry:
1940: A philosophy of science (576 p., New York; Isis 33, 144).
1948: The basis and structure of knowledge (462 p., New York; Isis 42, 68).
The author is a professor of philosophy.

Westaway, Frederic William:
1912: Scientific method, its philosophical basis and its modes of application (London, later editions 1919; Isis 4, 119-22; 1924, 1931; 1937, Isis 28, 579).
1920: Science and theology, their common aims and methods (350 p., London; Isis 4, 119-22; new ed., 1932).
1942: Science in the dock: guilty or not guilty? (143 p., London).
The author was formerly an inspector of English schools.

Weyl, Hermann:
1932: The open world, three lectures on the metaphysical implications of science (88 p., New Haven; Isis 23, 281-84).
1934: Mind and nature (106 p., Philadelphia; Isis 23, 281).
1949: Philosophy of mathematics and natural science (320 p., Princeton; Isis 41, 236-37).

Whitehead, Alfred North (1861-1947):
1919: Enquiry concerning the principles of natural knowledge (212 p., Cambridge).—Reprinted 1925.
1920: The concept of nature (212 p., Cambridge; Isis 4, 212).—Reprinted 1926, 1930.
1925: Science and the modern world (308 p., Cambridge).—Often reprinted.
1938: Modes of thought (New York; Isis 32, 239).
WHITEHEAD was a mathematician and philosopher.

Wolf, Abraham (1876-   ):
1925: Essentials of scientific method (160 p., London; Isis 8, 604).—Often reprinted.
The author was professor of the subject in the University of London and wrote books on the history of science.

This list is very incomplete; it includes only the books which have come to the author's knowledge and which he has remembered.   The books mentioned illustrate a great variety of purposes and offer a sufficient choice to meet the reader's first needs, whichever they be.
See the Critical Bibliographies of Isis, section 18 Philosophy of Science.

8. SCIENCE AND SOCIETY

Some historians of science are interested in the many complex questions concerned with the impact of society upon science and with the impact of science upon society. The following books deal with those questions, but they are not absolutely separate from the books dealing with the philosophy of science. The philosophy of science and the sociology of science[87] are two overlapping fields; the nature and extent of the overlapping vary with each author.

Baker, John Randal (1900-   ):
1943: The scientific life (154 p., New York; Isis 35, 191-92).
1945: Science and the planned state (120 p., London; Isis 36, 224; 37, 250).
English biochemist, leading opponent of "planning" in science.—*See* also MEES.

Bennett, Jesse Lee (1885-   ):
1942: The diffusion of science (150 p., Baltimore; Isis 34, 374).

Bernal, John Desmond (1901-   ):
1929: The world, the flesh and the devil; an enquiry into the future of the three enemies of the rational soul (96 p., London).
1939: The social function of science (498 p., London).
1949: The freedom of necessity (448 p., London).
English physicist, Marxist.

Blackett, Patrick Maynard Stuart:
1949: Fear, war and the bomb, military and political consequences of atomic energy (252 p., New York; Isis 41, 86).
English physicist.

Bridgman, Percy Williams (1882-   ):
1938: The intelligent individual and society (312 p., New York; Isis 30, 310-12, 37, 128).
American physicist.

Bryson, Lyman (1888-   ):
1947: Science and freedom (202 p., New York).
American educator.

Bush, Vannevar (1890-   ):
1946: Endless horizons (191 p., Washington, D. C.; Isis 37, 250).
The author is a mathematician and engineer, president of the Carnegie Institute of Washington.

Coates, J. B.:
1949: The crisis of the human person (256 p., London).

Cohen, I. Bernard (1914-   ):
1948: Science, servant of man. A layman's primer for the age of science (376 p., 8 pl., Boston; Isis 40, 73-75).
The author is professor of the history of science in Harvard University.

Crowther, James Gerald (1899-   ):
1930: Science in Soviet Russia (128 p., 13 pl., London).
1936: Soviet science (352 p., London; Isis 27, 90-92).

---

[87] What I call here sociology of science is implicitly defined in the preceding sentence; it is somewhat different from the Wissenssoziologie about which *see* ROBERT K. MERTON: The sociology of knowledge (Isis 27, 493-503, 1937). Wissenssoziologie is more ambitious from the metaphysical and epistemological point of view than my sociology of science.

1935: British scientists of the nineteenth century (345 p., 12 pl., London; Isis 28, 507-08).

1937: Famous American men of science (430 p., New York; Isis 28, 507-08). These two books containing 9 biographies of physicists (5 English and 4 American) are quoted because of the social theory which inspires them.

1941: The social relations of science (697 p., New York; Isis 33, 345-47). English scientific journalist.

Darlington, Cyril Dean (1903-   ):
1948. The conflict of science and society. Conway Memorial Lecture (61 p., London; Isis 41, 319).
English geneticist, director of the John Innes Horticultural Institution.

Gellhorn, Walter (1906-   ):
1950: Security, loyalty and science (Cornell, Ithaca, N Y.).

Haldane, John Burdon Sanderson (1892-   ):
1923: Daedalus, or science and the future (100 p., London).
1938: The Marxist philosophy and the sciences (183 p., London).
1938: Heredity and politics (202 p., New York; Isis 29, 565).
1940: Science and everyday life (284 p., New York; Isis 33, 142).
1940: Adventures of a biologist (290 p., New York; Isis 33, 297-98, 524-25).
1947: What is life? (251 p., New York).
English biologist, Marxist.

Hogben, Lancelot (1895-   ):
1937: Mathematics for the million (660 p., New York; Isis 28, 138-40).
1938: Science for the citizen (1114 p., New York; Isis, 31, 467-69).
1940: Dangerous thoughts (285 p., New York; Isis 33, 144).
English physiologist, biologist.

Huxley, Julian Sorell 1887-   ):
1923: Essays of a biologist (321 p., London).
1931: What dare I think? The challenge of modern science to human action and belief (287 p., London).
1934: Scientific research and social needs (304 p., 40 pl., London).—American edition titled: Science and social needs (304 p., New York 1935; Isis 24, 188).
1936: Africa view (463 p., London; Isis 28, 150-51). Impact of science on colonial administration.
1941: The uniqueness of man (313 p., London).—American edition titled: Man stands alone (307 p., New York 1941; Isis 33, 409).
1944 (editor): Reshaping man's heritage. Biology in the service of man (96 p., 7 pl., London; Isis 36, 59).
1944: On living in a revolution (256 p., ill., New York).
1946: UNESCO, its purpose and philosophy (63 p., London; Washington, D.C. 1947; Isis 39, 116).
1947: Man in the modern world (281 p., London).
The author is an English biologist and was the first general director of UNESCO, hence very well placed to study the impact of science on international life.

Lilley, Samuel:
1948: Man, machines and history, a short history of tools and machines in relation to social progress (240 p., ill., London).
1949: Social aspects of the history of science (Archives internationales d'histoire des sciences, 28, 378-443).
Report prepared for the International Union of the History of Science. The author is an English historian of physics.

Lindsay, Jack (1900-   ):
1949: Marxism and contemporary science, or the Fullness of life (261 p., London; Isis 41, 320).

Mees, Charles Edward Kenneth (1882-   ) (with the coöperation of John R.
Baker):
1946: The path of science (262 p., New York; Isis 37, 251).
The author is Vice-president in charge of research of the Eastman Kodak Co.,
Rochester, N. Y. His field of research is photography.

Merton, Robert King:
1938: Science, technology and society in seventeenth century England (Osiris
4, 360-632; Bruges).
The author is professor of sociology in Columbia University, New York.

Nathanson, Jerome (editor):
1946: Science for democracy (180 p., New York; Isis 40, 385).

Needham, Joseph (1900-   ):
1944: An international science cooperation service (Nature 154, 657-60).
1945: The place of science and international scientific cooperation in post-war
world organization. Memorandum III (42 typewritten pages, Chungking; Isis 37,
251).
The author is an English biochemist, who has done service in China and in
UNESCO and is very alert concerning the social and international implications of
science.

Pla, Cortes (1898-   ):
1950: Ciencia y sociedad (230 p., Buenos Aires).

Science and Society, a Marxian quarterly. Vol. 1, no. 1, 126 p., Cambridge, Mass.,
1936 (Isis 27, 165).
The existence of this journal, is a witneess of the efforts made by Marxist scientists to diffuse their views on the sociology of science.

Sigerist, Henry Ernest (1891-   ):
1932: Man and medicine (350 p., New York; Isis 21, 337-38).—First published
in German, under title: Einführung in die Medizin (412 p., 1931).
1941: Medicine and human welfare (161 p., 20 ills., New Haven; Isis 33, 553).
1943: Civilization and disease (266 p., ill., Ithaca, N. Y.; Isis 35, 220).
1946: The university at the crossroads (171 p., New York; Isis 37, 275).
1947: Medicine and health in the Soviet Union (383 p., New York; Isis 39, 202-
03).
The author is a Swiss historian of medicine, whose teaching leads to a sociology
of medicine, largely based upon historical knowledge. The Marxist interpretation
of history appeals very much to him.

Soddy, Frederick (1877-   ):
1920: Science and life (242 p., London).
c. 1922: Cartesian economics. The bearing of physical science upon state
stewardship (32 p., London).
1924: The inversion of science and a scheme of scientific reformation (54 p.,
London).
1935: (editor) The frustration of science (144 p., New York; Isis 25, 274).
English chemist and physicist.

Thornton, Jesse Earl (editor):
1939: Science and social change (readings, 588 p., Washington, D.C.; Isis 32,
465).

Watson, David Lindsay (1901-   ):
1938: Scientists are human (269 p., London; Isis 31, 466-67).
American physico-chemist, born in Scotland; interested in the philosophy of
natural and social sciences.

Weaver, Warren (editor) (1894-   ):
    1947: The scientists speak (382 p., New York; Isis 39, 191-92).
    Collection of radio talks by 81 eminent scientists, explaining their views of the present and future of science.   The editor is director for the natural sciences of the Rockefeller Foundation, New York.

Znaniecki, Florjan (1882-   ):
    1940: The social role of the man of knowledge (216 p., New York, Columbia; Isis 33, 395).
    Sociologist of Polish birth, professor of sociology in the University of Illinois.

    See the Critical Bibliographies of Isis, sections 17. Organization of science, 43. Sociology, jurisprudence and positive polity, 48. History of philosophy.

9. CATALOGUES OF SCIENTIFIC LITERATURE

JOHANN CHRISTIAN POGGENDORFF (1796-1877): Biographisch-literarisches Hand-wörterbuch (1863-1940; reprint 10 vols. Ann Arbor 1945). For more details, *see* end of section 6 above.

ROYAL SOCIETY OF LONDON, **Catalogue of Scientific Papers**, 1800-1900 (Cambridge, 1867-1925, 19 vols.). Subject index (1908-14, 4 vols.).

This work is so important that we must pause a moment to describe it. Its compilation was first suggested at the Glasgow meeting of the B.A.A.S. in 1855 by JOSEPH HENRY (1797-1878), secretary of the Smithsonian Institution, and the plan was drawn up in 1857. After many years of preparation and considerable expenditure, the first volume appeared in 1867, and the publication continued as follows:

First series.   Vols. i-vi, cataloguing the papers of 1800-63, 1867-77.
Second series.   Vols. vii-viii, literature of 1864-73, 1877-79.
Third series.   Vols. ix-xi, literature of 1874-83, 1891-96.
Vol. xii.   Supplement to the previous volumes, 1902.
Fourth series.   Vols. xiii-xix, literature of 1884-1900, 1914-25.

To give an idea of the size of this catalogue it will suffice to remark that the papers catalogued in the fourth series alone, for the period 1884-1900, number 384,478, by 68,577 authors.

The compilation of a subject index, without which the work loses much of its value, was already contemplated in the first plan (1857). It was finally decided to arrange it in accordance with the International Catalogue of Scientific Literature (*see below*). This meant that it would include seventeen volumes, one for each of the seventeen sciences recognized in that catalogue. The first volume, Pure Mathematics, appeared in 1908; the second, Mechanics, in 1909, the third, Physics, in two instalments, Generalities, Heat, Light, Sound in 1912, Electricity and Magnetism in 1914. The publication seems to have been finally discontinued, which is a great pity. Whatever be the fate of the International Catalogue may be, there is no justification for leaving the *Royal Society Catalogue* essentially incomplete, and thus nullifying a large part of the past labor and expenditure.

International Catalogue of Scientific Literature. Published for the International Council by the Royal Society of London.

This is an outgrowth of the Royal Society Catalogue, as it was felt that the scientific literature of our century was too extensive to be dealt with by a single scientific society. Its organization was arranged at the initiative of the Royal Society by an international conference which met in London in 1896, then again in 1898, in 1900, etc. It was decided to divide science into seventeen branches:

A. MATHEMATICS.
B. MECHANICS.
C. PHYSICS.
D. CHEMISTRY.
E. ASTRONOMY.
F. METEOROLOGY (incl. TERRESTRIAL MAGNETISM).
G. MINERALOGY (incl. PETROLOGY and CRYSTALLOGRAPHY).
H. GEOLOGY.
J. GEOGRAPHY (MATHEMATICAL and PHYSICAL).
K. PALAEONTOLOGY.
L. GENERAL BIOLOGY.
M. BOTANY.
N. ZOOLOGY.
O. HUMAN ANATOMY.
P. PHYSICAL ANTHROPOLOGY.
Q. PHYSIOLOGY (incl. EXPERIMENTAL PSYCHOLOGY, PHARMACOLOGY, and EXPERIMENTAL PATHOLOGY).
R. BACTERIOLOGY.

A large number of annual volumes were actually published from 1902 to 1916, but the gigantic undertaking was a victim of the first World War and of the national selfishness and loss of idealism which the War induced. The volumes published cover the scientific literature for the period from 1901 to about 1913.[88]

[88] The publication includes 254 octavo volumes, varying in thickness from half an inch to two inches, and the original price was about £260. The stock has been sold to William Dawson and Sons, London, who offered a complete set for the price of £60 unbound, or £100 bound (November 1935). Unfortunately most of Messrs. Dawson's stock was lost, by enemy action, during the second World War and these volumes are now almost unobtainable.

10. UNION LISTS OF SCIENTIFIC PERIODICALS

The two most important lists of that kind are:

1) **The Union List of Serials in Libraries of the United States and Canada** (New York, 1927, one very large quarto volume of 1588 p.).

Registering some 70,000 journals and serials, of every kind, dead or alive, published in some 70 languages, and available in some 225 American libraries. Two supplements have already appeared, bringing the list down to 1932.

Second edition by the same editor, WINIFRED GREGORY (3065 p., New York 1943). This lists between 115 and 120,000 items. Supplement to the end of 1943 (New York 1945).

2) **A World List of Scientific Periodicals published in the years 1900-1921** (2 vols. London 1925-27), listing over 24,000 periodicals. Second edition for the years 1900-34 (1 vol. 794 p., London 1934). Item 2 is less comprehensive than 1 because it is restricted to contemporary scientific publications, it includes some 36,000 entries in 18 languages (for statistics, *see* Isis, vol. 23, p. 578). A new edition is in preparation.

These two lists are useful, first, to identify a certain journal, secondly, to find in what libraries (British or American) sets of it are available, and, finally, to judge of its importance, or at least of its popularity, by the number of sets available in the English-speaking world. This last judgment is possible only in the case of publications which are not distributed mostly by gift or exchange.

11. GENERAL SCIENTIFIC JOURNALS

For the study of modern science and the determination of the main impulses and tendencies of modern contemporary research, it is necessary to consult journals devoted to science in general. The leading journals of that kind are listed below in chronological order, and under their original or main title. The titles of some journals were changed more than once but a record of such changes is not in scope of our list. Should the reader wish for such information he would find it conveniently in the Union List of Serials (ULS) or in bibliographical lists of serial publications.

Since the purpose of such a list is to enable the historian of science to obtain quickly a general view of scientific problems and novelties *at a definite chronological level* some of the older and now deceased publications are also included.

XVIITH and XVIIITH CENTURY PERIODICALS

1665-   : **Journal des savants.** Paris.
A new series of the journal began in 1903. There has been a 'pirate' edition of this periodical running from 1665 to 1763, issued from Amsterdam. It has 164 volumes.

1682-1779: **Acta eruditorum.** Leipzig.
After 1732 its title was "Nova acta eruditorum." It has several supplements and a 6-volume index.

1772-1787: **Allgemeines Schwedisches Gelehrsamkeits-Archiv.** Leipzig. Edited by C. W. LÜDEKE; complete in 7 volumes.

1798-   : **Philosophical magazine and Journal of science.** London.
After 1850 it is called The London, Edinburgh, and Dublin Philosophical Magazin, etc. It is still current and comprises now several hundred volumes in seven series.

XIXTH CENTURY PERIODICALS

1817-1835: **Isis; oder, Enzyklopaedische Zeitung.** Jena & Leipzig. Edited by L. OKEN; comprises 23 volumes.
Originally a political periodical until 1824, it changed title to Enzyklopädische Zeitschrift vorzüglich für Naturgeschichte, etc. As a supplement it had a "Literarischer Anzeiger."

1818-   : **American journal of science (Silliman's journal).** New Haven.
Vol. 50 is an index to vols. 1-49, after that every tenth volume contains an index to ten volumes.

1823-1831: **Bulletin des annonces et des nouvelles scientifiques.** Paris.
Title varies: Bulletin universel (des sciences et de l'industrie); divided into sections according to branches of science.

1845-1921: **Scientific American.** New York.
Merged in 1921 with the Scientific American monthly.

1846-   : **Archives des sciences physiques et naturelles; Bibliothèque universelle.** Genève.

1850-   : Natuurwetenschappelijk tijdschrift voor Nederlandsch-Indië. Batavia, Weltevreden.
Later called Chronica naturae. Index v. 1-60, 1850-1900; v. 61-90, 1901-30.

1853-1918: Zeitschrift für Naturwissenschaften. Halle & Leipzig. Edited by GIEBEL, SIEWERT, et al.; 86 volumes; slight variation in title.

1857-1875: Année (L') scientifique et industrielle. Paris.

1857-   : Moniteur scientifique du Dr Quesneville; journal des sciences pures et appliquées. Vol. 100 was published in 1928.

1863-   : Revue scientifique (Revue rose illustrée) Paris. Index 1863-81.

1866-   : Archives néerlandaises des sciences exactes et naturelles. Haarlem.
Its 3rd series started in 1911 with three divisions: 3A for exact sciences, 3B for natural sciences and 3C for physiology.

1867-   : The American naturalist. Boston & New York.
Beginning with vol. 85, 1951, it became the official journal of the American Society of Naturalists.

1869-   : Nature. London.

1869-   : Természettudományi közlöny (Naturwissenschaftlicher Anzeiger). Budapest.

1872-1915: Popular science monthly. New York.
Weekly; continued as Scientific Monthly; index vol., 1-40, 1872-92.

1873-   : La Nature. Paris. Four decennial indices for the period 1873-1912.

1876-   : Scientific American supplement (1876-1919) New York.
Continued by Scientific American monthly (1920-21). In Nov. 1921, merged into Scientific American; rejuvenated in May 1948 (vol. 178, 5). Index: 1876-1910.

1877-   : Revue des questions scientifiques. Louvain. Indices: v. 1-50, 1877-1901; v. 51-80, 1902-21; v. 81-110, 1922-36.

1883-   : Science. Cambridge, Mass., & New York.

1886-1912: Naturwissenschaftliche Rundschau. Braunschweig. Complete in 27 vol.; continued as Die Naturwissenschaften.

1887-   : Naturwissenschaftliche Wochenschrift. Edited by H. POTONIÉ; vol. 37, 1922.

1890-   : Revue générale des sciences pures et appliquées. Paris. Index: v. 1-25, 1890-1914, issued in vol. 25.

1890-1920: Prometheus; illustrierte Wochenschrift für die Fortschritte (der angewandten Naturwissenschaften) in Gewerbe, Industrie und Wissenschaft. Berlin. In 1921, merged into Umschau; completed in 31 vols.

1897-   : Umschau; Übersicht über die Fortschritte und Bewegungen auf dem Gesamtgebiete des Wissenschaft, Technik, etc. Frankfurt a.M. Edited by J. H. BECHHOLD.

XXTH CENTURY PERIODICALS

1903-   : South African journal of science. Cape Town.

1906-   : Science progress in the twentieth century. London.

1907-   : Scientia. Bologna. Index: 1907-29.

1909-1914: **Natura;** rivista di scienze naturali. Pavia.

1912-   : **Priroda.** Leningrad.

1913-   : **American scientist;** Sigma XI quarterly.   Champaign, Illinois.

1913-   : **Naturwissenschaften.** Berlin.
Continues Naturwissenschatfliche Rundschau (1886-1912).

1915-   : **Scientific monthly.** New York & Lancaster, Pennsylvania.

1915-   : **K'o-hsüeh** [Science]. Shanghai.
Monthly; contains bibliographies, progress reports and reviews in Chinese.

1918-   : **Nauka polska.** Warszawa.
For progress of science in Poland.

1920-   : **Discovery.** London.

1922-   : **Ergebnisse der exakten Naturwissenschaften.** Berlin.
Annual; long reviews on progress of certain problems of exact sciences.

1925-   : **Forschungen und Fortschritte.** Berlin.

1932-   : **Current science.** Bangalore, Mysore.

1934-   : **Ciencias;** revista trimestrial. Madrid.

1935-   : **Science and culture.** Calcutta.

1938-   : **Australian journal of science.** Sidney.

1940-   : **Ciencia;** revista hispano-americana de ciencias puras y aplicadas.   Mexico, D. F.

1942-   : **Endeavour.** London.[89]

1942-   : **Experientia.** Basel.

1945-   : **Ciencia e investigación.** Buenos Aires.

1946-   : **Zeitschrift für Naturforschung.** Wiesbaden.

1948-   : **Naturwissenschaftliche Rundschau.** Stuttgart.

1949-   : **Ciencia e cultura.** São Paulo.

The most convenient of all these journals is probably *Nature*, but it began only in 1869 and has no general indices.   One must consult the indices of each volume, which is a tedious process (by the end of 1950, 166 volumes had appeared).   Complete sets of these journals are very bulky and the historian of modern science can hardly have them near him, but he should try to keep close at hand a few general indices.   (*N.B.* The present efforts of modern technicians to reduce the bulk of accumulated literature by means of microfilms, microprints and similar other devices will have but little practical value for historians of any kind.)   (C. F. M.)

In many cases, the historian of science would be obliged to consult also journals devoted to special sciences, or the *abstracting journals* concerned with special subjects.   Any attempt to enumerate all these journals would be futile and outside the scope of this guide-book.   Every specialized man of science is familiar with the journals devoted to his special studies.   Moreover, there are many special lists of sci-

---

[89] "Endeavour, a quarterly review designed to record the progress of the sciences in the service of mankind," is published by the Imperial Chemical Industries, London.   It serves as a means of propaganda for British science and industry, but the articles are as impartial as they would be in any scientific journal; they are admirably illustrated.   In addition to the English edition of Endeavour, there are also editions in French, Spanish, German and (beginning with vol. VII, no. 25, Jan. 1948) Italian.

entific journals available, in addition to the union catalogs and world lists, which contain the needed references to such special serials.

Many more journals could be quoted in various languages, not counting the publications of the academies and learned societies, but those quoted are more than sufficient for the general purpose.[90] If a historian wished to have a general view of science in 1895, the simplest way of obtaining it would be to consult the periodicals which appeared in that year. Many of these periodicals, if not all of them, are available in every good research library.

---

[90] Some journals which ran only for a few years and have long been out of circulation and forgotten (in spite of their goodness) have been omitted, because they are difficult to find except in the oldest and largest libraries.

12. ABSTRACTING AND REVIEW JOURNALS
(by CLAUDIUS F. MAYER)

For the historian of any branch of science the so-called abstracting journals are very convenient indicators, first-aid tools in a quick approach to past decades or centuries. While they help him in his effort to revive the contemporary ideology of a chosen subject and to re-create the scientific atmosphere of any era of his choice, they are not more than indicators to be used with proper criticism. The information that they convey should never be accepted without an ultimate recourse to the original sources. For the historian who is engaged in specific bio-bibliographical studies the abstracting journals are especially valuable because they may help him to detect many details in the literary activities and in the life histories of even the lesser stars of science.

The historian has to be reminded, however, that the literature of any scientific subject is much wider and the literary production of any man is much larger than it could be revealed by any abstracting journal. Repeated statistical studies showed that it is not more than about 20% of the world's current scientific literature which the current abstracting journals are able to comprehend. The percentage of abstracted literature may be higher and the value of older abstracting journals may be greater for earlier decades and centuries when the bulk of scientific publishing has been small. The value of these journals as secondary sources for the historian to prepare bio-bibliographies depends also upon the professional education of the makers of the abstracting journals and subject bibliographies. If the compiler or editor was a scientist, expert in his subject, the historian may be assured of the completeness and accuracy of the subject bibliographies and the abstracts though they are secondary records only.

The abstracting journal is by no means a 20th century innovation of scientific journalism, though this century may have an increased demand for it. Indeed, the precursors of the modern abstracting journals could be retraced to the earliest printed magazines, and, even beyond those, to the medieval encyclopedias, formularies, pandects, furthermore to the various written collections of scientific knowledge made already a couple of thousand years B.C.

The earliest scientific periodicals as well as many publications of the first scientific societies in the 17th and 18th centuries either consisted exclusively of abstracts and digests or included much of these to form a large part of an issue. Many of the general scientific periodicals listed above in this chapter do the same. In Chapter 20 there are special journals for the historian of science; many of them abound in abstracts of articles related to the history of sciences. At the end of Chapter 20 (p. 246-48) there is a short appendix of journal titles; in a way, most of those journals were chiefly filled with abstracts.

There is a steady growth in the number of journals that are devoted exclusively to abstracting the contents of other scientific periodicals. At the beginning of 1951 there were some 300 of them. A correct count is almost impossible, and not needed. Many more may be in existence, and many are defunct now. Recently, D. E. GRAY listed 145 current abstracting (and indexing) services for the field of physics alone (Am. J. Physics, 1950, 18: 274-99; 417-24). Yet, only two of these journals have been used by more than 90% of the people he questioned.

Besides GRAY's article there are very few other publications for listing such journals. A list was prepared by RUTH COBB with the title *Periodical bibliographies and abstracts for scientific and technological journals of the world* (Washington, U. S. National Research Council, 1920). The Library Association of Great Britain has published a *Class Catalogue*, &c. (Lond., 1912; 38p.). The latest of such lists is a document of the International Federation for Documentation, under the title *List of current specialized abstracting and indexing services* (The Hague, 1949).

It is a very tentative list which excuses itself with the sentence that "The present status of the abstracting work in the whole world is still very confusing."

The following selective alphabetical list includes a few abstracting journals chiefly of older vintage or of long standing which, in the opinion of the compiler, are of some value as secondary indicative sources for the historian of science.

(1785)1793- (1800)1807: **Allgemeines Repertorium der Literatur.** Jena; Weimar. Edited by J. S. Ersch; 3 series; in many sections.

1827-1844: **Allgemeines Repertorium der gesamten deutschen medizinisch-chirurgischen Journalistik.** Leipzig. Edited by C. F. Kleinert; 18 vols; ca 5,000 references a year.

(1825-)1829-   : **American journal of pharmacy.** Philadelphia.

1876-   : **Analyst.** Cambridge, Engl.

1886-   : **Anatomischer Anzeiger.** Jena.

1895-   : **Année (L') biologique.** Paris.

1862-1877: **Année (L') géographique.** Paris.

1850-1871: **Annual (The) of scientific discovery.** Boston. Limited to discoveries in the U. S. only.

1890-   : **Anthropologie.** Paris.

1906-   : **Anthropos.** St Gabriel; Freiburg (Sw.).

(1827)1828- (1837)1838: **Arcana of science** [and art]. London.

1822-   : **Archiv der Pharmazie.** Berlin.

1834-1914: **Archiv für Naturgeschichte.** Berlin.

1882-   : **Archives italiennes de biologie.** Pisa.

1922-   : **Australian science abstracts.** Sydney. From v. 17, 1938, issued as supplement of Australian journal of science.

1877-1919: **Beiblätter; Annalen der Physik.** Leipzig. In 1920, continued as Physikalische Berichte.

1893-1913: **Bibliographia physiologica . . . répertoire des travaux de physiologie de l'année.** Bruxelles; Wien. Edited by Richet; in 3 series.

1697-1699: **Bibliotheca librorum novorum.** Utrecht. Five vol. in 3; issued bimonthly from Apr./May 1697 to Nov./Dec. 1699; perhaps the earliest book-review journal; edited by Ludolph Küster(=Neocorus) and Henrik Sikio(=Sickius).

1851-1887: **Bibliotheca historico-naturalis et physicochemica** [et mathematica]. Göttingen.

1796-1835: **Bibliothèque britannique.** Genève. First series, 1796-1816, in three sections: *a*) littérature, 60v., *b*) sciences et arts, 60v., *c*) agriculture, 20v., plus 4v. index. Continued as Bibliothèque universelle des sciences, and had another series from 1816 to 1835; a third series began in 1858.

1902-1910: **Biochemisches Zentralblatt.** Berlin.

1881-   : **Biologisches Zentralblatt.** Leipzig.

1918-1926: **Botanical abstracts.** Baltimore. Continued as part of Biological Abstracts (1926-   ).

1880-   : Botanisches Zentralblatt. Kassel; Jena, &c.

1843-1910: Botanische Zeitung. Berlin; Leipzig.

1757-1763: Bremisches Magazin zur Ausbreitung der Wissenschaften. Hannover.

1836-1877: British and foreign medical [medico-chirurgical] review. London.

1855-1861: Bulletin de bibliographie, d'histoire et de biographie mathématiques. Paris. Edited by TERQUEM; 6 vols.

1903-   : Bulletin de l'Institut Pasteur. Paris.

1854-   : Bulletin de la Société botanique de France. Paris.

1858-   : Bulletin de la Société chimique de France. Paris. From 1858 to 1863: Répertoire de chimie, &c.

1809-1813: Bulletin des neuesten und wissenswürdigsten aus den Naturwissenschaften. Berlin.

1870-   : Bulletin des sciences mathématiques. Paris.

1907-   : Chemical abstracts. Columbus; Washington.

1830-   : Chemisches Zentralblatt. Berlin. 1830-1849: Pharmaceutisches Centralblatt; 1850-1858: Chemisch-pharmaceutisches Centralblatt.

1862-1901: Chemisch-technisches Repertorium. Berlin.

1752-1798: Commentarii de rebus in scientia naturali et medicina gestis. Leipzig.

1913-   : Critical bibliography of the history and philosophy of science. (Published in *Isis*).

1897-1920: Dermatologisches Zentralblatt. Leipzig.

1712-1739: Deutsche acta eruditorum, oder Geschichte der Gelehrten. Leipzig. 240 nos. in 20 vols.

1880-   : Elektrotechnische Zeitschrift. Berlin.

1772-1814: Esprit(L') des journaux français et étrangers. Liége; Paris; Bruxelles. 480 vols. for 23 years.

(1891)1892-1929: Excerpta medica; monatliche Journalauszüge. Leipzig; Basel.

1904-   : Folia haematologica. Berlin; Leipzig.

1902-   : Folia otolaryngologica. Leipzig.

1910-1932: Fortschritte der naturwissenschaftlichen Forschung. Berlin, &c.

(1845)1847- (1918)1919: Fortschritte der Physik. Berlin; Braunschweig. Continued as Physikalische Berichte (1920-   ).

(1874)1875- (1884)1889: Geological record. London.

1901-   : Geologisches Zentralblatt. Leipzig; Berlin.

1739-1860: Göttingische gelehrte Anzeigen. Göttingen. 1753-1802: Göttingischer Anzeiger von gelehrten Sachen.

1907-1917: Gynaekologische Rundschau. Berlin.

1852-   : Hedwigia; Organ für Kryptogamenkunde und Phytopathologie nebst Repertorium für Literatur. Dresden.

1687(Sept.)- 1709(June): **Histoire des ouvrages des scavans.** Rotterdam.

1891-1922: **Hygienische Rundschau.** Berlin.

1859-   : **Ibis; a quarterly journal of ornithology.** London.

1935-   : **Indian science abstracts.** Calcutta.

1908-1923: **Internationale Revue der gesamten Hydrobiologie and Hydrographie.** Leipzig.

1884-1922: **Internationales Zentralblatt für Laryngologie,** etc. Berlin.

1918-   : **Italia che scrive.** Roma.

1865-1901: **Jahrbuch der Erfindungen und Fortschritte aus dem Gebiete der Physik, Chemie und chemischen Technologie, der Astronomie und Meteorologie.** Leipzig.

(1868)1871-   : **Jahrbuch über die Fortschritte der Mathematik.** Berlin.

1867-1919: **Jahresbericht über die Leistungen und Fortschritte in der gesamten Medicin.** Berlin.

1863-   : **Journal of botany.** London.

1809-   : **Journal de pharmacie et de chimie.** Paris.
1. ser., 1809-1814: Bulletin de pharmacie et des sciences accessoires; in many volumes, grouped into several sets, each with its own cumulative index.

1872-   : **Journal de physique et le radium.** Paris.

1912-   : **Kongresszentralblatt für die gesamte innere Medizin.** Berlin.

1843-1860: **Leipziger Repertorium der deutschen und ausländischen Literatur.** Leipzig.

1850-   : **Literarisches Zentralblatt für Deutschland.** Leipzig.

1901-   : **Man; a monthly record of anthropological science.** London.

1781-1794: **Medicinische Litteratur.** Leipzig. Edited by J. C. T. SCHLEGEL.

1876-   : **Mind; a quarterly review of psychology and philosophy.** London.

1876-   : **Mineralogical magazine.** London.

1715-1797: **Neue Zeitungen von gelehrten Sachen.** Leipzig. Edited by JOH. GOTTL. KRAUSE and O. MENCKE; a rival of the Acta eruditorum; includes reviews of articles on science and literature.

1882-1921: **Neurologisches Zentralblatt.** Berlin.

1821-1849: **Notizen aus dem Gebiete der Natur- und Heilkunde.** Erfurt; Weimar; Jena. Edited by L. F. v. FRORIEP; 101 vols. in 3 series.

1733-1736: **Nützliche und auserlesene Arbeiten der Gelehrten im Reich.** Nürnberg.

1898-   : **Orientalistische Literaturzeitung.** Berlin; Leipzig.

1893-   : **Ornithologische Monatsberichte.** Berlin.

1855-   : **Petermanns (Dr. A.) Mitteilungen aus Justus Perthes' Geographischer Anstalt.** Gotha.

1859-   : **Pharmazeutische Zentralhalle.** Berlin; Dresden.

1921-   : **Photographic abstracts.** London.

1895-1904: **Photographisches Zentralblatt.** München.

1893-   : **Physical review.** New York, etc.

1904-1909: **Physikalisch-chemisches Zentralblatt.** Leipzig.

1920-   : **Physikalische Berichte.** Braunschweig.
Continuation of Fortschritte der Physik; begins with reviews of 1918 literature.

1916-1938: **Physiological abstracts.** London.

1907-1917: **Progressus rei botanicae.** Jena.
Founded by JOH. PAULUS LOTSY (1867-1931); also called Fortschritte der Botanik; 5 vols.

(1872)1873- (1879)1886: **Repertorium annuum literaturae botanicae periodicae.** Haarlem. Edited by J. A. VAN BEMMELEN and others; 8 vols.

1822-1825: **Repertorium der mathematischen Literatur.** Augsburg; Leipzig.

1869-1871: **Repertorium der technischen, mathematischen und naturwissenschaftlichen Journal-Literatur.** Berlin.

(1823)-1912: **Repertorium der technischen Literatur.** Berlin.
In 1909, title reads: Fortschritte der Technik (1909-1912).

1840-1893: **Repertorium der Tierheilkunde.** Stuttgart.

1815-1851: **Repertorium der Pharmacie.** Nürnberg.

(1805)1806- (1813)1815: **Retrospect of philosophical, mechanical, chemical and agricultural discoveries.** London.

1840-1901: **Retrospect of practical medicine** [and surgery]. London.

1913-   : **Review of applied entomology.** London. Ser. A: Agricultural; Ser. B: Medical and veterinary.

1890-1936: **Review of reviews.** London.

1866-1935: **Revue critique d'histoire et de littérature.** Paris.

1873-1898: **Revue des sciences médicales en France et à l'étranger.** Paris. Edited by G. HAYEM; 52 vols.

1862-1880: **Revue des sociétés savantes.** Paris.

1856-1882: **Revue des sociétés savantes des départements.** Paris.

1917-   : **Revue générale de l'électricité.** Paris.

1893-1934: **Revue sémestrielle des publications mathématiques.** Amsterdam; Leipzig.

1907-   : **Rivista delle riviste.** (*In:* Scientia. Bologna).

1834-1922: **Schmidt's Jahrbücher der in- und ausländischen gesamten Medizin.** Leipzig; Bonn.
V. 1-40, 1834-1843, as Jahrbücher . . . ; 341 vols. in 9 series; includes ca 800,000 abstracts and references.

1898-   : **Science abstracts.** London.
From 1903, it runs in two sections (physics, electrical engineering).

1916-   : **Science et industrie.** Paris.

1828-1843: **Summarium des neusten aus der** [gesammten] **Medicin.** Leipzig.

1908-   : Technique (La) moderne; revue universelle des sciences appliquées à l'industrie. Paris.

1912-   : Tropical diseases bulletin. London.

1740-1759: Wöchentliche Nachrichten von gelehrten Sachen. Regensburg.
A rarity and curiosity; includes reviews, abstracts, personal notices, etc.; copy in British Museum.

1913-   : Zeitschrift für ophthalmologische Optik. Berlin.

1884-   : Zeitschrift für wissenschaftliche Mikroskopie. Leipzig.

1882-1919: Zentralblatt für allgemeine Gesundheitspflege. Bonn.

1890-   : Zentralblatt für allgemeine Pathologie und pathologische Anatomie. Jena.

1896-1912: Zentralblatt für Anthropologie, Ethnologie, und Urgeschichte. Jena.

1887-   : Zentralblatt für Bakteriologie. Jena.
Later in two sections, one of them running in 2 parts (Originale, Referate).

1874-   : Zentralblatt für Chirurgie. Leipzig.

1911-1930: Zentralblatt für die gesamte Kinderheilkunde. Berlin.

1900-1911: Zentralblatt für die gesamte Physiologie und Pathologie des Stoffwechsels. Berlin; etc.

1889-1906: Zentralblatt für die Krankheiten der Harn- und Sexualorgane. Hamburg, etc.

1863-1915: Zentralblatt für die medizinischen Wissenschaften. Berlin.

1877-   : Zentralblatt für Gynaekologie. Leipzig.

1931-   : Zentralblatt für Mathematik und ihre Grenzgebiete. Berlin.

1878-1910: Zentralblatt für Nervenheilkunde und Psychiatrie. Leipzig.

1904-1914: Zentralblatt für normale und pathologische Anatomie. Berlin; Wien.

1887-1921: Zentralblatt für Physiologie. Leipzig; Wien.

1877-1919: Zentralblatt für praktische Augenheilkunde. Leipzig.

1910-1919: Zentralblatt für Röntgenstrahlen, Radium und verwandte Gebiete. Wiesbaden.

1913-   : Zentralorgan für die gesamte Chirurgie. Berlin; Leipzig.
Title varies.

1864-   : Zoological record. London.
V. 1-6, 1864-1869, as Record of zoological literature.

1878-1896: Zoologischer Anzeiger. Leipzig; Zürich.
1896-1914, v. 1-25, as Bibliographia zoologica.

1894-1918: Zoologisches Zentralblatt. Leipzig.
Title of last six volumes: Zentralblatt für Zoologie.

13. NATIONAL ACADEMIES
AND NATIONAL SCIENTIFIC SOCIETIES

The scientific academies created in the seventeenth century and later, being supported by the prince or government took naturally a national aspect. Thus, the *Accademia dei Lincei* became eventually (much later) the outstanding academy of Italy, the *Académie des Sciences* and the *Royal Society* became the scientific academies of France and of England, etc. Those academies took some interest in the history of science, chiefly but not exclusively, as far as it had developed in their own territory. Thus, the Institut de France prepared by order of NAPOLEON reports on the progress of science from 1789 to 1810.

J. B. J. DELAMBRE, Rapport historique sur les progrès des sciences mathématiques depuis 1789 et sur leur état actuel (272 pp.). Including mechanics, astronomy, geography, arts and industries. GEORGES CUVIER, Rapport historique sur les progrès des sciences naturelles (298 pp.). Including chemistry, physics, physiology, natural history, medicine, agriculture. BON JOSEPH DACIER, Rapport historique sur les progrès de l'histoire et de la littérature ancienne (263 pp.). The three quarto volumes were published at Paris in 1810.

The series of books on the history of science written at the initiative of the Academy of Bavaria is so important that a complete description of it is given on p. 124-25.

Moreover, as the early academies grew older, they became naturally more concerned with their own glorious past, with the history of their achievements and institutions and the biographies of their members, and this has often induced them to promote historical investigations. The jubilee publications of those bodies sometimes contain historical memoirs of real value, which do not always receive the publicity they deserve and thus are relatively unknown.

A history of the main academies, however brief, would take too much space here. We have already spoken of the oldest ones, the *Accademia dei Lincei*, the *Accademia del Cimento*, the *Académie des Sciences*, the *Royal Society*. There are various historical accounts of each of them, so many in fact, that the history of each academy requires a bibliography of its own. The same remark applies to the other national academies, many of which are a century or two old. More of them were created in the twentieth century and at present there are almost as many national academies as there are nations in the United Nations. The creation of the younger academies was due partly to the feeling that national prestige required their existence and partly to the requirement of the International Union of Academies.

It is impossible to give here a complete bibliography of academies, or even to enumerate them and for each of them the main historical publications. We must limit ourselves to mentioning a few general studies.

MARTHA ORNSTEIN: The role of scientific societies in the seventeenth century (second ed., University of Chicago 1928; Isis 12, 154-56). The first edition appeared in 1913; the second edition was reprinted in 1938 (322 p.; Isis 31, 87-89). HARCOURT BROWN: Scientific organizations in seventeenth century France, 1620-80 (328 p., Baltimore 1934; Isis 22, 542).

The Royal Society of London publishes a journal "Notes and Records" which contains many historical articles in addition to other news of social, non-technical interest. Vol. 1, no. 1 appeared in April 1938, vol. 8, no. 1 in October 1950. Address: Royal Society, Burlington House, London W.1.

In addition to their national academies many countries have another kind of national organization of their men of science. This takes the form of an annual scientific congress, meeting each year in another city of the national (or colonial) territory. Academies are exclusive organizations, the membership of which is generally restricted to elected fellows. The number of members may be very small as in the Académie des sciences, or larger as in the Royal Society; in any case, it is limited, and nobody can join the Academy without a formal invitation after a regular election.[91] The annual congresses are far more democratic; their purpose is to bring together each year in one place as many men of science as possible.

The initiative of those annual congresses was taken in Switzerland. In 1797, some scientists of Bern invited Swiss men of science to meet at Herzogenbuchsee, and they constituted the Société générale helvétique des amis des sciences physiques et naturelles. Political events discouraged further meetings. In 1801 a similar effort was made, by German men of science, in Stuttgart and was equally abortive.

The Swiss idea was renewed and realized in 1815 by HENRI ALBERT GOSSE and meetings held on Oct. 6 at Mornex and Geneva. We may thus place the Swiss Society at the head of our list.

1) 1815: Société helvétique des sciences naturelles (the title occurs also in German, Italian, and Romansh). Since 1915, annual meetings have taken place each year in a different city. The centenary was celebrated at the birthplace of the society, Geneva, in 1915. The proceedings of that centenary appeared in vol. L of the Nouveaux mémoires de la Société helvétique (Zürich 1915); they contain a history of the Swiss organization. Shorter account by THÉOPHILE STUDER *in* PAUL SEIPPEL (*editor*): La Suisse au dix-neuvième siècle (3 vols., Lausanne 1899-1901; vol. 2, 195-200, 1900).—The 129th annual meeting occurred in Lausanne, 1949.

Inspired by the Swiss organization, LORENZ OKEN (1779-1851; editor of Isis from 1817 to 1848) proposed in 1820 to the Kaiserlich Leopoldinische Akademie der Naturforscher to constitute a similar one in Germany. The Leopoldina declined to do so, but the German society was constituted two years later.

2) 1822: (GDNA) Gesellschaft deutscher Naturforscher und Ärzte.—First meeting in Leipzig in 1822. Accounts of meetings 1 to 8 appeared in OKEN's Isis; reports of later meetings in the Amtlicher Bericht, Tageblatt der Versammlung, etc.; since 1924, they appear as supplements to Die Naturwissenschaften. KARL SUD-HOFF: Hundert Jahre Deutscher Naturforscher Versammlungen (80 p., Leipzig 1922). This booklet, published to celebrate the centenary of the German society, contains a history of the society and a list of its meetings, the main discourses of each being mentioned, from the first, Leipzig 1822 to the 86th, Bad Nauheim 1920. The centennial meeting of Leipzig 1922 was not the hundredth one, but the 87th, some annual meetings having been omitted because of war or unrest.

3) 1831: (BAAS) British Association for the Advancement of Science. This association met for the first time at York in 1831, and has met almost every year since in a different town of Great Britain, the British Empire or Ireland. The Reports published annually in separate volumes since 1831, constitute a valuable collection for the historian of science (as opposed to the German reports which being scattered and irregularly published are so difficult to consult in their entirety that one does not try to do so). Vols. 1 to 108 of the Reports were published from 1831 to 1938 (no meetings in 1917, 1918); two volumes of general indexes cover respectively the years 1831-60, 1861-90. From 1939, the Reports appear under a new title "The advancement of science" in the form not of an annual but of a quarterly. Vol. 1, part 1, Oct. 1939, part 4, July 1940.

Address: Burlington House, London W.1. The official residence of the Permanent Secretary is now at Down House, at Downe, Kent, formerly DARWIN's home (Isis 23, 533, 534).

4) 1848: (AAAS) American Association for the Advancement of Science. Proceedings published in annual volumes since the first meeting (Philadelphia 1848) until 1910. Since then the full proceedings appear in Science, and only Summarized Proooceedings from time to time in book form. *E.g.*, summarized Proceedings for the period from Jan. 1934 to Jan. 1940 with Directory of members as of July 1, 1940 (1120 p., Washington, D. C., 1940). That volume contains a brief history of AAAS from 1848 to 1940 (p. 1-87).

Address of the Permanent Secretary: Smithsonian Institution, Washington, D. C.

---

[91] In America, the name "academy" has been assumed by at least one society of which almost anybody can become a member by paying the annual subscription. That form of exploitation of snobbishness is certainly wrong.

In 1920, a special section (L) was devoted to the "Historical and philological sciences." The original idea, promoted by FREDERICK E. BRASCH was to have a section devoted to the "history of science," but the AAAS considered that the history of science was too small a subject to have a section for itself and entitled the new section "Historical and philological sciences." It was as if it were making a subsection of the American Historical Association and of the Philological Association—the whole of history and philology was only a part of the AAAS. A section devoted to the "history of science" would have been very natural, this one was preposterous. It must be added, however, that the great majority of the papers read before section L were papers on the history of science.

FREDERICK E. BRASCH (Science 52, 559-62, 1920; 53, 315-18, 1921).

5) 1872: (AFAS) **Association française pour l'avancement des Sciences.** First annual meeting in Bordeaux 1872. Meetings are held almost every year in a different French-speaking town. The 67th meeting took place in Geneva (Switzerland) in 1948.

Comptes rendus of the annual meetings appear in book form; those of the first meeting (Bordeaux 1872) in Paris 1873; those of the 63rd meeting (Liége, Belgium, 1939) in 1941.

There is also a Revue de l'Association etc. entitled Sciences giving miscellaneous information. I have seen no. 59, 75. année, juillet-sept. 1948, p. 433-51, i-ix. 75th year refers to the age of the AFAS, not of "Sciences."

Address of the Secretary: 28 rue Serpente, Paris 6.

As in the case for the other national societies, the actual foundation was preceded by tentatives which are traced back to 1864 (LEVERRIER) and 1865 (FREDERIC KUHLMANN). The Association was constituted at a meeting held in Paris on 22 April 1872 under the presidency of CLAUDE BERNARD.

6) 1907: (SIPS) **Società italiana per il progresso delle scienze.** The first annual meeting took place in Parma 1907. Annual meetings have taken place since then almost every year, each time in a different Italian town.

The proceedings are published in book form, Atti della Società, etc. (vol. 1, Roma 1908). The Atti of the first 18 annual meetings from 1907 to 1929 appeared in 18 volumes. A new series of the Atti began with the meeting of Florence 1929 (2 vols., 1930). The 28th meeting took place in Pisa 1939, and its Atti edited by LUCIO SILLA bear the subtitle Celebrazione del 1° centenario. *See also:*—

LUCIO SILLA (*editor*): Un secolo di progresso scientifico italiano, 1839-1939 (7 vols., Roma 1939-40; Isis 35, 190; 36, 223). This very useful but disingenuous work bears a misleading subtitle "Società italiana per il progresso delle scienze. Anno 100° della prima riunione degli scienziati italiani." Hasty readers might conclude that these volumes celebrate the centenary of the Società, which in 1939 was only 32 years old. The subtitle refers to a meeting of the "Congresso dei dotti," which took place in Pisa 1839. That Congresso having taken a patriotic and revolutionary character (we must remember that Italy was not unified until 1870), it was suppressed after its ninth meeting held in Venice 1847. Italian scientists met again in Siena 1862, Rome 1873, Palermo 1875. In short, Italian scientists held twelve annual meetings during the period 1839-1907, or forty during the period 1839-1939.

General indexes to the Atti. Indici della prima serie (vol. I-X, 1907-19; 1926), della seconda serie (riun. 11-20, 1921-31; 1932).

The Società also publishes an Annuario containing the list of its members (last vol. seen 1935-XIII); it began in 1937 the publication of Scienza e Tecnica, a monthly supplement to the Atti; vol. 2 (1938) was issued independently with subtitle Rivista generale di informazione scientifica.

Address of SIPS: Piazzale delle Scienze 7, Palazzo del Consiglio Nazionale delle Ricerche, Roma.

The description of these six associations must suffice; they are still the most important, the first because of chronological precedence and the five others because of the great achievements of German, English, American, French and Italian men of science. Similar associations have been created in many countries in order to satisfy national ambitions, or sometimes the ambitions of a linguistic group. For example, the Flemish congress of science and medicine was created by JULIUS MAC-

LEOD in Gent, 1897 (ten years before the Italian congress!).   The history of that
Flemish congress from 1897 to 1944 was told in Dutch by one of the founders,
A. J. J. VAN DE VELDE (Antwerpen 1944; Isis 39, 116).

The publications of these national congresses constitute an important documentation for the study of the history of science, chiefly (but not exclusively) in
the countries concerned.   The publications of the Swiss, German, British, American,
French and Italian congresses have also some international significance, because each
of these congresses invited or welcomed foreign guests.   The scientific achievements of the nations using languages of international currency (chiefly EFGILS)[92]
are so considerable that the annual discussions of them are of interest not only to
the countries immediately concerned but also to a very large part of the civilized
world.

[92] SARTON: Tower of Babel (Isis 39, 3-15, 1948).

C. HISTORY OF SCIENCE

14. CHIEF REFERENCE BOOKS
ON THE HISTORY OF SCIENCE

LUDWIG DARMSTAEDTER (1846-1927): **Handbuch zur Geschichte der Natur-wissenschaften und der Technik** (Zweite Auflage, 1272 p., Berlin 1908). Chrono-logical list of discoveries year by year. Valuable, but to be used with caution.

GEORGE SARTON: **Introduction to the History of Science.** Vol. 1, From HOMER to OMAR KHAYYAM (Baltimore, 1927). Vol. 2, in two parts. From RABBI BEN EZRA to ROGER BACON (1931). Vol. 3, in two parts. Science and Learning in the Fourteenth Century (1948).

This is a very elaborate treatise and bibliography, but it extends only to the year 1400. It is closely interlocked with Isis; there are references to Isis on almost every page, enabling the reader to obtain rapidly more information; on the other hand, errata and addenda are published from time to time in the Critical Bibliogra-phies of Isis.

See also biographical collections, especially those concerning men of science, dealt with in section 6.

15. TREATISES AND HANDBOOKS
ON THE HISTORY OF SCIENCE

The need of explaining the work accomplished by one's predecessors in any philosophic or scientific field and of recapitulating the results already obtained is natural enough. Every scholar who has raised himself above the lowest technical stage must have realized it, though he may have been unable to satisfy it. That need was felt just as soon as the development of knowledge had assumed sufficient complexity. Young students of the history of science may be astonished to find "historical outlines" even in early times, but there is nothing astonishing in that as long as one understands that those early times were not early at all from the contemporary point of view. The "father of medicine" HIPPOCRATES was a very sophisticated physician, who had been preceded by many generations of other physicians and thought of himself as a modern doctor. When we look backward from our privileged position, we see him standing, not at the beginning of a long line of physicians, but rather about half-way between our earliest Egyptian colleagues and ourselves. One of the early Hippocratic treatises deals with "ancient medicine."[93] The first book of ARISTOTLE's Metaphysics contains a history of early Greek philosophy; various philosophical problems are introduced as it were in their chronological order of appearance, a method which has been followed by many philosophers and is still popular in the teaching of philosophy. The history of philosophy is used to explain philosophy itself; in the same way, the history of science might be used to explain science, if one had time enough for that.[94] Science is so vast and complex that the teachers must use the shortest avenues of approach instead of the historical one which may be the most natural but is certainly the longest. This explains a paradoxical situation: while courses on the history of science are still very rare, courses on the history of philosophy are an intrinsic part of every philosophical curriculum.

To return to early histories of science the best examples of it were given by EUDEMOS OF RHODES (IV-2 B.C.), who tried to explain the historical development of arithmetic, geometry and astronomy. EUDEMOS' histories are lost but many fragments of them have been preserved in later writings.[95] Unfortunately, that example was not as fruitful as the one given by ARISTOTLE and the history of science was not cultivated as it might have been. The decadence and fall of ancient science and the very slow and precarious revival in mediaeval times may be the cause of the historical silence. There are some mediaeval books which might be considered attempts in the direction of the history of science, but such attempts are rare and weak. The best work in that line was done by Arabic scholars such as the Andalusian, IBN SĀʿID (XI-2), the Egyptian, IBN AL-QIFṬĪ (XIII-1), the Syrian, IBN ABĪ UṢAIBIʿA (XIII-1). These books stem from the Arabic interest in the classification of the sciences, in bibliography, and in biography; they are hardly more than lists of scientific books (very precious indeed) with short biographical notes on their authors.

A fairly large number of books on the history of this or that science, or on the history of science in general, appeared in the eighteenth century. Their purpose was the popularization of science, and the historical approach being as natural as it is,

---

[93] Περὶ ἀρχαίης ἰητρικῆς. Text with French translation in Littré (vol. 1, 1839); text with English translation by W. H. S. JONES in the Hippocrates of the Loeb collection (vol. 1, 3-64, 1923).

[94] This was tried by many people, the most successful attempt being that of POUL LACOUR and JACOB APPEL: Historisk fysik (in Danish, 2 vols., Copenhagen 1896-7; German translation, 2 vols., Braunschweig 1905). The method is excellent to teach the elements of science, but beyond that point it breaks down because science is far too complex. Still, historical digressions will often help teachers of science in their task.

[95] LEONARDUS SPENGEL: Eudemi Rhodii peripatetici fragmenta quae supersunt (188 p., Berlin 1866). HERMANN DIELS: In Aristotelis physicorum libros commentaria (Commentaria in Aristotelem graeca, 9, 10; 2 vols., Berlin 1882-95).

it was often resorted to.   The authors were not critical historians but they often had
the advantage of being relatively close to the events which they described; they
were able to tell stories taken from the lips of contemporaries.   Therefore, the best
of those eighteenth century histories (*e.g.*, those of Priestley and Montucla) are
valuable sources of information to this day.

The following list includes large treatises and smaller handbooks; it did not seem
practical to separate the latter from the former.   Therefore, they are all listed together in the alphabetic order of the authors' names.   I am unable to choose between
them, because there are many which I have not read, and some of which I have
never used.   When a wise and experienced scholar writes an elementary book, we
may be sure that it contains worthwhile novelties, yet those novelties are necessarily lost in a mass of commonplace.   Such books are written for novices and old
scholars can hardly be expected to read them for the sake of finding a few novelties.

When scholars are beginning to take an interest in our studies, their first query
is, naturally enough, "Could you recommend a single volume giving an outline of
the whole subject?"   Such a volume does not yet exist, and this is not surprising
when one knows how the matter stands with regard to treatises.   Elementary books
can only be written in a satisfactory way when elaborate treatises are available.
It is possible to-day to write a little book covering the whole of, say English literature, or the Reformation, or any other standardized subject, and to be confident that,
however small the scale, nothing essential, from the standpoint of that scale, is likely
to be overlooked.   For the history of science such a feat of selection and com-
pression is still impossible, because the introductory analyses and surveys have not
yet been completed; or, if not impossible, it is very much of a wager and a gamble.

If we had to select a guidebook to Europe, purporting to indicate and to
explain within the covers of a single volume the chief curiosities of the whole continent, our first question would concern the personality of the author.   Of course
we should have more confidence in him if we knew he had himself travelled all
over Europe than if we discovered that he had compiled his guide in the New York
Public Library.   In a similar way, for the appreciation of a handbook on the history
of science, the prime consideration must be the wisdom and experience of the
writer.   Therefore, we shall try to indicate in each case the author's background, as
much as this can be done in a few words.

Baden-Powell: *see* Powell, Baden.

Boynton, Holmes (*editor*):
1948: The beginnings of modern science.   Scientific writers of the 16*th*, 17*th*
and 18*th* centuries (655 p., New York; Isis 40, 163).

Butterfield, Herbert:
1949: The origins of modern science 1300-1800 (228 p., London; Isis 41,
231-33).
The author is a professor of history in Cambridge.

Candolle, Alphonse de (1806-93):
1873: Histoire des sciences et des savants depuis deux siècles.   (489 p., Genève).
—German translation by Wilhelm Ostwald (Grosse Männer, vol. 2; 486 p., Leipzig
1911; Isis 1, 132).
Alphonse de Candolle was a Swiss (Genevese) botanist.

Conant, James B.:
1947: On understanding science.   An historical approach (160 p., 10 fig., New
Haven; Isis 38, 125-27).
Examination of a few "cases" illustrating the methods and progress of science.   Dr. Conant was trained as a chemist.   He was for a time professor of
organic chemistry in Harvard University, and is now the president of that university.
1950*f.*: Harvard case histories in experimental science (Harvard, Cambridge,
Mass.; Isis 42, 65).   Thus far, four case histories have been published, nos. 1-2
edited by Conant, 3 by Duane Roller, and 4 by Leonard K. Nash).

Cuvier, Georges (1769-1832):
1841-45: Histoire des sciences naturelles depuis leur origine jusqu'à nos jours chez tous les peuples connus (5 vols. Paris).
Completed by T. Magdeleine de Saint Agy. Cuvier was the greatest naturalist of his age.

Dampier, Sir William Cecil (1867-   ):
1912 (with his wife Catherine Durning Whetham): Science and the human mind (304 p., Cambridge; Isis 1, 125-32).
1924 (with his daughter, Margaret Dampier Whetham): Cambridge Readings in the history of science (288 p., 8 pl., Cambridge).
1929: History of science and its relations with philosophy and religion (535 p., 14 fig., Cambridge; Isis 14, 263-65). Third edition revised and enlarged (598 p., Cambridge 1942; Isis 34,448). Fourth edition, 1949.
1944: Shorter history of science (200 p., 9 pl., Cambridge; Isis 36, 50).
The author's name was originally William Cecil Dampier Whetham; it was classified under Whetham, later under Dampier-Whetham, finally under Dampier. Sir William is an English physico-chemist, but for the last forty years he had devoted much time and thought to the history and cultural aspects of science.

Dannemann, Friedrich (1859-1936):
1910-13: Die Naturwissenschaften in ihrer Entwicklung und in ihrem Zusammenhange (4 vols., Leipzig; 2nd ed., 4 vols., 1920-23; Isis 2, 218-22; 4, 110, 563; 6, 115).
Strange to say, this is still today the largest history of science available in any language. It is elementary and imperfect, yet Dannemann was a pioneer and deserves our gratitude. Wolf's work is partly derived from it.

Draper, John William (1811-82):
1874: History of the conflict between religion and science (395 p., New York).
Man of science, historian, educator.

Enriques, Federigo (1871-1946); **Santillana, George de:**
1937: Compendio di storia del pensiero scientifico (487 p., Bologna; Isis 28, 577).
Enriques was a distinguished mathematician and the founder of the institute for the history and philosophy of science at the University of Rome; Santillana was an assistant of his in Rome and now teaches the history of science and the humanities at the Massachusetts Institute of Technology, Cambridge, Massachusetts.

Francesco, (Mrs.) Grete de:
1939: The power of the charlatan (296 p., ill., New Haven, Yale University Press; Isis 32, 406-08). Translated from the German: Die Macht des Charlatans (258 p., ill., Basel 1937).

Ginzburg, Benjamin:
1930: The adventure of science (504 p., 8 port., New York; Isis 16, 157-58).
The author is a scientific journalist and teacher in the New School for Social Research in New York City.

Günther, Siegmund (1848-1923):
1909: Geschichte der Naturwissenschaften (2 vols. in 1, 16 pl., Leipzig). That is the 2nd ed.; 3rd ed., 1917-19.
Little book containing so many facts that it is unreadable. It is as if one crowded too many names on a small map. Günther was one of the founders of the history of science in Germany, and the author of many books and memoirs on the history of mathematical and physical sciences.

Hannequin, Arthur (1856-1905):
1908: Etudes d'histoire des sciences et d'histoire de la philosophie (2 vols., Paris).
Including biography and portrait of the author, a French philosopher.

Jastrow, Joseph (1863-   ), *editor:*
1936: The story of human error (464 p., New York; Isis 30, 545-47) .
American psychologist.

Laminne, Jacques (1864-1924):
1903-4: Les quatre éléments. Le feu, l'air, l'eau, la terre. (Mémoires couronnés de l'Académie royale de Bruxelles, vol. 65, 194 p.)

Lange, Friedrich Albert (1828-75):
1879-81: History of materialism and criticism of its present importance (3 vols., London).—Third ed., 1925. The German original appeared in Iserlohn 1866 and was often reprinted and expanded; 9*th* ed., 2 vols., Leipzig 1914-15.
German philosopher.

Lasswitz, Kurd (1848-1910):
1890: Geschichte der Atomistik vom Mittelalter bis NEWTON (2 vols., Hamburg).
—New edition 1926.
German philosopher.

Le Lionnais, François (1902-   ):
1950: Les sciences (*in* Cinquante Années de découvertes. Bilan 1900-50. Paris, p. 173-326).
The same volume contains surveys of literature, philosophy, music and dance, arts and movies, technology. The last-named subject was dealt with by JACQUES BERGIER.

Lenard, Philipp (1862-1947):
1933: Great men of science, a history of scientific progress (410 p., portrait, New York; Isis 22, 596). The German original appeared in 1929.
German physicist.

Libby, Walter (1867-   ):
1917: Introduction to the history of science (300 p., 8 pl., Boston; Isis 5, 478-79).

Mabilleau, Léopold (1853-   ):
1895: Histoire de la philosophie atomistique (568 p., Paris).
French philosopher.

Merz, John Theodore (1840-1922):
1896-1914: A history of European thought in the nineteenth century (4 vols.).
Vol. 1 first printed 1896, second ed. 1904; vol. 2, 1903; vol. 3, 1912; vol. 4, 1914.
Vols. 1-2 deal with science; vols. 3-4 with philosophy (Isis 5, 524).
This does not really cover the whole century, because the author's scientific documentation ceased to be creative long before the end of the century. MERZ was primarily a philosopher.

Milhaud, Gaston (1858-1918; Isis 3, 391-95, portr.):
1906: Etudes sur la pensée scientifique chez les Grecs et chez les modernes (275 p., Paris).
1911: Nouvelles études sur l'histoire de la pensée scientifique (237 p., Paris).
MILHAUD was professor of philosophy in Montpellier, later at the Sorbonne.

Montucla, Jean Etienne (1725-99):
1758: Histoire des mathématiques (to the end of the seventeenth century, 2 vols., Paris).—Second ed. (2 vols., Paris 1799).
1802: Vols. 3-4 to end of the eighteenth century (2 vols., Paris).
In spite of its title, this book deals not only with mathematics, but also with mechanics, physics and astronomy. It is a history of the physical sciences centered upon their mathematical nucleus. *See* my study on MONTUCLA (Osiris 1, 519-67, 1936).

Pledge, Humphry Thomas:
1939: Science since 1500. A short history of mathematics, physics, chemistry and biology (359 p., 15 pl., 6 charts, 6 maps, London; Isis 33, 74).
The author is librarian of the Science Museum, Kensington, London, and has been able to avail himself of its rich collections.

Powell, Baden (1796-1860):
1834: Historical view of the progress of the physical and mathematical sciences from the earliest ages to the present time (412 p. London). *In* DIONYSIUS LARDNER (1793-1859), Cabinet cyclopaedia. Natural philosophy. New edition, 1837.
Pioneer history of mathematical and physical sciences, preceding WHEWELL's. The author was Savilian professor of geometry in Oxford from 1827 to 1860. His children adopted the surname BADEN-POWELL; one of them, Lord ROBERT BADEN-POWELL (1857-1941) inaugurated the Boy Scout movement in 1908 and his sister, AGNES, the Girl Guides in 1910.

Rossiter, Arthur Percival:
1939: The growth of science. An outline history (372 p., Cambridge Ortho-logical Institute; Isis 33, 74).
The author is concerned chiefly with the relations of science and society; his book is written in Basic English.

Sedgwick, William Thompson (1855-1921); Tyler, Harry Walter (1863-1938):
1917: A short history of science (New York).—This unsatisfactory primer was considerably improved in the second edition prepared after SEDGWICK's death by TYLER with ROBERT PAYNE BIGELOW (1863-   ) (New York 1939; Isis 32, 464; 33, 74).
SEDGWICK and BIGELOW were professors of biology and TYLER, of mathematics, in the Massachusetts Institute of Technology, Cambridge, Massachusetts; SEDGWICK and TYLER gave one of the pioneer courses in the history of science in that institute. Biography of TYLER by BIGELOW *in* Isis (31, 60-64, 1939).

Singer, Charles:
1941: A short history of science to the nineteenth century (414 p., 94 ills., Oxford, Clarendon Press; Isis 34, 177-80).
SINGER is the leading historian of science in the British Empire; his scientific training was in medicine and biology.

Tannery, Paul (1843-1904):
1912-43: Mémoires scientifiques, edited by MARIE TANNERY and others (16 vols.; for reviews *see* Isis 38, 49 or Introd. 3, 1906).
The French mathematician, TANNERY, was one of the earliest and greatest historians of science. His main investigations concerned ancient science, mediaeval science and the seventeenth century, but his range of knowledge was truly encyclopaedic. *See* biography by SARTON (Isis 38, 33-51, 1947).

Taylor, Frank Sherwood (1897-   ):
1939: Short history of science (334 p., 14 pl., 36 fig., London).—The American edition has an additional title: The march of mind (New York 1939; Isis 32. 465; 34, 74). New edition 1949 (Isis 41, 391).
1945: Science, past and present (275 p., ill., London).
TAYLOR is a chemist and classical scholar and is much interested in the vulgarization of science, and the relations of science with religion, especially with Catholicism. He was director of the Ashmolean Museum in Oxford and is now director of the Science Museum in London.

Thorndike, Lynn (1882-   ):
1923-41: A history of magic and experimental science during the first thirteen centuries of our era (2 vols., New York: Isis 6, 74-89); . . . in the fifteenth century (2 vols., New York 1934; Isis 23, 471-75); The sixteenth century (2 vols., New York 1941; Isis 33, 691-712).

The author is a mediaevalist who has edited an extraordinary large number of MSS concerning science and magic. He was professòr of mediaeval history in Columbia University, New York. Apart from these six heavy volumes he had published a great many papers, some of which are listed in almost every Critical Bibliography of Isis.

Uccelli, Arturo (1889-   ), *editor:*
1941: Enciclopedia storica delle scienze e delle loro applicazioni. Vol. 1, Le scienze fisiche e matematiche (folio 753 p., 1788 figs., 9 pl., Milano; Isis 36, 51).
Book of the same kind as the French one by URBAIN and BOLL, including a large number of illustrations of historical interest.
1946: Scienza e tecnica del tempo nostro (Milano).—Originally planned as vol. 2 of the Enciclopedia storica (vol. 1, 846 p. 2137 ill., 6 pl., Milano; Isis 41, 85).

Urbain, Georges (1872-1938); **Boll, Marcel** (*editors*):
1933-34: La science, ses progrès, ses applications (2 folio vols. of the Larousse collection, richly illustrated, Paris; Isis 22, 397; 23, 578). Includes some 2500 illustrations a great many of which are historical documents.

Whetham, *see* **Dampier.**

Whewell, William (1794-1866):
1837: History of the inductive sciences from the earliest to the present times (3 vols. London).—Revised ed., 1847; 3. ed., 1857. Pioneer work which has been discussed in the text above.

White, Andrew Dickson (1832-1918):
1896: History of the warfare of science with theology in Christendom (2 vols., New York).—Reprinted in 1923.
WHITE was an educator and diplomat, the first president of Cornell University in Ithaca, New York. He was deeply interested in cultural history, and we might even say in the history of science. He received much help from his former student, GEORGE LINCOLN BURR (1857-1938), himself a very distinguished American historian (Isis 35, 147-52, 1944).

Wightman, William P. D.:
1934: Science and monism (416 p., London).
1950: The growth of scientific ideas (508 p., 8 pl., Edinburgh; Isis 42).

Wolf, Abraham (1876-   ):
1935-39: History of science, technology and philosophy in the sixteenth and seventeenth centuries. With the cooperation of F. DANNEMANN and A. ARMITAGE (719 p., 316 illus., London; Isis 24, 164-67); *idem* in the eighteenth century (814 p., ill., London 1939; Isis 31, 450-51).
This work, stemming out of the DANNEMANN one quoted above, deals only with three centuries, the sixteenth to the eighteenth.

See in the Critical Bibliographies of Isis, section 16. History of science.

16. SCIENTIFIC INSTRUMENTS

Bell, Louis (1864-1923):
1922: The telescope (296 p., New York; Isis 5, 280). Popular account; the first 56 p. are historical.

Boffito, Giuseppe (1869-1944):
1929: Gli strumenti della scienza e la scienza degli strumenti, con l'illustrazione della Tribuna di Galileo (234 p., 136 pl., Firenze).

Clay, Reginald Stanley; Court, Thomas H.:
1932: History of the microscope up to the introduction of the achromatic microscope (280 p., 164 fig., London; Isis 21, 227-30).

Disney, Alfred N.; with Hill, Cyril F. and Baker, Wilfred E. Watson:
1928: Origin and development of the microscope (303 p., 30 pl., 36 fig., Royal Microscopical Society, London; Isis 20, 495-97).

Garcia Franco, Salvador (1884-   ):
1945: Catálogo critico de astrolabios existentes en España (454 p., 84 fig., Madrid; Isis 40, 168).

Greeff, Richard (1862-   ):
1921: Die Erfindung der Augengläser. Kulturgeschichtliche Darstellungen nach urkundlichen Quellen (120 p., 10 pl., Berlin).

Gunther, Robert Theodore (1869-1940):
1932: The astrolabes of the world (quarto, 2 vols., ill. University Press, Oxford). Vol. 1, Eastern astrolabes; vol. 2, Western ones (Isis 20, 310-16, 492-95).

Michel, Henri:
1939: Introduction à l'étude d'une collection d'instruments anciens (quarto, 110 p., 15 pl., Anvers; Isis 32, 468).
1947: Traité de l'astrolabe (quarto 210 p., 24 pl., Paris; Isis 39, 194).

Pendray, Edward (1901-   ):
1935: Men, mirrors and stars (New York). Rev. ed. 1946, 345 p., ill.

Repsold, Johann Adolf (1838-   ):
1908: Zur Geschichte der astronomischen Messwerkzeuge von PURBACH bis REICHENBACH, 1450 bis 1830. (140 p., 128 pl., Leipzig).

Rohde, Alfred (1892-   ):
1923: Die Geschichte der wissenschaftlichen Instrumente vom Beginn der Renaissance bis zum Ausgang des 18. Jahrhunderts. (Monographien des Kunstgewerbes, XVI; 125 p., 139 fig., Leipzig).

Rohr, Moritz v. (1868-1940):
1907: Die binokularen Instrumente (228 p., Berlin).—2nd ed., 320 p., Berlin 1920.
1908: Abhandlungen zur Geschichte des Stereoskops (Ostwald's Klassiker no. 168; 130 p., 4 pl.).
1911: Die Brille als optisches Instrument (182 p.).—Second ed. (268 p., 112 fig., Berlin 1921).
1927-28: Aus der Geschichte der Brille mit besonderer Berücksichtigung der auf der Greeffschen beruhenden Jenaischen Sammlung (Beiträge zur Geschichte der Technik 17, 30-50, 20 fig.; 18, 95-117, 34 fig., 1928; Isis 13, 546).

1934: (with HANS BOEGEHOLD): Das Brillenglass als optisches Instrument (291 p., 119 fig., Berlin).   This is a complete revision of the book first published in 1911.

Rouyer, Joseph:
1901: Coup d'oeil rétrospectif sur la lunetterie. Précédé de recherches sur l'origine du verre lenticulaire et sur les instruments servant à la vision (275 p., Paris).

Schmidt, Fritz (of Neustadt a. d. H.):
1935: Geschichte der geodätischen Instrumente und Verfahren im Altertum und Mittelalter (400 p., 26 pl., Neustadt a. d. H.; Isis 26, 224-28).

Thompson, Charles John Samuel (1862-1943):
1942: History and evolution of surgical instruments (113 p., 115 fig., New York).

See also sections devoted to Photography and to Chronometry and Horology.

17. HISTORY OF SCIENCE IN SPECIAL COUNTRIES

Before enumerating books devoted to the history of science in this or that country, we should speak of one national achievement of that kind which assumed international importance. That is the collection of books written by order and under the auspicies of the Royal Academy of Bavaria. Its general title was: **Geschichte der Wissenschaften in Deutschland. Neuere Zeit.** Herausgegeben durch die historische Commission bei der königl. Academie der Wissenschaften, München.

As the title indicates, the general purpose, the publication of histories of all the sciences ("Wissenschaften" in the broadest meaning; science and learning), was limited in two ways. It was restricted (1) to Germany, (2) to modern times. These restrictions were understood differently in each volume, according to the subject and to the author. The temporal restrictions can easily be applied: one can decide to begin one's account in the sixteenth century or later (with or without restrospective intermezzi in the text or footnotes); on the other hand, it is generally impossible to give an intelligible account of the development of science in one country without referring to work done in other countries. Many of the Bavarian books were of international interest and received international recognition. The first volume appeared in 1864 and the twenty-fourth and last in 1913. The delay in publication of this last volume was accidental, however (Isis 1, 527-29); the whole collection appeared within the nineteenth century, except the last part of the book on the German study of law (delayed until 1910) and the book on the history of physics (delayed until 1913). As this collection is the most ambitious effort of its kind, we give the list of these 24 works in chronological order of publication. For each work we name the author, then his subject (botany means history of botany) with its temporal restriction as indicated in the title, finally the date of first edition.

1. JOHANN CASPAR BLUNTSCHLI. Constitutional law and politics, from the sixteenth century. 1864.
2.° FRANZ KOBELL (1803-82). Mineralogy 1650-1860. 1864.
3.° KARL FRAAS (1810-75). Agriculture and forestry from the sixteenth century. 1865.
4.° OSCAR PESCHEL (1826-75). Geography to ALEXANDER VON HUMBOLDT and CARL RITTER. 1865 (revised 1877).
5. ISAAC AUGUST DORNER. Protestant theology. 1867.
6. KARL WERNER. Catholic theology from the Council of Trent. 1866.
7. HERMANN LOTZE. Aesthetics. 1868.
8. THEODOR BENFEY. "Sprachwissenschaft" and oriental philology from the beginning of the nineteenth century with retrospective views. 1869.
9. RUDOLF VON RAUMER. Germanic philology. 1870.
10.° HERMANN KOPP (1817-92). Chemistry. 1873.
11.° KARL KARMARSCH (1803-79). Technology from the middle of the eighteenth century. 1872.
12.° JULIUS VICTOR CARUS (1823-1903). Zoology until JOH. MÜLLER and DARWIN. 1872.
13. EDUARD ZELLER. German philosophy from LEIBNIZ. 1873.
14. WILHELM ROSCHER. National economy. 1874.
15.° JULIUS VON SACHS (1832-97). Botany from the sixteenth century until 1860. 1875.
16.° RUDOLF WOLF (1816-93). Astronomy. 1877.
17.° KARL IMMANUEL GERHARDT (1816-99). Mathematics. 1877.
18. RODERICH STINTZING. German law (3 vols. in 5). 1880-1910.
19. KONRAD BURSIAN. Classical philology in Germany from its beginning (2 vols.). 1883.

20. FRANZ XAVER VON WEGELE. German historiography from the beginning of
    humanism. 1885.
21.* MAX JÄHNS (1837-1900). Military science (3 vols.). 1889-91.
22.* AUGUST HIRSCH (1817-94). Medicine. 1893.
23.* KARL ALFRED VON ZITTEL (1839-1904). Geology and paleontology. 1899.
24.* ERNST GERLAND (1838-1910). Physics from the earliest times to the end of
    the eighteenth century. 1913 (Isis 1, 527-29).

The items which concern more directly the history of science (as we understand
it) have been marked with an asterisk; there are 13 of them out of 24. Some of
these thirteen works were translated into English or into French; many were reprinted. These thirteen works belong to the general literature of our field.

For books dealing with the history of science in special countries, it will be convenient to list them in alphabetical order of these countries. It should be noted that
the largest of those histories (as for example the French one) are also of international
interest. This is unavoidable. It is always worth while to consult the history of
science of a special nation (as well as national bibliographies, encyclopaedias, atlases
and gazetteers) whenever one has to investigate persons or events concerning that
particular nation.

AMERICA, see UNITED STATES OF AMERICA, see also CANADA.

For pre-Columbian America, see in the Critical Bibliographies of Isis the section
entitled Ethnology (Primitive and popular science) and (beginning with the 60th
Critical Bibliography in vol. 33, 1941) the section entitled America (part 2, IV A).

— ARGENTINA —

Babini, José (1897-   ):
    1949: Historia de la ciencia argentina (218 p., Mexico; Isis 41, 84).

— BELGIUM —

Quetelet, Adolphe (1796-1874):
    1864: Histoire des sciences mathématiques et physiques chez les Belges (480 p.,
Bruxelles).
    1866: Sciences mathématiques et physiques chez les Belges au commencement
du XIXe siècle (760 p., Bruxelles).

Van Overbergh, Cyrille:
    1907-1908: Le mouvement scientifique en Belgique, 1830-1905 (2 vols., Bru-
xelles).
    Account prepared by order of the Belgian government for the International Exhi-
bition of Liége, 1905.

Vincent, Auguste:
    1938: Histoire des sciences en Belgique jusqu'à la fin du XVIIIe siècle (160 p.,
Bruxelles).
    This is only the catalogue of an exhibition organized by the Bibliothèque Royale,
but it may be useful (Isis 29, 526).

— CANADA —

Tory, Henry Marshall (editor):
    1939: A history of science in Canada (152 p., 9 ill., Toronto; Isis 33, 142).

Wallace, William Stewart (1884-   ) (editor):
    1949: Centennial volume of the Royal Canadian Institute (241 p., ill., Toronto).

— DENMARK —

Meisen, V. (editor):
    1932: Prominent Danish scientists through the ages, with facsimiles from their

work (195 p., Copenhagen 1932; Isis 23, 276-78).

This is an exemplary publication.   The method followed would not be suitable for the larger countries, but it is excellent for the smaller ones.

ENGLAND, *see* GREAT BRITAIN

— FRANCE —

1915: **La science française** (2 vols., Paris).

These two volumes were published by the Ministère de l'éducation publique at the time of the International Exhibition of San Francisco.   No editor is named but the general preface is written by LUCIEN POINCARÉ.   Many portraits and bibliographies.   Science is taken in a general sense, it includes all the sciences and the humanities.   Each article is written by a master of the subject.

1924: **Histoire des sciences en France** (2 vols. quarto, illustr., being vols. 14 and 15 of the Histoire de la Nation française edited by GABRIEL HANOTAUX, Paris; Isis 7, 514-16; 8, 602).   General preface by EMILE PICARD.   Vol. 1 dealing with mathematical and physical sciences was written by HENRI ANDOYER, CHARLES FABRY, PIERRE HUMBERT, ALBERT COLSON; vol. 2 contains the history of biological sciences by MAURICE CAULLERY, and the history of philosophy by RENÉ LOTE.

Caullery, Maurice:

1933: La science française depuis le XVIIe siècle (214 p., Paris; Isis 22, 395).

1934: French science and its principal discoveries since the seventeenth century (240 p., New York; Isis 24, 266).

— GERMANY —

See the note at the beginning of this chapter describing the Geschichte der Wissenschaften in Deutschland (Munich 1864-1913), edited by the Bavarian Academy.

Abb, Gustav (*editor*):

1930: Aus fünfzig Jahren deutscher Wissenschaft.   Die Entwicklung ihrer Fachgebiete in Einzeldarstellungen (508 p., Berlin).

This description of German science and learning in the period just preceding the Nazi destruction was prepared in the form of a Festschrift dedicated to FRIEDRICH SCHMIDT-OTT.

Schnabel, Franz (1887-   ):

1949: Deutsche Geschichte im neunzehnten Jahrhundert.   Band 3, Erfahrungswissenschaften und Technik, Freiburg im Breisgau).

I have seen only the first edition of the whole work (4 vols., 1929-37).   The first edition of vol. 3 appeared in 1934.   It begins with a chapter on HEGEL and his time.

— GREAT BRITAIN —

Schuster, Arthur (1851-1934) and **Shipley, Arthur E.:**

1917: Britain's heritage of science (350 p., 15 ports., London).

Gunther, Robert Theodore (1869-1940):

1920-45: Early science in Oxford (14 vols. Oxford).

1937: Early science in Cambridge (525 p., Oxford; Introd. 3, 1886).

HOLLAND, *see* THE NETHERLANDS.

— INDIA —

See next chapter under India; for Pakistan, *see* next chapter under India and also under Islam.

— ITALY —

Caverni, Raffaello (1837-1900):

1891-1900: Storia del metodo sperimentale in Italia (6 vols., Firenze).

Savorgnan di Brazzà, Francesco (1883-   ):
1933: Da Leonardo a Marconi, invenzioni e scoperte italiane (357 p., 48 pl., Milano).

Silla, Lucio (editor):
1939-40: Società italiana per il progresso delle scienze. Un secolo di progresso scientifico italiano 1839-1939 (7 vols., Roma; Isis 35, 190; 36, 223).

— Japan —
See next chapter under Far East.

— The Netherlands —
Barnouw, A. J.; Landheer, B. (editors):
1943: The contribution of Holland to the sciences. (400 p., 13 ills., New York; Isis 35, 189-90).

Sevensma, T. P. (editor):
1946:Nederlandsche helden der wetenschap (351 p., Amsterdam; Isis 40, 164).
Biographies with portraits of the nine Dutch scientists who received the Nobel prize, a large number for so small a country.

Gerrits, G. C.:
1948: Grote Nederlanders bij de opbouw der natuurwetenschappen (530 p., ill., Leiden).

For the Netherlands Indies, see next chapter under Far East.

— New Zealand —
Jenkinson, Sidney Hartley:
1940: New Zealanders and science (176 p., 9 ill., Wellington, N. Z.).

— Poland —
A collection of 34 pamphlets dealing with the history of various sciences and branches of learning in Poland is being published in Krakow 1948-49 under the general title Historia nauki polskiej w monografiach (History of Polish science in monographs) under the auspices of the Polska akademia umiejętności (Polish Academy of Sciences). I have seen 26 of these pamphlets. Each is written by a separate author and followed by a French summary. These pamphlets are enumerated in the 76th Critical Bibliography (Isis 41, 394 etc.), each in its section: mathematics, physics, chemistry, etc.
I owe communication of these 26 pamphlets to the friendliness of Professor Mieczyslaw Choynowski (Isis 37, 78) president of the Konwersatorium naukoznawcze (Cercle pour la science de la science) of Krakow. Seven pamphlets (out of the 34) are in preparation or printing (July 1949).

— Russia —
Congress of American-Soviet Friendship, Second Congress, New York 1943:
1944: Science in Soviet Russia. Preface by Walter B. Cannon (1871-1945; Isis 36, 258-59, portr.) (108 p., Lancaster, Pennsylvania; Isis 36, 39).

Crowther, James Gerald (1899-   ):
1930: Science in Soviet Russia (128 p., London).
1936: Soviet Science (352 p., 16 pl., New York; Isis 27, 90-92).
1942: Soviet science (191 p., New York, Penguin).

Needham, Joseph (1900-   ) (editor):
1942: Science in Soviet Russia by seven British scientists (65 p., London).

Petrunkevitch, Alexander Ivanovitch (1875-   ):
1920: Russia's contribution to science (Transactions of the Connecticut Academy, vol. 23, 211-41, New Haven).

Sigerist, Henry Ernest (1891-   ):
1947: Medicine and health in the Soviet Union.   With the cooperation of JULIA
OLDER (383 p., New York; Isis 39, 202-03).

— SOUTH AFRICA —

Council for Scientific and Industrial Research:
1949: Science in South Africa (176 p., Pretoria).

— SPAIN —

Carracido, José Rodriguez:
1917: Estudios histórico-críticos de la ciencia española (2nd ed., 422 p., Madrid).
1935: Associación nacional de historiadores de la ciencia española.   Estudios
sobre la ciencia española del siglo XVII.   Prólogo de S. E. DON NICETO ALCALÁ-
ZAMORA (686 p., Madrid).

Menéndez y Pelayo, Marcelino:
1887-88: La ciencia española (3rd ed., 3 vols., Madrid).
Collected essays which hardly cover the ground; they deal with a few points of
the history of learning, rather than science.   First edition of vol. 1, 1876.

Millás Vallicrosa, José Maria:
1949: Estudios sobre historia de la ciencia española (512 p., 16 pl., Barcelona;
Isis 41, 229).
Dealing only with the Middle Ages.

— SWEDEN —

An elaborate history of science in Sweden is being prepared under the direction
of JOHANN NORDSTRÖM of Uppsala.

— SWITZERLAND —

Fueter, Eduard:
1939: Grosse Schweizer Forscher (308 p., ill., Zurich; Isis 32, 193-97); second
edition (340 p., Zurich 1941; Isis 37, 247).
1941: Geschichte der exakten Wissenschaften in der schweizerischen Aufklärung,
1680-1780 (352 p., Aarau; Isis 34, 32).

TURKEY, *see* ISLAM in next chapter.

UNITED KINGDOM, *see* GREAT BRITAIN.

— UNITED STATES OF AMERICA —

Youmans, William Jay (1838-1901):
1896: Pioneers of science in America.   Sketches of their lives and scientific work
(New York).

Goode, George Brown (1851-1896):
1897: The Smithsonian Institution, 1846-1946 (866 p., ill., Washington).
1901: A memorial of him together with a selection of his papers on museums and
on the history of science in America (527 p., ill., Washington, Smithsonian Institution).

Jordan, David Starr (1851-1931):
1910: Leading American men of science (New York).

Dana, Edward Salisbury (1849-1935) (*et alii*):
1918: A century of science in America with special reference to the American
Journal of Science 1818-1918 (458 p., New Haven, Yale).

Jaffe, Bernard:
1944: Men of science in America (640 p., ill., New York; Isis 36, 73-74).—Translated into French (s.a., Isis 37, 248); into German (Isis 39, 114); into Italian (s.a.,
Isis 37, 248).

Struik, Dirk J.:
  1948: Yankee science in the making (445 p., Boston; Isis 40, 62-64).

  This list could be indefinitely extended if to the books dealing with the history of science in separate countries were added those devoted to special provinces or cities, or to academies, universities, museums, scientific societies, etc. A few exceptions were made faute de mieux for the history of the Italian scientific congress (the Italian equivalent of AAAS) under Italy, and for Gunther's books under Great Britain.

  The bibliography of the history of science relative to each country is made difficult by the confusion of two ideas. For example, history of science in Poland may be understood in two very different ways, which are symbolized by the formulas

> *1*) (history of science) in Poland
> *2*) history of (science in Poland).

  Under (*1*) would be classified papers or books concerning the teaching and the study of the history of science (universal science) in Poland, under (*2*) the contributions made by Polish men of science, the biographies of these men, the development of each branch of science in Poland, etc.

18. HISTORY OF SCIENCE
IN SPECIAL CULTURAL GROUPS

This chapter completes the preceding one. The national subdivision does not suffice, for in addition to the many books dealing with the history of science in this or that country, there are many more dealing with cultural rather than national (or geographical) entities.

The items are classified under the following headings:

Antiquity (in general)
Ancient Near East (generalities, Egypt, Babylonia)
Classical Antiquity
Middle Ages
Byzantine and Slavonic
Israel
Islam
India
Far East and Eastern Indies (Indonesia)
China
Japan

ANTIQUITY (in general)

Forbes, Robert James:
1936: Bitumen and petroleum in antiquity (109 p., 6 tables, 2 maps, 54 fig., Leiden; Isis 26, 536).
1940- : Bibliographia antiqua. Philosophia naturalis. I. Mining and geology, 1940. II. Metallurgy, 1942. III. Building Materials, 1944. IV. Pottery, faience, glass, glazes, beads, 1944. Nederlandsch Instituut voor het Nabije Oosten, Leiden (Isis 36, 208). Parts V to X published in 1949-50.
1950: Metallurgy in antiquity (490 p., 98 ill., Leiden).

Partington, James Riddick (1886-   ):
1935: Origins and development of applied chemistry (610 p., London; Isis 25, 504-07).

ANCIENT NEAR EAST

Archibald, Raymond Clare:
1929: Bibliography of Egyptian and Babylonian mathematics. Appended to the edition of the Rhind mathematical papyrus (vol. 2), *see* CHACE, A. B. in the section on Egypt.

Neugebauer, Otto:
1934: Vorlesungen über Geschichte der antiken mathematischen Wissenschaften. 1. Band. Vorgriechische Mathematik (224 p., Berlin; Isis 24, 151-53).

Peet, Thomas Eric (1882-1934):
1931: Comparative study of the literatures of Egypt, Palestine and Mesopotamia. Egypt's contribution to the literature of the ancient world (144 p., London; Isis 21, 305-16).

Pritchard, James B. (*editor*):
1950: Ancient Near Eastern texts relating to the Old Testament (quarto 548 p., Princeton; Isis 42, 75).

See in the Critical Bibliography of Isis the section 1. Antiquity, and 8. Asia, Western Asia.

Breasted, James Henry (1865-1935; Isis 34, 289-91, portr.):
1930: The Edwin Smith surgical papyrus. Published in facsimile with trans-
literation, translation and commentary (2 vols., Oriental Institute, Chicago; Isis 15,
355-67).
1933: The dawn of conscience (460 p., New York; Isis 21, 305-16).

Chace, Arnold Buffum (1845-1932); **Bull, Ludlow; Manning, Henry Parker** (1859-);
Archibald, Raymond Clare:
1927-29: The Rhind mathematical papyrus (2 vols. Mathematical Association of
America, Oberlin, Ohio; Isis 14, 251-55).
Includes ARCHIBALD's bibliography of Egyptian and Babylonian mathematics in
both volumes.

Clarke, Somers (1841-1926):
1930: Ancient Egyptian masonry. The building craft (258 p., 269 ill., London).

Cumont, Franz (1868-1947):
1937: L'Egypte des astrologues (254 p., Bruxelles; Isis 29, 511).

Engelbach, Reginald (1888-1946):
1923: The problem of the obelisks, from a study of the unfinished obelisk at
Aswan (134 p., 21 pl., London).

Gillain, O.:
1927: La science égyptienne. L'arithmétique au moyen empire (342 p., Bruxelles; Isis, 11, 395-98).

Glanville, Stephen Ranulph Kingdon (1900-   ) (*editor*):
1942: The legacy of Egypt (444 p., 34 pl., Clarendon Press, Oxford; Isis 34,
441).

Grinsell, Leslie V.:
1947: Egyptian pyramids (194 p., 14 pls., 27 fig., 8 maps, Gloucester; Isis 41,
76).

Hurry, Jamieson Boyd (1857-1930):
1928: IMHOTEP. The vizier and physician of King ZOSER and afterwards the
Egyptian god of medicine (2nd ed., 227 p., 26 ill., Oxford; Isis 13, 373-75; 14, 226,
1 pl.).—First ed., 1926, 134 p., ill.

Lexa, François (1876-   ):
1925: La magie dans l'Egypte antique de l'ancien empire jusqu'à l'époque copte
(3 vols., Paris; Isis 9, 450-52).

Lucas, Alfred (1867-1945):
1926: Ancient Egyptian materials and industries (250 p., London).—2nd ed.
revised (459 p., London 1934).—3rd ed. revised (582 p., London 1948).

Petrie (Sir William Matthew) **Flinders** (1853-1942):
1940: Wisdom of the Egyptians (178 p., 128 figs., London; Isis 34, 261).

Pratt, Ida Augusta:
1925: Ancient Egypt. Sources of information in the New York Public Library
(502 p., New York).
Bibliography of science covers p. 220 to 238 (astronomy, geology, metals, botany,
zoology, mathematics, medicine and anatomy, metrology, industries and chemistry).
1942: Supplement 1925-41 (347 p., New York). Science, same classification
(p. 168-82).

Wainwright, Gerald Averay:
1938: The sky-religion in Egypt (137 p., Cambridge University; Isis 33, 126).
See in the Critical Bibliography of Isis section 2. Egypt.

— BABYLONIA —

This term is not quite correct in the present acception, Mesopotamia and its neighborhood;
scholars investigating that field are often called "Assyriologists" which is another incorrectness
of the same kind, to wit, the designation of a whole by one of its parts.

Boissier, Alfred:
1905-6: Choix de textes relatifs à la divination assyro-babylonienne (2 vols.,
Genève).
1935: Mantique babylonienne et mantique hittite (80 p., 5 pl., Paris; Introd. 3,
1103).

Budge, Sir E. A. Wallis (1857-1934):
1925: Rise and progress of Assyriology (340 p., 32 pl., London; Isis 9, 547).

Contenau, Georges (1877-   ):
1927-47: Manuel d'archéologie orientale (4 vols., 2378 p., ill., Paris; Isis 20,
474-78; 40, 153). For science, *see* p. 1871-1927.
1938: La médecine en Assyrie et en Babylonie (234 p., 60 fig., 1 map, Paris; Isis
31, 99-101).
1940: La divination chez les Assyriens et les Babyloniens (380 p., 8 pl., Paris).
1947: La magie chez les Assyriens et les Babyloniens (298 p., ill., Paris).

Gadd, Cyril John (1893-   ):
1936: The stones of Assyria. The surviving remains of Assyrian sculpture, their
recovery and their original position (285 p., 47 pl., 2 plans, London; Isis 27, 152).
This is a chapter of the history of Assyriology.

Kugler, Franz Xaver (1862-1929):
1907-35: Sternkunst und Sterndienst in Babel. Buch I, II und Ergänzungsheften
(Münster i. W.; Isis 25, 473-76).
Vol. 1 appeared in 1907, vol. 2 in 3 parts, 1909, 1912, 1924. Two supplements
were published by KUGLER in 1913 and 1914, a third supplement, posthumous, by
JOHANN SCHAUMBERGER in 1935.

Meissner, Bruno (1868-   ):
1920-25: Babylonien und Assyrien (2 vols., Heidelberg; Isis 8, 195-98).

Neugebauer, Otto:
1935-37: Mathematische Keilschrift-Texte herausgegeben und bearbeitet (3 vols.,
Berlin; Isis 26, 63-81; 28, 490-91).
1945: Mathematical cuneiform texts (with the assistance of A. SACHS and A.
GOETZE) (187 p., 49 pl., New Haven, Connecticut; Isis 37, 96-97, 231).

Pratt, Ida Augusta:
1918: Assyria and Babylonia, a list of references in the New York Public Library
(148 p., New York). For science, *see* p. 57-63.

Thureau-Dangin, François (1872-1944):
1938: Textes mathématiques babyloniens transcrits et traduits (283 p., Leiden;
Isis 31, 398-425).
1939: Sketch of a history of the sexagesimal system (Osiris 7, 95-141).

Thompson, Reginald Campbell (1876-1941):
1936: Dictionary of Assyrian chemistry and geology (314 p., Oxford, Clarendon;
Isis 26, 477-80).

Weidner, Ernst Friedrich:
1915: Handbuch der babylonischen Astronomie (vol. 1, 146 p., Leipzig).
See in the Critical Bibliography of Isis the section 3. Babylonia and Assyria.

CLASSICAL ANTIQUITY

Allbutt, Sir Thomas Clifford (1836-1925):
1921: Greek medicine in Rome. With other historical essays (647 p. London; Isis, 4, 355-57).
Greek and Byzantine medicine cover 424 pages; the rest of the book is devoted to other medico-historical essays.

Ashby, Thomas (1874-1931):
1935: The aqueducts of ancient Rome (356 p., ill., Oxford, Clarendon).

Bailey, Cyril (1871-   ) (*editor*):
1924: The legacy of Rome (524 p., 76 ill., Clarendon Press, Oxford).

Bailly, Jean Sylvain (1736-93; Isis 11, 393-95):
1775: Histoire de l'astronomie ancienne depuis son origine jusqu'à l'établissement de l'école d'Alexandrie (550 p., Paris).—Second ed., 1781.

Berger, Hugo (1836-1904):
1903: Geschichte der wissenschaftlichen Erdkunde der Griechen (2nd ed. 666 p., 19 fig., Leipzig).—First ed. in 4 parts, Leipzig 1887-93.

Berthelot, Marcelin (1827-1907):
1888: Collection des anciens alchimistes grecs (4 vols., ill., Paris).

Blake, Marion Elizabeth:
1947: Ancient Roman construction in Italy from the prehistoric period to AU-GUSTUS (quarto 444 p., 57 pl. Washington, Carnegie Institution; Isis 40, 279).

Boll, Franz (1867-1924):
1903: Sphaera. Neue griechische Texte und Untersuchungen zur Geschichte der Sternbilder (576 p., ill., Leipzig).
1910-20: Griechische Kalender, herausgegeben und erläutert (5 vols., pl., Heidelberg).
1914-1930: Stoicheia. Studien zur Geschichte des antiken Weltbildes und der griechischen Wissenschaft (9 vols., Leipzig). Vols. 1 to 7 were edited by him.
1917: Sternglaube und Sterndeutung. Die Geschichte und das Wesen der Astrologie (Leipzig).
Not seen the first edition. Second ed. with the collaboration of CARL BEZOLD (1859-1922) (120 p., 1 map, 20 fig., Leipzig 1919; Isis 3, 482), 3rd ed. (posthumous) prepared by WILHELM GUNDEL (1880-1945) (234 p., 48 fig., 20 pl., 1 map, 1926; Isis 9, 476-77), 4th ed. (1931).

Bouché-Leclerc, Auguste (1842-1923):
1879-82: Histoire de la divination dans l'antiquité (4 vols., Paris).
1899: L'astrologie grecque (678 p., Paris).

Brunet, Pierre (1893-1950); **Mieli, Aldo** (1879-1950):
1935: Histoire des sciences. Antiquité (1224 p., 109 fig., Paris; Isis 24, 444-47).
Anthology of selected extracts in French translation with commentaries.

Bunbury, Sir Edward Herbert (1811-95):
1879: History of ancient geography among the Greeks and Romans till the fall of the Roman Empire (2 vols., 20 maps, London).—Second ed. 1883.

Cohen, Morris (1880-1947); **Drabkin, Israel Edward** (1905-   ):
1948: Source book in Greek science (600 p., ill., New York; Isis 40, 277).

Cozzo, Giuseppe:
1928: Ingegneria romana (320 p., ill., Roma).

Cumont, Franz (1868-1947):
1912: Astrology and religion among the Greeks and the Romans (235 p., New York).
1949: Lux perpetua (558 p., portrait, Paris; Isis 41, 371).

Davies, Oliver:
1935: Roman mines in Europe (303 p., ill., 6 maps, London; Isis 25, 251).

Delambre, Jean Baptiste Joseph (1749-1822):
1817: Histoire de l'astronomie ancienne (2 vols., Paris).

Delatte, Armand (1886-   ):
1936: Herbarius. Recueil sur le cérémonial usité chez les anciens pour la cueillette des simples et des plantes magiques (Bulletin de l'Académie de Belgique, classe des lettres, 22, 227-348, Bruxelles) (Isis 27, 531-32).—Second ed. (177 p. Liége 1938; Isis 30, 395).

Diepgen, Paul (1878-   ):
1937: Geschichte der Frauenheilkunde (Handbuch der Gynäkologie, hrg. v. W. Stoeckel; vol. 12, München). 1. Teil, Paul Diepgen: Die Frauenheilkunde der Alten Welt (358 p., ill.; Isis 28, 123-26).

Enriques, Federigo (1871-1946); **Santillana, Giorgio de:**
1932: Storia del pensiero scientifico. Vol. 1, Il mondo antico (682 p., 120 ill., Milano; Isis 23, 467-69).

Farrington, Benjamin (1891-   ):
1936: Science in antiquity (London, Home University Library).—Reprinted 1947.
1939: Science and politics in the ancient world (243 p., London; Isis 33, 270-73).
1944: Greek science, its meaning for us (143 p., London, Penguin Books).

Gest, Alexander Purves (1853-   ):
1930: Engineering (Our debt to Greece and Rome, 236 p., New York).

Gilbert, Otto (1839-1911):
1907: Die meteorologischen Theorien des griechischen Altertums (750 p., Leipzig).

Günther, Siegmund (1848-1928); **Windelband, Wilhelm** (1848-1915):
1888: Geschichte der antiken Naturwissenschaft und Philosophie (Handbuch der klassischen Altertums-Wissenschaft 5, 1; 344 p., Nördlingen).
The second ed. (322 p., München 1894) bears the title "Geschichte der alten Philosophie von W. Windelband," Günther's summary of the history of ancient science being published in the form of an appendix.

Gundel, Wilhelm (1880-1945; Isis 39, 103):
1922: Sterne und Sternbilder im Glauben des Altertums und der Neuzeit (Bonn).
1933: Sternglaube, Sternreligion und Sternorakel (Leipzig).
1934: Astronomie, Astralreligion, Astralmythologie und Astrologie (Jahresbericht über die Forschritte der klass. Altertumswissenschaft, vol. 243, 1-162).
1936: Dekane und Dekansternbilder. Ein Beitrag zur Geschichte der Sternbilder der Kulturvölker. Mit einer Untersuchung über die altägyptischen Sternbilder und Gottheiten der Dekane von S. Schott (462 p., 33 pl., Bibliothek Warburg, Hamburg 1936; Isis 27, 344-48).
1950: Planeten (PW col. 2017-86). Completed by his son, H. Gundel.

Heath, Sir Thomas (1861-1940; Osiris 2, portr.):
1921: History of Greek mathematics (2 vols., Oxford, Clarendon Press; Isis 4, 532-35).

1931: Manual of Greek mathematics (568 p., Oxford, Clarendon Press; Isis 16, 450-51).
1932: Greek astronomy (250 p., London; Isis 22, 585).
Translated selections from the Greek astronomical writings.

Heiberg, Johan Ludvig (1854-1928; Isis 11, 367-74, port.):
1922: Mathematics and physical science in classical antiquity (110 p., Oxford; Isis 5, 531).
Original German text published in Leipzig 1912, 2nd ed. 1920.

Heidel, William Arthur (1868-1941):
1933: The heroic age of science; the conception, ideals and methods of science among the ancient Greeks (210 p., Washington, Carnegie Institution; Isis 21, 220-24).

Honigmann, Ernst (1892-):
1929: Die sieben Klimata und die πόλεις ἐπίσημοι. Eine Untersuchung zur Geschichte der Geographie und Astrologie im Altertum und Mittelalter. (247 p., 4 fig., Heidelberg; Isis 14, 270-76).

Hultsch, Friedrich (1833-1906):
1862: Griechische und römische Metrologie (338 p., Berlin).—Second ed. much enlarged (760 p., Berlin 1882).

Jaeger, Werner Wilhelm (1888-):
1939-44: Paideia, the ideals of Greek culture (3 vols., Oxford University Press: Isis 32, 375-76; 35, 188-89; 37, 99-100).—Translated from the German (1934 ff.).

Jennison, Madge:
1949: Roads (370 p., London).
History of roads in antiquity.

Lenz, Harald Othmar (1799-1870):
1856: Zoologie der alten Griechen und Römer (680 p., Gotha).

Livingstone, Sir Richard Winn (1880-) (editor):
1922: The legacy of Greece (436 p., 36 ill., Clarendon Press, Oxford).

Loria, Gino:
1914: Le scienze esatte nell'antica greca (2nd ed., 997 p., 122 ill., Milano; Isis 1, 714-16).

Marrou, Henri Irénée:
1948: Histoire de l'éducation dans l'antiquité (595 p., Paris; Isis 40, 295).

Michel, Paul-Henri:
1950: De Pythagore à Euclide. Contribution à l'histoire des mathématiques préeuclidiennes (700 p., Paris; Isis 42, 61).

Milhaud, Gaston (1858-1918):
1893: Leçons sur les origines de la science grecque (306 p., Paris).
1900: Les philosophes géomètres de la Grèce, PLATON et ses prédécesseurs (388 p., Paris).

Neuburger, Albert (1867-):
1930: The technical arts and sciences of the ancients (550 p., 676 ill., London).— German original, Leipzig 1919; 2nd ed. 1921 (Isis 4, 423; 6, 129-31).

Ninck, Martin:
1945: Die Entdeckung von Europa durch die Griechen (287 p., 36 fig., Basel; Isis 39, 105).

Rey, Abel (1873-1940):
1930-46: La science dans l'antiquité (Paris). Four volumes have appeared in HENRI BEHR's collection: L'évolution de l'humanité.

Vol. 1, 1930: La science orientale avant les Grecs.

Vol. 2, 1933: La Jeunesse de la science grecque (that is, the period from 600 to 450; Isis 21, 224-26).

Vol. 3, 1932: La maturité de la pensée scientifique en Grèce (down to ARISTOTLE included; Isis 32, 167).

Vol. 4, 1946: L'apogée de la science technique grecque (Isis 40, 70).

These four volumes do not complete the history of Greek science; the last, posthumously published, is very unbalanced: mathematics is explained only down to PLATO, but astronomy down to HIPPARCH, etc.

Reymond, Arnold:
1927: History of the sciences in Greco-Roman antiquity (255 p., London).
—Translated from the French (Paris 1924; Isis 7, 252).

Robin, Léon (1866-   ):
1928: Greek thought and the origins of the scientific spirit (429 p., map, London).—Translated from the French original (504 p., Paris 1923; Isis 6, 557-59); revised ed. 1928.
1942: La pensée hellenique des origines à EPICURE. Questions de méthode, de critique et d'histoire (554 p., Paris).

Rochas d'Aiglun, Albert de (1837-1914):
1883: La science dans l'antiquité. Les origines de la science et ses premières applications (290 p., 117 fig., Paris).

Sarton, George:
1952: Ancient science to EPICUROS (the book is completed but not yet published; Harvard University Press, Cambridge, Mass.).

Schiaparelli, Giovanni Virginio (1835-1910):
1925: Scritti sulla storia della astronomia antica. Parte prima. Scritti editi (470 p., port., Bologna; Isis 8, 503-6).

Schuhl, Pierre Maxime:
1934: Essai sur la formation de la pensée grecque. Introduction historique à une étude de la philosophie platonicienne (475 p., Paris; Isis 23, 469-70).—Second edition with 30 additional pages (Paris 1949; Isis 41, 227).

Simon, Maximilian (1844-1918):
1909: Geschichte der Mathematik im Altertum in Verbindung mit antiker Kulturgeschichte (418 p., Berlin).

Singer, Charles:
1922: Greek biology and Greek medicine (128 p., ill., Oxford; Isis 5, 532).
1927: The herbal in antiquity (Journal of Hellenic studies 47, 1-52, 10 pl., 46 fig.; Isis 10, 519-21).

Smith, David Eugene (1860-1944):
1923: Mathematics (Our debt to Greece and Rome; 185 p., Boston: Isis 6, 188).

Tannery, Paul (1843-1904; Isis 38, 33-51):
1887: Pour l'histoire de la science hellène. De THALÈS à EMPÉDOCLE (404 p., Paris).—Revised edition by A. DIÈS (460 p., Paris 1930; Isis 15, 179-80).
1887: La géométrie grecque. Comment son histoire nous est parvenue et ce que nous en savons (196 p., Paris).
1893: Recherches sur l'histoire de l'astronomie ancienne (378 p., Paris).

Taylor, Henry Osborn (1856-1941):
1922: Greek biology and medicine (166 p., London; Isis 5, 532).

Thirion, Julien (1852-1918):
1900: Evolution de l'astronomie chez les Grecs (286 p., 5 ill., Bruxelles).

Thomas, Ivor (1905-   ):
1939-41: Selections illustrating the history of Greek mathematics, with English translation (2 vols., Loeb Classical Library, Cambrige, Harvard University Press).

Thomson, J. Oliver:
1948: History of ancient geography (436 p., 2 pl., 66 fig., Cambridge University; Isis 40, 244).

Tozer, Henry Fanshawe (1829-1916):
1897: History of ancient geography (406 p., 10 maps, Cambridge University).— Second edition in 1935 with 34 p. of notes by MAX CARY (Isis 26, 537).

Van Deman, Esther Bose (1862-1937):
1934: The building of the Roman aqueducts (quarto, 452 p., ill., Washington, Carnegie Institution; Isis 23, 470-71).

Viedebantt, Oskar (1883-   ):
1923: Antike Gewichtsnormen und Münzfüsse (172 p., Berlin).

Warmington, Eric Herbert (1898-   ):
1934: Greek geography (317 p., London).
Anthology of translated fragments of the Greek geographers.

Wycherley, R. E.:
1949: How the Greeks built cities (250 p., 52 ill., 16 pl., London).

Zeuthen, Hieronymus Georg (1839-1920):
1896: Geschichte der Mathematik im Altertum und Mittelalter (350 p., ill., Copenhagen).—First published in Danish (Copenhagen 1893); reprint of the Danish edition with additions by O. NEUGEBAUER (Copenhagen 1949; Isis 42). French translation by JEAN MASCART (310 p., 31 ill., Paris 1902).

See in the Critical Bibliography of Isis the sections entitled 1. Antiquity, 4. Greece, 5. Rome.

MIDDLE AGES

Beazley, Sir Charles Raymond (1868-   ):
1897-1906: The dawn of modern geography (3 vols., London).

Berthelot, Marcelin (1827-1907):
1893: Histoire des sciences. La chimie au Moyen âge (3 vols., Paris).

Chevalier, Ulysse (1841-1923):
1894-1903: Répertoire des sources historiques du Moyen âge. Topobibliographie (2 vols., Montbéliard).
1905-7: Répertoire des sources historiques du Moyen âge. Biobibliographie (4832 col. in 2 vols., Paris).

Crump, Charles George (1862-1935); **Jacob, Ernest Fraser** (1894-   ):
1926: The legacy of the Middle Ages (562 p., 42 pl., Clarendon Press, Oxford).

De Bruyne, Edgar:
1946: Etudes d'esthétique médiévale (3 vols., 795 p., Bruges; Isis 39, 188-90).

Delambre, Jean Baptiste Joseph (1749-1822):
1819: Histoire de l'astronomie au Moyen âge (774 p., Paris).

De Wulf, Maurice (1867-1947):
1909: History of medieval philosophy (532 p., London).—New ed., 2 vol. 1926, 3rd ed. 1935-38. Original French ed., Louvain (488 p., 1900); 2nd ed., 3 vols., Louvain 1934-47.

Fischer, Hermann (1884-   ):
1929: Mittelalterliche Pflanzenkunde (334 p., 70 ill., München; Isis 15, 365-70).

Gilson, Etienne (1884-   ):
1922: La philosophie au Moyen âge (2 small vols., 326 p., Paris; Isis 5, 537).— Second ed. revised and much increased (782 p., Paris 1944).
1936: The spirit of mediaeval philosophy (Gifford Lectures 1931-32, 500 p., New York).
Original French edition (299 p., Paris 1932); 2nd ed. (450 p., Paris 1944).

Haskins, Charles Homer (1870-1937; Isis 28, 53-56, portr.):
1924: Studies in the history of mediaeval science (425 p., Cambridge, Harvard; Isis 7, 121-24).—Second ed., 1927.
1929: Studies in mediaeval culture (303 p., Oxford; Isis 14, 433-36).

Hecker, Justus Friedrich Karl (1795-1850):
1835: Epidemics of the Middle Ages (London, Sydenham Society).— Reprinted 1837, 1844, 1846, 1859. German edition by AUGUST HIRSCH, Berlin 1865.

Kibre, Pearl:
1948: The nations in mediaeval universities (252 p., Mediaeval Academy, Cambridge, Massachusetts).

Kimble, George Herbert Tinsley (1908-   ):
1938: Geography in the Middle Ages (284 p., 20 pl., London; Isis 30, 540-42).

Klebs, Arnold Carl (1870-1943):
1938: Incunabula scientifica et medica. Short title list (Osiris 4, 1-359).

Lacroix, Paul (Bibliophile Jacob, 1806-84):
1878: Science and literature in the Middle Ages and at the period of the Renaissance (quarto, 569 p., over 400 woodcuts, port., maps, London).—The French original: Sciences et lettres au Moyen âge (2nd ed., quarto, 616 p., ill.) was published in Paris, 1877.

Lelewel, Joachim (1786-1861):
1850-52: Géographie du Moyen âge (4 vols. in 2, atlas of 50 pl., Bruxelles).
1857: Epilogue (316 p., 8 pl., Bruxelles).

Nordenskiöld, Adolf Erik (1832-1901):
1897: Periplus. An essay on the early history of charts and sailing directions (Folio, 218 p., 100 ill., 60 maps, Stockholm).

Picavet, François (1851-1921):
1905: Esquisse d'une histoire générale et comparée des philosophies médiévales (400 p., Paris).

Sarton, George:
1927-48: Introduction to the history of science (3 vols. in 5, Baltimore). Covers the Middle Ages, East and West, down to 1400.
1938: The scientific literature transmitted through the incunabula (Osiris 5, 41-245, 60 facs., Bruges). Study based on KLEBS (1938).

Singer, Charles (1876-   ):
1928: From magic to science, essays on the scientific twilight (272 p., 14 pl., 108 fig., London; Isis 13, 225).

Strunz, Franz (1875-   ):
1910: Geschichte der Naturwissenschaften im Mittelalter (126 p., 1 fig., Stuttgart).

Sudhoff, Karl (1853-1938):
1908: Deutsche medizinische Inkunabeln (Studien zur Geschichte der Medizin, nos. 2/3) (302 p., 40 fig., Leipzig).
1908: Beitrag zur Geschichte der Anatomie im Mittelalter, speziell der anatomischen Graphik nach Handschriften des 9. bis 15. Jahrh. (Studien zur Geschichte der Medizin, no. 4: 94 p., 3 fig., 24 pl., Leipzig).

1914-18: Beiträge zur Geschichte der Chirurgie im Mittelalter. Graphische und Textliche Untersuchungen in mittelalterlichen Handschriften (Studien zur Geschichte der Medizin, nos. 10-12; 956 p., ill., 95 pl., Leipzig).

Thompson, James Westfall (1869-1941):
1939: The medieval library (700 p., University of Chicago Press, Chicago; Isis 32, 175-77).

Thorndike, Lynn:
1923-41: History of magic and experimental science (6 vols., Columbia University Press, New York).
1923: Vols. 1, 2, First thirteen centuries of our era (Isis 6, 74-89).—Reprinted with corrections, 1929.
1934: Vols. 3, 4, Fourteenth and fifteenth centuries (Isis 23, 471-75).
1941: Vols. 5, 6, The sixteenth century (Isis 33, 691-712).
1929: Science and thought in the fifteenth century (402 p., New York; Isis 14, 235-40).
1944: University records and life in the Middle Ages (Records of civilization, no. 38) (493 p., 1 map, Columbia University Press, New York; Isis 36, 211).

Wickersheimer, Ernest (1880-):
1936: Dictionnaire biographique des médecins en France au Moyen âge (878 p., Paris; Isis 26, 187-89).

Wright, John Kirtland (1891-):
1925: Geographical lore of the time of the Crusades (584 p., American Geographical Society, New York; Isis 7, 495-98).
See in the Critical Bibliography of Isis, section 6. Middle Ages.

BYZANTINE AND SLAVONIC
BYZANTINE

Baynes, Norman Hepburn (1877-); Moss, Henry St. L. B. (editors):
1948: Byzantium. An introduction to East Roman civilization (468 p., 48 pl., 3 maps, Clarendon Press, Oxford; Isis 41, 78).

Delatte, Armand:
1927-29: Anecdota atheniensia. (Bibliothèque de la Faculté de philosophie et lettres de l'Université de Liége.) 2 vols.—1927: Vol. 1, 748 p. (Isis 12, 328-30).—1939: Vol. 2, 512 p. (Isis 33, 274-78).
1947: Les portulans grecs (433 p., Liége; Isis 40, 71-72).

Krumbacher, Karl (1856-1909):
1897: Geschichte der byzantinischen Litteratur von Justinian bis zum Ende des Oströmischen Reiches, 527-1453 (Handbuch der klassischen Altertumswissenschaft, 9. Bd., 1. Abt.; Zweite Aufl., 1213 p., München).—First edition 1891, 506 p.
See in the Critical Bibliographies of Isis the section 7. Byzantium.

SLAVONIC
See the section on Russia in chapter 15. For a general, if brief, account of the scientific contributions of Slavonic peoples, see JOSEPH S. ROUCEK: Slavonic Encyclopaedia (p. 1116-33, New York 1949; Isis 41, 96). That article deals with Bulgaria, Czechoslovakia, Poland, Russia, USSR, Ukraine, Yugoslavia.

ISRAEL
Bevan, Edwyn R.; Singer, Charles (editors):
1927: The legacy of Israel (592 p., 83 fig., Oxford, Clarendon).

Ebstein, Wilhelm (1836-1912):
1901: Die Medizin im Alten Testament (192 p., Stuttgart).
1903: Die Medizin im Neuen Testament und im Talmud (345 p., Stuttgart).

Encyclopaedia Judaica:
1928-34: 10 vols. published (to Lyra). Edited by JACOB KLATZKIN (Berlin). Abbr. EJ.

Feldman, William Moses (1879-   ):
1931: Rabbinical mathematics and astronomy (252 p., London; Isis 19, 208-12)

Friedenwald, Harry (1864-1950):
1944: The Jews and medicine (2 vols., 1242 p., Baltimore; Isis 35, 346).
1946: Jewish luminaries in medical history and a Catalogue of works bearing on the subject (208 p., Baltimore; Isis 37, 239).

Gandz, Solomon (1887-   ):
1932: The Mishnat ha-middot, the first Hebrew geometry of about 150 C.E. and the geometry of MUHAMMAD IBN MŪSĀ AL-KHOWĀRIZMĪ, the first Arabic geometry (c. 820) representing the Arabic version of the Mishnat ha-middot. Edition of the Hebrew and Arabic texts with introduction, translation and notes (Quellen und Studien zur Geschichte der Mathematik, A 2; 104 p., 14 fig., 4 pl. Berlin; Isis 20, 274-80).
1932-33: Hebrew numerals (Proceedings American Academy for Jewish research 4, 53-112; Isis 22, 390).

Jewish Encyclopaedia:
1901-6: 12 vols. edited by CYRUS ADLER, ISIDORE SINGER, etc. (Funk and Wagnalls, New York). Abbr. JE.

Krauss, Samuel (1866-   ):
1910-12: Talmudische Archäologie (3 vols., Leipzig).
Does not deal with science proper but there are chapters in vol. 2 (1911) on agriculture, arts and industries, metrology, in vol. 3 (1912) on writing, books and education.

Löw, Immanuel (1854-1944):
1926-34: Flora der Juden (4 vols.; Isis 6, 428; 8, 210; 23, 573).

Meyerhof, Max (1874-1945; see Osiris 9):
1938: Mediaeval Jewish physicians in the Near East, from Arabic sources (Isis 28, 432-60).

Preuss, Julius (1861-   ):
1911: Biblisch-talmudische Medizin (742 p., Berlin).

Roback, Abraham Aaron (1890-   ):
1929: Jewish influence in modern thought (506 p., Cambridge, Massachusetts; Isis 13, 522).

Roth, Cecil (1899-   ):
1938: The Jewish contribution to civilisation (372 p., 8 pl., London).

Schleiden, Matthias Jakob (1804-81):
1877: Die Bedeutung der Juden für Erhaltung und Wiederbelebung der Wissenschaften im Mittelalter (41 p., Leipzig).—Fifth ed., 54 p., Leipzig 1912.
SCHLEIDEN was one of the founders of the cellular theory (1838), as well as one of the founders of modern botany.

Snowman, Jacob (1871-   ):
1935: Short history of Talmudic medicine (94 p., London; Isis 25, 265).
See also in the Critical bibliographies of Isis section 12. Israel.

ISLĀM

Adnan (-Adïvar), Abdulhak:
1939: La science chez les Turcs Ottomans (182 p., Paris; Isis 32, 186-89.—Re-

vised and amplified translation into Turkish (225 p., 3 pl., Istanbul 1943; Isis 38, 121-25).

Arnold, Sir Thomas Walker (1864-1930); **Guillaume, Alfred** (*editors*):
1931: The legacy of Islam (432 p., 42 pl., Clarendon Press, Oxford).

Brockelmann, Carl (1868-   ):
1898-42: Geschichte der arabischen Litteratur.—1898: Vol. 1 (540 p., Weimar).
—1902: Vol. 2 (726 p., Berlin).—1937: Suppt. to vol. 1 (993 p., Leiden).— 1938: Suppt. to vol. 2 (1066 p., Leiden).—1939-42: Suppt. vol. 3 1338 p., Leiden).
This volume deals with modern Arabic literature but includes (p. 1191-1326) addenda and errata to vols. 1 and 2.
1943: Geschichte der arabischen Litteratur. Zweite den Supplement-bänden angepasste Auflage (Leiden).— 1943: Vol. 1 (686 p..).—1944-49: Vol. 2 (702 p.).
This is mainly what the title says, a reprint of the first edition, the additions of the supplements being inserted in their proper places.

Browne, Edward Granville (1862-1926):
1906-24: Literary history of Persia (4 vols. University Press, Cambridge).— 1908, reprinted 1909: Vol. 1, From the earliest times until FIRDAWSĪ.—1906: Reprinted 1915. Vol. 2, From FIRDAWSĪ to SAʿDĪ.—1920: Reprinted 1928. Vol. 3, Tartar dominion. 1265-1502.—1924: Reprinted 1928. Vol. 4, Modern times. 1500-1924.
1921: Arabian medicine. Being the Fitzpatrick lectures delivered at the College of Physicians in November 1919 and November 1920. (146 p., 1 pl., University Press, Cambridge; Isis 4, 349-50).
1933: La médecine arabe. Edition française mise à jour et annotée par H. P. J. RENAUD (186 p., Paris; Isis 21, 435).

Campbell, Donald (1883-   ):
1926: Arabian medicine and its influence on the Middle Ages (2 vols., 458 p., London; Isis 9, 559).

Carra de Vaux, Bernard (1867-   ):
1921-26: Penseurs de l'Islam (5 vols., Paris).
1921: Vol. 1, Les souverains. L'histoire et la philosophie politique (Isis 4, 618).
1921: Vol. 2, Les géographes, les sciences mathématiques et naturelles (Isis 5, 165-67).
1923: Vol. 3, L'exégèse. La tradition et la jurisprudence (Isis 7, 272).
1923: Vol. 4, La scolastique, la théologie et la mystique. La musique (Isis 8, 598).
1926: Vol. 5, Les sectes. Le libéralisme moderne (Isis 10, 245).

Encyclopaedia of Islam:
1908-38: A dictionary of the geography, ethnography and biography of the Muhammedan peoples. Edited by M. TH. HOUTSMA, T. W. ARNOLD, R. BASSET, R. HARTMANN, A. J. WENSINCK, W. HEFFENING, E. LÉVI-PROVENÇAL, H. A. R. GIBB (4 vols. plus supplement, Leiden and London).

Erlanger, Rodolphe d' (1872-   ):
1930-39: La musique arabe (4 vols., Paris; Isis 20, 280-82; 26, 552; 30, 334; 32, 458).

Farmer, Henry George (1882-   ):
1929: History of Arabian music to the thirteenth century (280 p., 3 pl., London; Isis 13, 375-76).
1930: Historical facts for the Arabian music influence (388 p., London; Isis 15, 370-72).
1940: The sources of Arabian music. Annotated bibliography of Arabic MSS (100 p., Bearsden, Scotland; Isis 32, 458).

Ferrand, Gabriel (1864-c.1935) (*editor*):
1928: Introduction à l'astronomie nautique arabe (284 p., Paris; Isis 13, 127).

Fonahn, Adolf Mauritz (1873-1940):
1910: Zur Quellenkunde der persischen Medizin. (158 p., Leipzig).
1922: Arabic and Latin anatomical terminology chiefly from the Middle Ages. (Norwegian Academy, hist. class., 1921, no. 7). (176 p., Kristiania; Isis 5 170-72; 37, 81).

Hirschberg, Julius (1843-1925):
1905: Die arabischen Lehrbücher der Augenheilkunde. Unter Mitwirkung von J. LIPPERT und EUGEN MITTWOCH (1876-1942) (117 p., Abh., Preuss. Akad., Berlin).

Khairallah, Amin A.:
1946: Outline of Arabic contributions to medicine and the allied sciences (228 p., ill., Beirūt; Isis 40, 381).

Leclerc, Lucien (1816-   ):
1876: Histoire de la médecine arabe (2 vols., Paris).

Meyerhof, Max (1874-1945; Osiris 9):
1919: Die Optik der Araber (Zeitschrift für ophthalmologische Optik, vol. 8, 16-29, 42-54, 86-90, Berlin; Isis 4, 431).
1940: Un glossaire de matière médicale de MAIMONIDE, édité et traduit (403 p., Le Caire; Isis 33, 527-29).

Mieli, Aldo (1879-1950):
1939: La science arabe et son rôle dans l'évolution scientifique mondiale. (408 p., Leiden; Isis 30, 291-95).

Miles, George Carpenter (1904-   ):
1948: Early Arabic glass weights and stamps (174 p., American Numismatic Society, New York; Isis 40, 381).

Nallino, Carlo Alfonso (1872-1938):
1944: Raccolta di scritti editi e inediti. Vol. 5. Astrologia, astronomia, geografia (558 p., Roma; Isis 38, 120).
The Raccolta fills 6 vols. (1939-48); vol. 6 includes an index to vols. 3 to 6 and Nallino's biography (Isis 34, 177; 40, 161).

Pines, Salomon (1908-   ):
1936: Beiträge zur islamischen Atomenlehre (150 p., Berlin; Isis 26, 557).

Ribera y Tarragó, Julian (1858-1934):
1929: Music in ancient Arabia and Spain. Translated by ELEANOR HAGUE and MARION LEFFINGWELL (296 p., Stanford University; Isis 34, 46).
Abridged translation of La musica de las cantigas (Madrid 1922). For this work and others by RIBERA on Andalusian and Arabic music *see* Isis (11, 496-97; 12, 163).

Suter, Heinrich (1848-1922) (Isis 18, 166-83):
1900: Die Mathematiker und Astronomen der Araber und ihre Werke. (Abhandlungen zur Geschichte der mathematischen Wissenschaften, Heft 10) (288 p., Leipzig).
1902: Nachträge und Berichtigungen. (Abhandlungen zur Geschichte der mathematischen Wissenschaften, Heft 14, p. 155-85). (Leipzig; Isis 5, 409-17).
See in the Critical Bibliographies of Isis, section 14. Islam.

INDIA

Barnett, Lionel David (1871-   ):
1913: Antiquities of India. An account of the history and culture of ancient

Hindustan (322 p., 25 pl., 3 maps, London; Isis 2, 408-10).
Chapters 6 to 9, p. 188-231, deal with science.

Behanan, Kovoor Thomas:
1938: Yoga. A scientific evaluation (292 p., London; Isis 32, 451).

Brennand, W.:
1896: Hindu astronomy (346 p., London).

Chakraberty, Chandra:
1923: Interpretation of Hindu medicine (620 p., Calcutta; Isis 7, 267).
1923: Comparative Hindu materia medica (208 p., Calcutta; Isis 7, 266).

Cultural Heritage:
1936-37: The Cultural heritage of India. Sri Ramakrishna centenary memorial.
A symposium by some 100 authors (Quarto, 3 vols., c. 1950 p., 164 ill., Calcutta).
Only a part of vol. 3 (p. 337-481) deals with science proper; the main emphasis is on religion, philosophy, art. SRI RĀMAKRISHNA (1836-86) is a religious leader who has exerted a deep influence upon his countrymen (Isis 36, 214, 215).

Cumming, Sir John (1868-   ) (editor):
1939: Revealing India's past. A cooperative record of archaeological conservation and exploration in India and beyond by 22 authorities British, Indian and continental (394 p., 33 pl., 1 map, 2 fig., London).

Cunningham, Sir Alexander (1814-93):
1871: Ancient geography of India (609 p., 13 maps, London).—New edition by SURENDRANATH MAJUMDAR SASTRI (842 p., map, Calcutta 1924).

Dasgupta, Surendra Nath (1887-   ):
1922-49: History of Indian philosophy (4 vols., Cambridge University).—Vol. 1 reprinted in 1932; vol. 4, 1949 (Isis 41, 79).
1924: Yoga as philosophy and religion (210 p. London).
1930: Yoga philosophy in relation to other systems of Indian thought (390 p., Calcutta).

Datta, Bibhutibhusan:
1932: The science of śulba. A study in early Hindu geometry (256 p., University of Calcutta; Isis 22, 272-77).
1935-38 (with Singh, Avadhesh Narayan): History of Hindu mathematics. A source book. Part 1. Numeral notations and arithmetic (282 p., Lahore; Isis 25, 478-88). Part 2. Algebra (330 p., Lahore).

Dey, Nundo Lal:
1927: Geographical Dictionary of ancient and mediaeval India. (Calcutta Oriental series, no. 21, E. 13.). Second ed., quarto (272 p., London).
First edition, Calcutta 1899. Second edition printed in sheets in The Indian antiquary, issued as a volume by Quaritch, London 1921. The edition of 1927 was printed in Bombay; the preface is dated Chinsurah 1922.

Edgerton, Franklin:
1931: The elephant lore of the Hindus. The elephant sport of Nilakantha (148 p., New Haven; Isis 41, 120-23).

Eliade, Mircea (1907-   ):
1936: Yoga. Essai sur les origines de la mystique indienne (Bibliothèque de philosophie roumaine) (255 p., Paris).
The book is more comprehensive than its title indicates, for it contains a comparative study of yoga theories and practices, not only in India but all over the world.

Finot, Louis (1864-1935):
1896: Les lapidaires indiens (Bibliothèque de l'Ecole des hautes études, fasc. 111; 336 p., Paris).

Garratt, Geoffrey Theodore (1888-   ) (*editor*):
1937: The legacy of India (446 p., 24 pl., 1 map, Clarendon Press, Oxford).

Hoernle, August Friedrich Rudolf (1841-1918):
1907: Studies in the medicine of ancient India. Vol. 1, Osteology (264 p., Oxford).—No others published.

Keith, Arthur Berriedale (1879-   ):
1921: Indian logic and atomism. An exposition of the Nyāya and Vaiçeṣika systems. (291 p., Clarendon Press, Oxford; Isis 4, 535-36).
1928: History of Sanskrit literature. (612 p., Clarendon Press, Oxford).

Law, Narendra Nath:
1915: Promotion of learning in India by early European settlers, up to c. 1800 (188 p., 2 fig., London).
1916: Promotion of learning in India during Muhammadan rule, by Muhammadans (308 p., ill., London).
1921: Aspects of ancient Indian polity (248 p., Oxford, Clarendon; Isis 5, 164-65).

Majumdar, Girija Prasanna:
1927: Vanaspati. Plants and plant life as in Indian treatises and traditions. (276 p., Calcutta; Isis 25, 259, 198).

Mariadassou, *see* Paramānanda.

Markham, Sir Clements (1830-1916):
1871: Memoir of the Indian Surveys (328 p., 4 fold. maps and charts, London). —Second ed. 1878 (510 p., 5 fold. maps and charts, London).

Masson-Oursel, Paul:
1920: Bibliographie sommaire de l'Indianisme (Isis 3, 171-218).

Mookerji, Radhakumud (1884-   ):
1912: Indian shipping. History of the seaborne trade and maritime activity of the Indians from the earliest times (310 p., 20 pl., London).
1947: Ancient Indian education (691 p., 26 pl., London).

Paramānanda Mariadassou:
1906: Moeurs médicales de l'Inde et leurs rapports avec la médecine européenne (178 p., Pondichéry).
1913: Le jardin des simples de l'Inde (286 p., Pondichéry).
1934-35: Médecine traditionnelle de l'Inde (3 vols., Pondichéry).

Phillimore, Reginald Henry (1879-   ):
1945-   : Historical records of the Survey of India. Vol. 1, 18th century (436 p., 21 pl., Dehra Dūn; Isis 37, 207).

Rādhākumuda Mukhopādhyāya, *see* Mookerji, Radhakumud.

Ramakrishna, Sri (1836-86; Isis 36, 214-15):
See Cultural heritage.

Ray, Dhirendra Nath:
1937: The principle of tridoṣa in Āyurveda (376 p., Calcutta; Isis 34, 174-177).

Rāy, Praphulla Chandra (1861-1944) (Isis 27, 515-16):
1902-9: History of Hindu chemistry from the earliest times to the middle of the sixteenth century (2 vols., Calcutta; Isis 3, 68-73).—Second ed. of vol. 1, 1903.

Sarkar, Benoy Kumar (1887-   ):
   1914: The positive background of Hindu sociology. Book 1. Non political
(390 p., Allahabad; Isis 3, 63-64). With appendices by B. SEAL.
   1918: Hindu achievements in exact sciences (98 p., London; Isis 3, 139).

Seal, Sir Brajendranath (1864-1938):
   1915: The positive sciences of the ancient Hindus (304 p., London; Isis 3,
139, 474).

Sewell, Robert (1845-1925):
   1896: (with SANKARA BĀLKṚISHṆA DIKSHIT) The Indian calendar, with tables
for the conversion of Hindu and Muhammadan into A.D. dates and vice versa. With
tables of eclipses visible in India by ROBERT SCHRAM (318 p., London).
   1898: Eclipses of the moon in India (quarto, 74 p., London).
   1912: Indian chronography. An extension of the "Indian calendar" with
working examples (quarto, 200 p., London).

Thomas, Edward (1813-86):
   1874: Ancient Indian weights (82 p., London).

Winternitz, Moriz (1863-1937):
   1907-22: Geschichte der indischen Litteratur (3 vols., Leipzig).
   1907: Vol. 1, Einleitung. Der Veda. Die volkstümlichen Epen und die
Purānas. Zweite Ausgabe (520 p.).
   1920: Vol. 2, Die buddhistische Litteratur und die heiligen Texte der Jainas.
(416 p.).
   1922: Vol. 3, Die Kunstdichtung. Die wissenschaftliche Litteratur. Neu-
indische Litteratur. Nachträge zu allen drei Bänden (710 p.).
   1927-33: A history of Indian literature. English translation by Mrs. SHRIDAR
VENKATESH KETKAR and her sister, HELEN KOHN, revised by the author (University of Calcutta).
   1927: Vol. 1, Introduction. Veda, national epics, purāṇas and tantras. (654
p.).
   1933: Vol. 2, Buddhist and Jaina literature (693 p.).

Zimmer, Henry R. (1890-1943):
   1948: Hindu medicine (275 p., Baltimore; Isis 41, 120-23).
   For Hindu logic as preserved in the Buddhist world, see in chapter 17, the sec-
tion on Logic, Eastern Logic. For Pakistan and more generally for Muslim
India, see also Islām.
   See also in the Critical Bibliographies of Isis the section 9. India.

FAR EAST AND EASTERN INDIES (INDONESIA)

Chikashige Masumi (1870-   ):
   1936: Alchemy and other chemical achievements of the ancient orient (112 p.,
ill., Tokyo; Isis 27, 79).

Cordier, Henri (1849-1925):
   1912-32: Bibliotheca indosinica (5 vols., Paris; Introd. 3, 1879).

Duong-Bá Banh:
   1947: Histoire de la médecine du Viet-Nam (88 p., Hanoi; Isis 41, 380; 42, 64).

Gimlette, John D. (1867-1934):
   1939: Dictionary of Malayan medicine. Edited and completed by H. W.
THOMSON (275 p., London; Isis 33, 130).

Honig, Pieter; Verdoorn, Frans (editors):
   1945: Science and scientists in the Netherlands Indies (514 p., 134 fig., New
York; Isis 36, 260-61).

Huard, Pierre:
  1949: La science et l'Extrême Orient (68 p., Hanoi; Isis 41, 380).

Mikami Yoshio:
  1913: The development of mathematics in China and Japan (355 p., Leipzig).

Rutten, Louis Martin Robert (1884-1946):
  1929: Science in the Netherlands East Indies (440 p., Amsterdam; Isis 25, 564).
  Book prepared under the auspices of the Koninklijke Akademie van Wetenschappen (Royal Dutch Academy, Amsterdam) on the occasion of the Fourth
Pacific Science Congress, Java.

Sallet, Albert:
  1931: L'officine sino-annamite en Annam. 1. Le médecin annamite et la
préparation des remèdes (170 p., 16 pl., Paris; Isis 22, 267-72).

Weck, Wolfgang (1881-   ):
  '937: Heilkunde und Volkstum auf Bali (260 p., 27 fig., Stuttgart; Isis 28,
235).
  See in the Critical Bibliographies of Isis, section 8. Asia, Eastern Asia.

CHINA

Carter, Thomas Francis (1882-1925):
  1925: The invention of printing in China and its spread westward (300 p.,
ill., New York; Isis 8, 361-73).—New ed. 1931 (308 p., 40 ill., New York; Isis 19,
426).

Cordier, Henri (1849-1925):
  1904-24: Bibliotheca sinica (2nd ed., 5 vols., Paris; Introd. 3, 1879).

Couling, Samuel (1859-1922):
  1917: Encyclopaedia Sinica (642 p., London).

Forke, Alfred (1867-1944):
  1925: The world conception of the Chinese. Their astronomical, cosmologi-
cal and physico-philosophical speculations (314 p., London; Isis 8, 373-75).

Fung (Fêng) Yu-lan (1895-   ):
  1937: History of Chinese philosophy. Vol. 1 translated by DERK BODDE
(Peiping). The second volume is available only in the Chinese original (2 vols.,
Peiping 1934).
  1947: The spirit of Chinese philosophy. Translated by E. R. HUGHES (238
p., London; Isis 40, 159).
  1948: Short history of Chinese philosophy. Edited by DERK BODDE (388 p.,
New York; Isis 40, 158).

Hartner, Willy:
  1941-42: Heilkunde im alten China (Extract from Sinica, vols. 16 and 17; 120
p., ill.; Isis 41, 230).

Hommel, Rudolf P.:
  1937: China at work. An illustrated record of the primitive industries of
China's masses whose life is toil, and thus an account of Chinese civilization
(Quarto, 378 p., 536 ill., Bucks County Historical Society, Doylestown, Pennsylvania; Isis 31, 219).

Hübotter, Franz (1881-   ):
  1913: Beiträge zur Kenntnis der chinesischen sowie der tibetisch-mongolischen
Pharmakologie (Quarto, mimeographed copy of author's handwriting, 324 p.,
Berlin).
  1929: Die chinesische Medizin zu Beginn des XX. Jahrhunderts und ihr

historischer Entwicklungsgang (Quarto mimeographed copy of typewriting, 356 p., ill., Leipzig; Isis 14, 255-63).

Hughes, Ernest Richard (1883-   ):
1937: The invasion of China by the Western world (340 p., London).

Johnson, Obed Simon (1881-   ):
1928: Study of Chinese alchemy (170 p., Shanghai; Isis 12, 330-32).

Li Ch'iao-p'ing:
1948: Chemical arts of old China (226 p., ill., Easton, Pennsylvania; Isis 40, 281).

Mély, Fernand de (1851-   ):
1896: Les lapidaires chinois. Introduction, texte et traduction avec la collaboration de M. H. COUREL (Les lapidaires de l'antiquité et du moyen âge, tome 1; 366 p., 144 p. in Chinese, Paris).

Needham, Joseph (1900-   ):
1945: Chinese science (80 p., 95 ill., London; Isis 37, 238).

Needham, Joseph and Dorothy (*editors*):
1948: Science outpost. Papers of the Sino-British co-operation office (British Council Scientific Office in China) 1942-46 (313 p., 60 ill., 3 maps, London; Isis 40, 159).
The two NEEDHAM books deal with science in China now; yet they may be useful to the historians of old Chinese science.
NEEDHAM is preparing an elaborate work to be entitled Science and civilisation in China; the table of contents has appeared in the Archives intern. hist. sci. (30, 280-94, 1951).

Peake, Cyrus Henderson (1900-   ):
1932: Nationalism and education in modern China, 1860-1929 (254 p., New York; Isis 36, 217).
1934: Some aspects of the introduction of modern science into China (Isis 22, 173-219).

Purcell, Victor (1896-   ):
1936: Problems of Chinese education (270 p., London).

Read, Bernard Emms (1887-1949):
1931-39: Chinese materia medica. Animal drugs (9 parts published by the Peking Natural History Bulletin, Peking; Isis 20, 584).
1936: Chinese medicinal plants from the Pên ts'ao kang mu, 1596. Third ed. of a botanical, chemical and pharmacological reference list (406 p., Peking Natural History Bulletin, Peiping).—Second ed. 1927.
1936: Compendium of minerals and stones from the Pên ts'ao kang mu (2nd ed., 106 p., Peking Natural History Bulletin, Peiping.—First ed. 1928.
1946: Famine foods listed in the Chiu huang pên ts'ao (90 p., Shanghai; Isis 39,248).

Saussure, Léopold de (1866-1925; Isis 27, 286-305, port.):
1930: Les origines de l'astronomie chinoise (608 p., Paris; Isis 17, 267-71).

Schlegel, Gustave (1840-1903):
1875: Uranographie chinoise (944 p., plus atlas of 7 pl., La Haye).

Sowerby, Arthur de Carle (1885-   ):
1940: Nature in Chinese art (204 p., ill.; New York, Isis 34, 68).

Stuart, G. A.:
1911: Chinese materia medica. Vegetable kingdom. Extensively revised from the work of F. PORTER SMITH (568 p., Shanghai).

Wong, K. Chimin; Wu Lien-teh (1879-   ):
1932: History of Chinese medicine (724 p., 93 ill., map. Tientsin; Isis 20, 480-82).—Second ed. 1936 (934 p., ill., Shanghai; Isis 27, 341-42).

Yule, Sir Henry (1820-89):
1913-16: Cathay and the way thither, being a collection of medieval notices of China. Second ed. revised by HENRI CORDIER (4 vols., Hakluyt Society, London; Introd. 3, 1910)—First ed. 1866 (2 vols., London).
See in the Critical Bibliographies of Isis, section 10. China.

JAPAN

Cordier, Henri (1849-1925):
1912: Bibliotheca japonica (762 col., Paris).

Fujikawa Yu (d. 1940):
1934: Japanese medicine. Translated from the German (Tokyo 1911) by JOHN RUHRÄH, with a note on the recent history of medicine in Japan by AMANO, KAGEYAS WAT (1899-   ) (128 p., 8 ill., New York).
For FUJIKAWA, *see* Isis 24, 510; 29, 247.

Keenleyside, Hugh Llewellyn (1898-   ); **Thomas, Andrew Frank** (1896-   ):
1937: History of Japanese education and present educational system (378 p., Tokyo).

Shinjo, Shinzo (*editor*):
1926: Scientific Japan past and present. Prepared in connection with the Third Pan-Pacific Science Congress (368 p., 47 pl., 2 maps, Tokyo 1926; Isis 10, 83-88).

Smith, David Eugene (1860-1944); **Mikami Yoshio:**
1914: History of Japanese mathematics (294 p., Chicago; Isis 2, 410-13).
See in the Critical Bibliographies of Isis the section 11. Japan.

19. HISTORY OF SPECIAL SCIENCES

We now offer our readers a selection of books dealing with special sciences, and sometimes with special branches of those sciences. For example, some books cover the whole history of mathematics, others deal only with the history of geometry, others are restricted to the history of projective geometry, others still discuss but one aspect of that geometry, the introduction of imaginary elements. It is impossible to extend this bibliography to every ramification of each subject, nor is that necessary. The relatively few items mentioned will suffice to enable ingenious students to continue their bibliographical investigations as far as they may wish; the references to Isis will enable them to find a great many additional items classified together with the items specifically referred to.

This chapter is subdivided very much like Part III in the Critical Bibliography of Isis, except that a number of sections dealing with marginal subjects have been omitted, as well as the whole of the first group "Science in general" to which other chapters are devoted (for Bibliography of science, *see* chapters 9 to 12, for History of science, chapters 14 and 15, for Organization of science, chapter 8, for Philosophy of science, chapter 7). For the history of special instruments (telescope, microscope, etc.) *see* chapter 16. Photography and Chronometry, however, are dealt with below after Technology.

LOGIC

Historians of logic are seldom able to isolate their subject sufficiently from the history of epistemology or of other branches of philosophy. Any scholar interested in the history of logic would be obliged to use many books dealing with the history of philosophy (books which cannot be enumerated here). Historians of science who pay special attention to the logical problems will find pertinent data in the books dealing with the philosophy of science (*see* section 7).

WESTERN LOGIC

Adamson, Robert (1852-1902):
1911: A short history of logic (276 p., Edinburgh).

Boll, Marcel (1886-   ):
1948: Manuel de logique scientifique (554 p., 192 fig., tables, Paris).
Amplification of the author's Eléments de logique scientifique (250 p., Paris 1942).

Church, Alonzo (1903-   ):
1936: Bibliography of symbolic logic (from 1666 to 1935).
Reprinted from the Journal of Symbolic Logic (1, 121-218, Menasha, Wisconsin).

Enriques, Federigo (1871-1946):
1922: Per la storia della logica: I principii e l'ordine della scienza nel concetto dei pensatori matematici (302 p., Bologna; Isis 5, 469).—French translation (Paris 1926).—German translation (Leipzig 1927).—English translation (282 p., New York 1929).

Prantl, Carl von (1820-88):
1855-70: Geschichte der Logik im Abendlande (4 vols., Leipzig).

Scholz, Heinrich:
1931: Geschichte der Logik (86 p., Berlin).

Überweg, Friedrich (1826-71):
1871: System of logic and history of logical doctrines. Translated from the German with notes and appendices by THOMAS M. LINDSAY (610 p., London).— German ed., Bonn 1857; 5th ed. 1882.

EASTERN LOGIC

Keith, Arthur Berriedale (1879-1944):
1921: Indian logic and atomism. An exposition of the Nyāya and Vaiçeṣika systems (291 p., Clarendon Press; Oxford; Isis 4, 535-36).

Shcherbatskii, Feodor Ippolitovich (in French, TH. STCHERBATSKY):
1926: La théorie de la connaissance et la logique chez les Bouddhistes tardifs, traduit par Madame I. DE MANZIARLY et PAUL MASSON-OURSEL (Annales du Musée Guimet, vol. 36, 267 p., Paris).
The Russian original text appeared in 1909 as an introduction to the Russian translation of the Nyāyabindu (Introd. 1, 473) and is especially important for the interpretation of Dignāga (IV-2) and Dharmakīrti (VII-1). The French translation was ready in 1914, but publication was delayed on account of the war; a German translation appeared in Munich 1924. The work deals with metaphysics rather than with logic.
1930-32: Buddhist logic (2 vols. of the Bibliotheca Buddhica, 26, Leningrad; also 2 vols. Harvard University Press, Cambridge, 1934; Isis 24, 508).
This is a more elaborate work than the one which was translated into German and French. It includes an English translation of the Nyāyabindu of Dharmakīrti (VII-1) and of its commentary (ṭīkā) by DHARMOTTARA.

Sugiura Sadajiro:
1900: Hindu logic as preserved in China and Japan (114 p., University of Pennsylvania, Philadelphia).

Vidyābhūsana, Satis Chandra:
1921: A history of Indian logic (692 p., Calcutta University; Isis 10, 214).
See the Critical Bibliographies of Isis, section 19. Logic.

MATHEMATICS—BIBLIOGRAPHY

Loria, Gino:
1946: Guida allo studio della storia delle matematiche (2nd ed. revised and augmented, 405 p., Milano; Isis 37, 254).—First edition 1916 (244 p., Milano; Isis 3, 142).

Müller, Felix (1843-1928):
1909: Führer durch die mathematische Literatur, mit besonderer Berücksichtigung der historisch wichtigen Schriften (262 p., Leipzig).

Sarton, George:
1936: The study of the history of mathematics (114 p., Harvard University Press, Cambridge, Massachusetts).

HISTORY OF MATHEMATICS
General Mathematics and special subjects
not covered in the following sections.

Archibald, Raymond Clare (1875-   ):
1932-49: Outline of the history of mathematics. First ed. 1932 (53 p.; Isis 19, 434).—Second ed. 1934 (58 p., Oberlin, Ohio; Isis 23, 582).—Third ed. 1936 (62 p., Oberlin, Ohio; Isis 27, 172).—Fourth ed. 1939 (66 p., Oberlin, Ohio; Isis 31, 237).—Fifth ed. 1941 (76 p., Oberlin, Ohio; Isis 34, 73).—Sixth ed. 1949 (114 p., American Mathematical Monthly 56; Isis 40, 289).

Ball, Walter William Rouse (1850-1925; Isis 8, 321-24):
1888: Short account of the history of mathematics (London).—Fifth ed. 1912 (546 p.; Isis 1, 561).—Sixth ed. 1915.—Stereotyped ed. 1919.

Bell, Eric Temple:
1937: Men of mathematics (613 p., 29 ill., New York; Isis 28, 510-13).
1940: The development of mathematics (598 p., New York; Isis 33, 291-93).—Second ed. enlarged (651 p., 1945).

Bouligand, Georges (1889-   ):
1935: L'évolution des sciences physiques et mathématiques (Paris).
1949: Le déclin des absolus mathématico-logiques (Paris; Isis 42, 71), with JEAN DESGRANGES.

Boutroux, Pierre (1880-1922):
1914-19: Les principes de l'analyse mathématique. Exposé historique et critique (2 vols., Paris; Isis 1, 577-89, 734-42; 4, 96-107).
1920: L'idéal scientifique des mathématiciens (274 p., Paris; Isis 4, 93-96).—German translation (Leipzig 1927; Isis 11, 236).

Braunmühl, Anton von (1853-1908):
1900-03: Vorlesungen über Geschichte der Trigonometrie (2 vols., Leipzig).

Cajori, Florian (1859-1930; Isis 17, 384-407):
1894: History of mathematics (436 p., New York). Reprinted 1895, 1897, 1901, 1909.—Second ed. revised (516 p., New York 1919).
Almost half of the book (p. 278-516) deals with the nineteenth century.
1928-29: History of mathematical notations (2 vols., Chicago; Isis 12, 232-36; 13, 129-30).

Cantor, Moritz (1829-1920):
1880-1908: Vorlesungen über Geschichte der Mathematik (4 vols. Leipzig, Teubner).—Vol. 1, from the beginning to 1200. First ed. 1880; 2nd, 1894; 3rd, 1907.—Vol. 2, from 1200 to 1668. First ed. 1892, 2nd, 1899-1900; (reprinted 1913).—Vol. 3, from 1668 to 1758. First ed. 1898, 2nd, with only a few corrections, 1901.—Vol. 4, from 1759 to 1799. Published in 1908 by a group of specialists under Cantor's direction, his own contribution being restricted to a brief conclusion.
These volumes at the time of their publication were almost as good as any history can ever hope to be. To be sure, there were many mistakes concerning details, some of which were gradually corrected by GUSTAF ENESTRÖM (1852-1923; Isis 8, 313-20 portrait) and his collaborators in Bibliotheca Mathematica, but the general lines were remarkably sound. Since that time much progress has been made, especially with regard to the ancient and mediaeval period and oriental mathematics in general, and Cantor has now become very insufficient in those respects. If these defects were less fundamental, they might be corrected in a new edition; as it is, at least the history of ancient and mediaeval times must be entirely rewritten.

Coolidge, Julian Lowell:
1949: The mathematics of great amateurs (220 p., Clarendon Press, Oxford; Isis 41, 234-36).

Enriques, Federigo (1871-1946):
1938: Le matematiche nella storia e nella cultura (340 p., 22 pl., Bologna; Isis 31, 108-9).

Günther, Siegmund (1848-1923):
1908: Geschichte der Mathematik bis Cartesius (428 p., Leipzig). Continued by WIELEITNER, q.v.

Heilbronner, Johann Christoph (1706-c.47):
1742: Historia matheseos universae a mundo condito ad seculum P.C.N. XVI. Praecipuorum mathematicorum vitas, dogmata, scripta et manuscripta complexa. Accedit recensio elementorum, compendiorum et operum mathematicorum atque historia arithmetices ad nostra tempora (Quarto, 930 p. + elab. indices, Leipzig).

Hooper, Alfred:
1948: Makers of mathematics (402 p. London).

Kästner, Abraham Gotthelf (1719-1800):
1796-1800: Geschichte der Mathematik seit der Wiederherstellung der Wissenschaften bis an das Ende des achtzehnten Jahrhunderts (4 vols., Göttingen).
The title of this work is misleading. Vols. 1 and 2 (1786-97) deal with mathematics and mathematical sciences to the end of the sixteenth century, vol. 3 (1799) with mathematics to CARTESIUS, vol. 4 (1800) with mechanics, optics, astronomy from 1600 to 1650.

Klein, Felix (1849-1925):
1926-27: Vorlesungen über die Entwicklung der Mathematik im 19. Jahrhundert (2 vols., 608 p., Berlin, Springer; Isis 9, 447-49; 10, 505).

Le Lionnais, F. (*editor*):
1948: Les grands courants de la pensée mathématique (533 p., Cahiers du Sud, France; Isis 40, 78).

Loria, Gino (1862-   ; Osiris 7, 1939):
1929-33: Storia delle matematiche (3 vols. Torino; Isis 13, 228; 19, 231; 22, 598). Revised ed. in 1 vol. (1012 p., Milano 1950; Isis 42, 63).
1937: Scritti, conferenze, discorsi sulla storia delle matematiche (614 p., Padova; Isis 27, 522-24).

Marie, Maximilien (1819-91):
1883-88: Histoire des sciences mathématiques et physiques (12 vols., Paris).

Montucla, Jean Etienne (1725-99; Osiris 1, 519-67):
1758-1802: Histoire des mathématiques (2 vols., Paris 1758). Vol. 1 deals with the history down to 1600, vol. 2 with the seventeenth century.—New edition completed by JÉRÔME DE LALANDE (1732-1807), with two more volumes covering the eighteenth century (4 vols., Paris 1799-1802).
This is the best of the early histories; it deals not only with mathematics but also less elaborately with mathematical sciences (mechanics, physics, astronomy). It is especially valuable for the study of the seventeenth and eighteenth centuries.

Müller, Felix (1843-1928):
1892: Zeittafeln zur Geschichte der Mathematik, Physik und Astronomie bis zum Jahre 1500 (108 p., Leipzig).

Prasad, Ganesh (1876-   ):
1933: Some great mathematicians of the nineteenth century. Their lives and their works (Benares).—Vol. 1, 364 p., 1933 (Isis 22, 359).—Vol. 2, 342 p., 1934 Isis 22, 575).—No others published.

Sanford, Vera:
1930: Short history of mathematics (414 p., Boston; Isis 15, 293).

Schaaf, William L. (*editor*):
1948: Mathematics: our great heritage. Essays on the nature and cultural significance of mathematics (300 p., New York; Isis 40, 167) .

Sergescu, Petre (1893-   ):
1933: Les sciences mathématiques (182 p., extrait du Tableau du XXe siècle, Paris; Isis 23, 539).
XX*th* century mathematics in France.

Smith, David Eugene (1860-1944; Osiris 1, 1936):
1923-25: History of mathematics (2 vols., Boston; Isis 6, 440-44; 8, 221-25).—Revised edition 1928-30.
1929: Source book in mathematics (718 p., ill., New York; Isis 14, 268-70).

Sterner, Matthäus:
1891: Geschichte der Rechenkunst (545 p., München).

Struik, Dirk Jan:
1949: Concise history of mathematics (2 vols., 318 p., ill., New York; Isis 40, 287-89).

Suter, Heinrich (1848-1922; Isis 5, 409-17):
1873-75: Geschichte der mathematischen Wissenschaften (2 vols. in 1, 590 p., Zürich).

Taton, René:
1948: Histoire du calcul (127 p., Paris; Isis 40, 167).
1949: Le calcul méchanique (126 p., Paris; Isis 41, 395).

Tropfke, Johannes (1866-1939):
Geschichte der Elementar-Mathematik in systematischer Darstellung mit besonderer Berücksichtigung der Fachwörter.—1930: Vol. 1^3, Rechnen.—1933: Vol. 2^3, Allgemeine Arithmetik.—1937: Vol. 3^3, Proportionen, Gleichungen.—1923: Vol. 4^2, Ebene Geometrie.—1923: Vol. 5^2, Ebene Trigonometrie, Sphärik und sphärische Trigonometrie.—1924: Vol. 6^2, Analysis. Analytische Geometrie.—1924: Vol. 7^2, Stereometrie. Verzeichnisse.
First edition, 2 volumes, Leipzig 1902-3. Second edition, 7 volumes, Berlin 1921-24 (Isis 5, 182-86, 553; 6, 229; 7, 314). Third edition of volumes 1 to 3, Berlin 1930-37 (Isis 21, 451; 29, 167-69).
I cite the number of the volume with an exponent indicating the edition.

Wieleitner, Heinrich (1874-1931; Isis 18, 150-65):
1911-21: Geschichte der Mathematik von CARTESIUS bis zur Wende des 18. Jahrhunderts (2 parts, 486 p., Leipzig).
Continuation of the history by GÜNTHER.
1927-29: Mathematische Quellenbücher (4 small vols., Berlin; Isis 11, 240; 12, 413).

Zeuthen, Hieronymus Georg (1839-1920):
1896: Geschichte der Mathematik im Altertum und Mittelalter (350 p., Copenhagen).—French translation by JEAN MASCART, revised by the author (Paris 1902).
Not to be confused with an abridged ed. called Die Mathematik im Altertum und im Mittelalter (95 p. Berlin 1912; Isis 1, 719-21).
1903: Geschichte der Mathematik im XVI. und XVII. Jahrhundert (442 p., Leipzig, Teubner).

ARITHMETIC, ALGEBRA, THEORY OF NUMBERS

Brown, Richard (1856-   ):
1905: History of accounting and accountants (475 p., ill., Edinburgh).

Conant, Levi Leonard (1857-1916):
1896: The number concept; its origin and development (226 p., New York).

Dantzig, Tobias:
1930: Number, the language of science (272 p., 11 pl., New York, 1930; Isis 16, 455-59).—Second ed., revised (1933; Isis 20, 592).—Third ed. (1939; Isis 31, 475-76).—French translation (1931; Isis 18, 495).

Dickson, Leonard Eugene (1874-   ):
1919-23: History of the theory of numbers (3 vols., Carnegie Institution of Washington; Isis 3, 446-48; 4, 107-8; 6, 96-98).

Hartner, Willy:
1943: Zahlen und Zahlensystem bei Primitiv- und Hochkulturvölkern (Paideuma, Mitteilungen zur Kulturkunde, 2, 268-326, Leipzig; Isis 41, 87).

Karpinski, Louis Charles:
1925: The history of arithmetic (212 p., Chicago; Isis 8, 231-32). *See* SMITH, D. E.

Matthiessen, Ludwig (1830-1906):
1878: Grundzüge der antiken und modernen Algebra der litteralen Gleichungen (1018 p., Leipzig; 2nd ed., 1896).

Muir, Sir Thomas (1844-1934):
1906-30: The theory of determinants in historical order of development (4 vols., London 1906-23; supplement London 1930; Isis 4, 199; 16, 510).

Ore, Øystein (1899-   ):
1948: Number theory and its history (380 p., 22 fig., New York; Isis 41, 88).

Smith, David Eugene (1860-1944; Osiris 1, 1936):
1908: Rara arithmetica (524 p., 246 fig., Boston). Addenda (62 p., 20 fig., Boston 1939; Isis 32, 468).
1911 (wih L. C. KARPINSKI): The Hindu-Arabic numerals (164 p., Boston).

Yeldham, Florence A. (1877-1945):
1926: The story of reckoning in the Middle Ages (96 p., ill., London; Isis 10, 259).
1936: The teaching of arithmetic through four hundred years, 1535-1935 (143 p., ill., London; Isis 27, 92-94).

GEOMETRY

Amodeo, Federico (1859-   ):
1939: Origine e sviluppo della geometria proiettiva (175 p., Napoli).—Spanish translation (217 p., Rosario, Argentina, 1939).
1945: Sintesi storico-critica della geometria delle curve algebriche (420 p., 30 port., Napoli).

Bonola, Roberto (1874-1911):
1912: Non-Euclidean geometry, a critical and historical study of its development (280 p., Chicago).—Originally published in Italian (220 p., Bologna 1906).—German translation (Leipzig 1908, 2nd ed. 1919, 1921).—Second ed. of English translation (La Salle, Illinois, 1938).

Chasles, Michel (1793-1880; Osiris 1, 421-50):
1837: Aperçu historique sur l'origine et le développement des méthodes en géométrie (Bruxelles).—Second ed. (Paris 1875).
1870: Rapport sur les progrès de la géométrie (388 p., Paris).

Coolidge, Julian Lowell:
1940: History of geometrical methods (468 p., Clarendon Press, Oxford; Isis 33, 347-50).
1945: History of the conic sections and quadric surfaces (225 p., Clarendon Press, Oxford; Isis 37, 253).

Engel, Friedrich (1861-   ); **Stäckel, Paul** (1862-1919):
1895: Die Theorie der Parallellinien von EUKLID bis auf GAUSS (336 p., Leipzig).
1898-1913: Urkunden zur Geschichte der nichteuklidischen Geometrie (2 vols., Leipzig).

Kötter, Ernst:
1898-1901: Die Entwicklung der synthetischen Geometrie. Vol. 1, Von MONGE

bis auf STAUDT, 1847 (Jahresbericht der Deutschen Mathematiker Vereinigung, vol. 5, pt. 2, 514 p., Leipzig).

Loria, Gino (1862-   ; Osiris 7, 1939):
1921: Storia della geometrica descrittiva dalle origini sino ai giorni nostri (Milano; Isis 5, 181-82).
1931: Il passato e il presente delle principali teorie geometriche. Storie e bibliografia.—4th ed. totalmente rifatta (490 p., Padua; Isis 19, 229-31).—First ed., 1887; 2nd ed. 1897; 3rd ed., 1907. Partial English translation of 3rd ed. by G. B. HALSTED (1902-3).

Sommerville, Duncan M'Laren Young (1879-   ):
1911: Bibliography of non-Euclidean geometry, including the theory of parallels, the foundation of geometry and space of n dimensions (415 p., London).

MATHEMATICAL ANALYSIS

Boyer, Carl Benjamin (1906-   )
1939: The concepts of the calculus (352 p., New York, Columbia; Isis 32, 205-10).—Reprinted, New York 1949 (Isis 41, 87).

Casorati, Felice (1835-90):
1868: Teorica delle funzioni di variabili complesse (Vol. 1, Pavia). History of the subject down to 1865, 143 p.

Geymonat, Ludovico:
1947: Storia e filosofia dell'analisi infinitesimale (352 p., Torino).

Loria, Gino (1862-   ; Osiris 7, 1939):
1930: Curve piane speciali algebriche e trascendenti (2 vols., Milano; Isis 14, 542; 15, 467).—First published in German (2 vols.; Leipzig 1910-11).

Picard, Emile (1856-1941):
1905: Sur le développement de l'analyse et ses rapports avec diverses sciences. Conférences faites en Amérique (174 p., Paris). Partial English translation by GEORGE BRUCE HALSTED (Congress of Arts and Sciences, St. Louis 1904, vol. 1, 497-517, Boston 1905).

Todhunter, Isaac (1820-84):
1861: History of the calculus of variations during the nineteenth century (544 p., Cambridge University).

Weissenborn, Hermann (1830-96):
1856: Die Principien der höheren Analysis in ihrer Entwickelung von LEIBNIZ bis auf LAGRANGE (176 p., 3 folding pls., Halle a.S.).
See the Critical Bibliographies of Isis, Section 20. Mathematics.

STATISTICS

Information on the history of statistical methods is found in books of very different character, the two extreme kinds being the history of the calculus of probabilities at the one end and the history of statistical investigations in various countries at the other.

Funkhouser, Howard Gray:
1937: Historical development of the graphical representation of statistical data (Osiris 3, 269-404, Bruges).

Koren, John:
1918: The history of statistics. Their development and progress in many countries (785 p., New York; Isis 4, 387-89).

Meitzen, August (1822-1910):
1891: History, theory and technique of statistics (2 vols., 243 p., Philadelphia).—

Translated from the first German edition 1886; second German edition, Stuttgart 1903.

Todhunter, Isaac (1820-84):
1865: History of the mathematical theory of probability from the time of Pascal to that of Laplace (640 p., Cambridge).—Reprinted New Yoork 1931.

Walker, Helen Mary:
1929: Studies in the history of statistical method (237 p., Baltimore; Isis 13, 382-83).

Westergaard, Harald:
1932: Contributions to the history of statistics (288 p., London).
See the Critical Bibliographies of Isis, section 21. Statistics.

ASTRONOMY

Abetti, Giorgio (1882-   ):
1946: Storia dell'astronomia (370 p., 32 pl., Florence; Isis 42, 72).

Armitage, Angus (1902-   ):
1950: A century of astronomy (272 p., London).

Bailly, Jean Sylvain (1736-1793; Isis 11, 393-95):
1775: Histoire de l'astronomie ancienne depuis son origine jusqu'à l'établissement de l'école d'Alexandrie (549 p., Paris).—Second ed., 1781.
1785: Histoire de l'astronomie moderne depuis la fondation de l'école d'Alexandrie jusqu'à 1732.   New edition (3 vols., Paris).   First ed. of vol. 1, 1782.—German translation (2 vols., Leipzig 1796-97).
1787: Traité de l'astronomie indienne et orientale (607 p., Paris).

Berry, Arthur (1862-1929; Isis 28, 418-20):
1898: A short history of astronomy (470 p., ill., London).—Often reprinted, my copy is dated 1910.

Bigourdan, Guillaume (1851-1932):
1911: L'astronomie, évolution des idées et des méthodes (406 p., 50 figs., Paris).

Clerke, Agnes Mary (1842-1907):
1885: Popular history of astronomy during the nineteenth century (Edinburg).—Second ed. 1887 (518 p.); 3rd ed. 1893; 4th ed. 1902, reprinted in 1908 (505 p.).

Davidson, Martin:
1948: The stars and the mind (220 p., London; Isis 40, 386).

Delambre, Jean Baptiste Joseph (1749-1822):
1817: Histoire de l'astronomie ancienne (2 vols., Paris).
1819: Histoire de l'astronomie au Moyen âge (774 p., Paris).
1821: Histoire de l'astronomie moderne (2 vols., Paris).
1827: Histoire de l'astronomie au dix-huitième siècle (800 p., Paris).

Doig, Peter (1882-   ):
1950: Concise history of astronomy (326 p., London; Isis 42, 73).

Doublet, Edouard Lucien (1855-   ):
1922: Histoire de l'astronomie (580 p., Paris; Isis 5, 172).

Dreyer, John Louis Emil (1852-1926):
1906: History of the planetary systems from THALES to KEPLER (442 p., Cambridge University).

Duhem, Pierre (1861-1916):
1913-17: Le système du monde.   Histoire des doctrines cosmologiques de PLATON à COPERNIC (5 vols., Paris; Isis 2, 203-04; 3, 125; 26, 302-03).

Eisler, Robert (1882-1949):
1946: The royal art of astrology (296 p., 16 pl., 48 ill., London; Isis 40, 79-81).

Grant, Robert (1814-92):
1852: History of physical astronomy (657 p., London).

Houzeau, Jean Charles (1820-88); **Lancaster, Albert** (1849-1908):
1882-89: Bibliographie générale de l'astronomie (2 vols. in 3, Bruxelles).

Humbert, Pierre (1891-   ):
1948: Histoire des découvertes astronomiques (273 p., Paris).

Makemson, Maud Worcester (1891-   ):
1941: The morning star rises. An account of Polynesian astronomy (313 p., 5 fig., New Haven, Yale; Isis 34, 71).

Mitchell, Samuel Alfred (1874-   ):
1935: Eclipses of the sun (4th ed., 530 p., ill., New York; Isis 25, 496-504).— First ed. 1923, 3rd ed. 1932.

Sageret, Jules (1861-   ):
1913: Le système du monde des Chaldéens à NEWTON (280 p., ill., Paris).
1931: Le système du monde de PYTHAGORE à EDDINGTON (346 p., Paris).

Shapley, Harlow; Howarth, Helen E.:
1929: Source book in astronomy (428 p., ill., New York, Isis 13, 130-34).

Waterfield, Reginald L.:
1938: A hundred years of astronomy (526 p., London; Isis 31, 109-12).

Whitrow, G. J.:
1949: Structure of the universe. Introduction to cosmology (172 p., London).

Wolf, Rudolf (1816-1893):
1877: Geschichte der Astronomie (832 p., 36 ill., Munich).

Zinner, Ernst (1886-   ):
1925: Verzeichnis der astronomischen Handschriften des deutschen Kulturge-bietes (folio, 544 p., lithographed, München; Isis 8, 801; 15, 193-95).
1931: Die Geschichte der Sternkunde (684 p., Berlin; Isis 16, 161-67).
1941: Geschichte und Bibliographie der astronomischen Literatur in Deutschland zur Zeit der Renaissance (456 p., Leipzig; Isis 36, 261-66).
1943: Entstehung und Ausbreitung der Coppernicanischen Lehre (Sitzungsber. der Physik.-mediz. Societät zu Erlangen, 606 p., Erlangen; Isis 35, 61; 36, 261-66).
See the Critical Bibliographies of Isis, section 23. Astronomy.

PHYSICS

Books on the history of physics in general, and on special topics except those included in the following subsections entitled Mechanics, Heat and Thermodynamics, Optics, Electricity and Magnetism. Various books dealing with the history or philosophy of physical theories concern not only physics, but the physical sciences, and are listed in the sections on the Philosophy of Science, or on the History of Science.

Auerbach, Felix (1856-1933):
1910: Geschichtstafeln der Physik (150 p., Leipzig).
1923: Entwicklungsgeschichte der modernen Physik (352 p., Berlin; Isis 6, 444-47).

Buckley, H.:
1927: Short history of physics (275 p., London).

Cajori, Florian (1859-1930; Isis 17, 384-407):
    1899: History of physics in its elementary branches including the evolution of
physical laboratories (330 p., 18 ill., New York). Reprinted 1924. Revised edition
(438 p., ill. 1929).

Charbonnier, Prosper:
    1928: Essais sur l'histoire de la balistique (334 p., Paris; Isis 15, 376-80).

Chase, Carl Trueblood:
    1932: History of experimental physics (195 p., ill., New York; Isis 31, 240).
    1947: The evolution of modern physics (300 p., New York; Isis 40, 169).

Crew, Henry (1859-   ):
    1928: The rise of modern physics (471 p., Baltimore; Isis 11, 530).—Second edi-
tion (454 p., 1935; Isis 24, 449-50).

De Waard, Cornelis (1879-   ):
    1936: L'expérience barométrique. Ses antécédents et ses applications (198 p.,
1 pl., Thouars; Isis 26, 212-15).

Duckworth, W. Wilson:
    1950: A hundred years of physics (320 p., London).

Duhem, Pierre (1861-1916):
    1906-13: Etudes sur Léonard de Vinci. Ceux qu'il a lus et ceux qui l'ont lu (3
vols. Paris).
    1908: Essai sur la notion de théorie physique de PLATON à GALILÉE (144 p.,
Paris).

Einstein, Albert (1879-   ); Infeld, Leopold (1898-   ):
    1938: The evolution of physics. The growth of ideas from early concepts to
relativity and quanta (330 p., New York; Isis 30, 124-25).

Fischer, Johann Karl (1761-1833):
    1801-8: Geschichte der Physik seit Wiederherstellung der Künste und Wissen-
schaften bis auf die neuesten Zeiten (8 vols., 33 fol. pl., Göttingen).

Fraser, Charles G.:
    1948: Half hours with great scientists. The story of physics (547 p., University
of Toronto; Isis 41, 89).

Gerland, Ernst (1838-1910):
    1913: Geschichte der Physik von den ältesten Zeiten bis zum Ausgange des
achtzehnten Jahrhunderts (772 p., Munich; Isis 1, 527-29).

Gerland, Ernst; Traumüller, Friedrich (1845-1906):
    1899: Geschichte der physikalischen Experimentierkunst (458 p., 425 ill., Leip-
zig).

Heller, August (1843-1902):
    1882-84: Geschichte der Physik bis R. MAYER (2 vols., 1192 p., Stuttgart).

Hoppe, Edmund (1854-1928; Isis 13, 45-50):
    1926: Geschichte der Physik (544 p., Braunschweig; Isis 9, 571).—French trans-
lation (671 p., Paris 1928).
    1926: Geschichte der Physik (Handbuch der Physik, edited by H. GEIGER and
KARL SCHEEL, vol. 1, p. 1-179, Berlin; Isis 12, 416).
    Historical summary in chronological order, while the preceding volume written
by the same author, same title, same year, is arranged in systematic order: mechanics,
heat, light, etc.

Jeans, Sir James (1877-1946):
    1948: The growth of physical science (374 p., 9 pl., 39 fig., Cambridge Univer-
sity; Isis 40, 81).

La Cour, Poul (1846-1908); **Appel, Jakob:**
1905: Die Physik auf Grund ihrer geschichtlichen Entwicklung (2 vols., ill., Braunschweig).
The original Danish edition was published in Copenhagen (1896-97). This book is listed, because it was a remarkable attempt to teach physics by means of the history of physics.

Laue, Max von (1879-   ):
1946: Geschichte der Physik (176 p. Bonn; Isis 38, 258-60).—Second ed. 1947 (Isis 40, 169).

Magie, William Francis:
1935: A source book in physics (634 p., ill., New York; Isis 26, 176).

Massain, Robert
1948: Physique et physiciens (400 p., 52 ill., Paris; Isis 41, 89).
Anthology. First edition 1939.

Miller, Dayton Clarence (1866-1941):
1935: Anecdotal history of the science of sound (126 p., 15 pl., New York; Isis 26, 569).

Poggendorff, Johann Christian (1796-1877):
1879: Geschichte der Physik (937 p., Leipzig).
Stops at the beginning of the nineteenth century.

Rosenberger, Ferdinand (1845-99):
1882-90: Geschichte der Physik in Grundzügen mit synchronistischen Tabellen (3 vols. 1439 p., Braunschweig). Up to ca. 1880.

Schurmann, Paul F.:
1946: Historia de la fisica (2 vols., 1078 p., Buenos Aires).—First ed. Montevideo 1936 (Isis 29, 172-76).

Todhunter, Isaac (1820-84):
1886-93: History of the theory of elasticity and of the strength of materials from GALILEI to the present time. Edited and completed by KARL PEARSON (2 vols., Cambridge University).

MECHANICS, INCLUDING CELESTIAL MECHANICS

Borel, Emile (1871-   ):
1943: L'évolution de la mécanique (227 p., 26 ill., Paris).

Brunet, Pierre (1893-1950:
1938: Etude historique sur le principe de la moindre action (113 p., Paris; Isis 33, 329-34).

Chapuis, Alfred (1880-   ); **Gélis, Edouard:**
1928: Le monde des automates. Etude historique et technique (2 vols., 700 p., Neuchâtel).

Dircks, Henry (1806-73):
1861: Perpetuum mobile, or Search for self-motive power during the seventeenth, eighteenth and nineteenth centuries (600 p., London).
1870: Perpetuum mobile, or a History of the search for self-motive power from the thirteenth to the nineteenth centuries. Second series (400 p., London).

Dühring, Eugen Karl (1833-1921):
1873: Kritische Geschichte der allgemeinen Principien der Mechanik (544 p., Berlin).—Second ed., 582 p., 1877.—Third ed., 638 p., 1887.

Dugas, René:
1950: Histoire de la mécanique (650 p., 116 fig., Neuchatel; Isis 42).

Duhem, Pierre (1861-1916):
1905: L'évolution de la mécanique (348 p., Paris).
1905-6: Origines de la statique (2 vols., Paris).

Einstein, Albrecht:
1922: The meaning of relativity. Four lectures delivered at Princeton University, May 1921 (128 p., Princeton).—New ed. 141 p., Princeton 1945 (Isis 36, 203; 37, 254).

Frank, Philipp (1884-   ):
1950: Relativity, a richer truth (158 p., Boston).

Gent, Werner (1878-   ):
1926: Die Philosophie des Raumes und der Zeit. Die Geschichte der Begriffe des Raumes und der Zeit von ARISTOTELES bis zum vorkritischen KANT, 1768 (285 p., Bonn; Isis 10, 261).
1934: Das Problem der Zeit (200 p., Frankfurt a.M.).

Girvin, Harvey F.:
1948: Historical appraisal of mechanics (284 p., Scranton, Pennsylvania; Isis 40, 168).

Gunn, John Alexander (1896-   ):
1929: The problem of time, an historical and critical study (460 p., London).

Haas, Arthur Erich (1884-   ):
1914: Die Grundgleichungen der Mechanik, dargestellt auf Grund der geschichtlichen Entwicklung (220 p., 45 fig., Leipzig).

Hertz, Heinrich (1857-94):
1899: The principles of mechanics presented in a new form (304 p., London).
The German text appeared in HERTZ's Gesammelte Werke (vol. 3, Leipzig 1894) with a preface by HERMANN V. HELMHOLTZ, edited by PHILIPP LENARD.

Jouguet, Emile (1871-1943):
1924: Lectures de mécanique. La mécanique enseignée par les auteurs originaux (2 parts, 577 p., Paris; Isis 7, 156-58.—First edition in 1908-9.

Jourdain, Philip Edward Bertrand (1879-1919; Isis 5, 129-33, port.):
1913: The principle of least action (84 p., reprinted from the Monist 1912, 1913, Chicago; Isis 1, 278, 527).

Lagrange, Louis (1736-1813):
1788: Méchanique analitique (quarto 524 p., Paris).
Important historical notes on p. 1-12, 122-30, 158-89, 428-37.

Lecat, Maurice (1884-   ):
1924: Bibliographie de la relativité (352 p., Bruxelles; Isis 6, 567-68).

Lorentz, Hendrik Antoon (1853-1928):
1923: The principle of relativity, a collection of original memoirs on the special and general theory (New York).—First published in German (Leipzig 1913); 3rd ed. 1920; 5th ed. 1923.

Mach, Ernst (1838-1916):
1893: The science of mechanics (Chicago).—The German original appeared in Leipzig 1889; 3rd ed. 1897; 4th, 1901; 7th, 1912. The English edition was many times revised; 2nd ed. 1902; 3rd, 1907, 4th, 1919; 5th, 1942. Supplement to third English edition by PHILIP E. B. JOURDAIN (120 p., Chicago 1915). French translation, Paris 1904.

Marcolongo, Roberto (1862-   ):
1919: Il problema dei tre corpi da NEWTON (1686) ai nostri giorni (173 p., Milano; Isis 3, 483).

Michel, J.:
1927: Mouvements perpétuels. Leur histoire et leurs particularités depuis les premières tentatives du XIIe siècle jusqu'aux engins des inventeurs modernes (60 p., 82 fig., Paris; Isis 12, 414).

Rühlmann, Moritz (1811-96):
1885: Vorträge über Geschichte der technischen Mechanik und theoretischen Maschinenlehre sowie der damit in Zusammenhand stehenden mathematischen Wissenschaften. 1. Theil. Technische Mechanik (565 p., 85 ill., portr., Leipzig).
No others published.

Schneider, Ilse (now Mrs. **Rosenthal-Schneider**):
1921: Das Raum-Zeit Problem bei KANT und EINSTEIN (78 p., Berlin., Isis 37, 255).

Todhunter, Isaac (1820-84):
1873: History of the mathematical theories of attraction and the figure of the Earth from the time of NEWTON to that of LAPLACE (2 vols., London).

Windred, G.:
1933: History of mathematical time (Isis 19, 121-53; 20, 192-219).

Wintner, Aurel:
1941: The analytical foundations of celestial mechanics (460 p., Princeton; Isis 34, 230).

HEAT—THERMODYNAMICS

Bachelard, Gaston:
1927: Etude sur l'évolution d'un problème de physique, la propagation thermique dans les solides (184 p., Paris; Isis 12, 415).

Hardin, Willett Lepley:
1899: The rise and development of the liquefaction of gases (258 p., 42 fig., New York).

Mach, Ernst (1838-1916):
1896: Die Principien der Wärmelehre historisch-kritisch entwickelt (480 p., 105 fig., Leipzig).—Second ed. 1900, 3rd ed. 1919, 4th ed. 1923.

McKie, Douglas; Heathcote, Niels H. de V.:
1935: The discovery of specific and latent heats (152 p., 6 pl., 2 fig., London; Isis 25, 227).

Matschoss, Conrad (1871-1942):
1908: Die Entwicklung der Dampfmaschine (2 vols., 37 portr., Berlin).

Meyer, Kristine (née Bjerrum):
1913: Die Entwicklung des Temperaturbegriffs im Laufe der Zeiten sowie dessen Zusammenhang mit den wechselnden Vorstellungen über die Natur der Wärme (168 p., Braunschweig).

Pictet, Raoul (1846-):
1907: Die Entwicklung der Theorien und der Verfassungsweisen bei der Herstellung der flüssigen Luft (137 p., Weimar).
1914: Evolution des procédés concernant la séparation de l'air atmosphérique en ses éléments (288 p., Genève).

Planck, Max (1858-1947):
1887: Das Prinzip der Erhaltung der Energie (260 p., Leipzig).—Second ed. 1908, 5th ed. 1924.

Rey, Abel (1873-1940):
1927: Le retour éternel et la philosophie de la physique (320 p., Paris; Isis 9, 477-79).

OPTICS

Hoppe, Edmund (1854-1928; Isis 13, 45-50, port.):
1926: Geschichte der Optik (270 p., Leipzig).

Mach, Ernest (1838-1916):
1926: The principles of physical optics (335 p., 10 pl., London).
The German original was published in Leipzig 1921 (454 p., ill.; Isis 4, 560-62).

Mallik, D. N.:
1917: Optical theories (181 p., Cambridge University).—Second ed. rev. (210 p., 1921).

Maseres, Francis (1731-1824):
1823: Scriptores optici, or a collection of tracts relating to optics.   Edited by CHARLES BABBAGE (1792-1871) (523 p., London).

Pla, Cortes:
1949: La enigma de la luz (328 p., 15 pl., 48 fig., Buenos Aires; Isis 42, 164).

Priestley, Joseph (1733-1804):
1772: History and present state of discoveries relating to vision, light and colours (828 p., pls., London).

Ronchi, Vasco:
1939: Storia della luce (217 p., Bologna; Isis 33, 294-96).

Verdet, Emile:
1869-70: Leçons d'optique physique (2 vols., 1238 p., ill., Paris; vols. 5-6 of the Oeuvres de VERDET).—Including elaborate historical notes.

Wilde, Emil (1793-1859):
1838-43: Geschichte der Optik (Berlin, 2 vols.).
Stops at Euler. The work was planned in 3 vols., but the third did not materialize.

ELECTRICITY AND MAGNETISM

Appleyard, Rollo:
1930: Pioneers of electrical communication (356 p., London).

Bauer, Edmond:
1949: L'électromagnétisme.   Hier et aujourd'hui (348 p., ill., Paris; Isis 42).

Becquerel, Antoine César (1788-1878); Becquerel, Alexandre Edmond (1820-91) (father and son):
1858: Résumé de l'histoire de l'électricité et du magnétisme (316 p., Paris).

Benjamin, Park (1849-1922):
1895: The intellectual rise in electricity (down to FRANKLIN; 612 p., New York).
—Reprinted 1898.

British Association for the Advancement of Science:
1913: Reports of the Committee on electrical standards.   A record of the history of absolute units and of Lord KELVIN's work in connection with these (807 p., Cambridge University; Isis 2, 217).

Fröhlich, O.:
1905: Die Entwicklung der elektrischen Messungen (204 p., 124 fig., Braunschweig).

Gliozzi, Mario:
1937: L'elettrologia fine al VOLTA (2 vols., 523 p., Napoli; Isis 28, 516-20).

Helm, Georg (1851-   ):
1904: Die Theorien der Elektrodynamik nach ihrer geschichtlichen Entwicklung (172 p., Leipzig).

Hoppe, Edmund (1854-1928; Isis 13, 45-50, portr.):
1884: Geschichte der Elektrizität (642 p., Leipzig).

Miller, Dayton Clarence (1866-1941):
1939: Sparks, lightning, cosmic rays.   An anecdotal history of electricity (210 p., illus., New York; Isis 32, 382-83).

Mottelay, Paul Fleury (1841-1922):
1922: Bibliographical history of electricity and magnetism, chronologically arranged (693 p., London; Isis 6, 104-7).

O'Reilly, Michael Francis (Brother **Potamian** 1847-1917) and **Walsh, James J.**:
1909: Makers of electricity (408 p., ill., New York, Fordham).

Potamian, religious name of **O'Reilly, M. F.**

Priestley, Joseph (1733-1804):
1767: History and present state of electricity with original experiments (768 p.. 7 pl., London).

Ronalds, Sir Francis (1788-1873):
1880: Catalogue of books relating to electricity, magnetism, the electric telegraph, etc. (591 p., London).

Sartiaux, Eugène; Aliamet. Maurice:
1903: Principales découvertes et publications concernant l'électricité de 1562 à 1900 (278 p., 278 fig., Paris).

Turner, Dorothy M.:
1927: Makers of science.   Electricity and magnetism (200 p., 65 ill., Oxford; Isis 10, 266).

Weaver, William Dixon (1857-1919):
1909: Catalogue of the [Schuyler Skaats] Wheeler gift of books, pamphlets and periodicals to the Library of the American Institute of Civil Electrical Engineers (2 vols., 980 p., ill., New York; Isis 6, 104-7).

Whittaker, Edmund Taylor (1873-   ):
1910: History of the theories of aether and electricity from the age of DESCARTES to the close of the nineteenth century (480 p., London; Isis 2, 222-24).

Witz, Aimé (1848-1926):
1921: L'électricité.   Ses hypothèses et ses théories successives (174 p., Louvain; Isis 5, 561).

See Critical Bibliographies of Isis, section 22. Mechanics, 24. Physics.

CHEMISTRY

Berry, Arthur John (1886-   ):
1948: Modern chemistry, some sketches of its historical development (250 p., Cambridge University).

Berthelot, Marcelin (1827-1907):
1885: Les origines de l'alchimie (465 p., Paris).—Photographic reprint 1938.
1889: Introduction à l'étude de la chimie des anciens et du moyen age (342 p., ill., Paris).—German translation (140 p., ill., Leipzig 1909).—Photographic reprint of the French original edition (Paris 1938).

Bolton, Henry Carrington (1843-1903):
1893-1904: Select bibliography of chemistry, 1482-1892 (1225 p., Washington,

Smithsonian Institution 1893). Supt. 1, 1899, 498 p.; suppt. 2, 464 p., 1904 (same publishers).

Brown, James Campbell (1843-1910):
1913: History of chemistry (574 p., 107 ill., London; Isis 1, 279-80).

Browne, Charles Albert (1870-1947):
1944: Source book of agricultural chemistry (300 p., Charonica Botanica, vol. 8, Waltham, Massachusetts; Isis 39, 149).

Bugge, Günther (*editor;* 1885-1944):
1929-30: Das Buch der grossen Chemiker (2 vols., Berlin, 1929-30; Isis 15, 298).

Colson, Albert (1853-   ):
1910: Contribution à l'étude de la chimie à propos du livre de ALBERT LADEN-BURG (130 p., Paris).

Delacre, Maurice (1862-1938):
1920: Histoire de la chimie (648 p., Paris; Isis 4, 84).

Dumas, Jean Baptiste (1800-84):
1837: Leçons sur la philosophie chimique, professées au Collège de France (430 p., Paris). Reprinted in 1878 and 1937. German translation, Berlin 1839.

Duveen, Denis I.:
1949: Bibliotheca alchemica et chemica (677 p., 16 pl., London; Isis 40, 387).

Faerber, Eduard (1892-   ):
1921: Die geschichtliche Entwicklung der Chemie (324 p., 4 pl. Berlin; Isis 5, 465-66).
The author's name is now spelled EDWARD FARBER.

Farber, Edward, *see* **Faerber, Eduard.**

Ferchl, Fritz; Süssenguth, Armin (1880-   ):
1939: A pictorial history of chemistry (222 p., London; Isis 37, 257). Translated from the German edition of 1936 (Isis 28, 262).

Ferguson, John (1837-1916; Isis 39, 60-61):
1906: Bibliotheca chemica. A catalogue of the alchemical, chemical and pharmaceutical books in the collection of the late James Young (2 vols., Glasgow).

Fester, Gustav (1886-   ):
1923: Die Entwicklung der chemischen Technik bis zu den Anfängen der Grossindustrie (234 p., Berlin; Isis 6, 89-90).

Fierz-David, Hans Eduard (1882-   ):
1945: Die Entwicklungsgeschichte der Chemie (440 p., 106 fig., 4 tables, Basel; Isis 37, 105-06).

Findlay, Alexander (1874-   ):
1937: A hundred years of chemistry (352 p., 11 fig., New York; Isis 29, 176-79). Second ed. 1948.

Forbes, Robert James:
1948: Short history of the art of distillation, from the beginnings up to the death of Cellier Blumenthal (410 p., 203 ill., Leiden; Isis 41, 131-33).

Graebe, Carl (1841-1927):
1920: Geschichte der organischen Chemie (vol. 1, to 1890, 426 p., Berlin; Isis 4, 361-65).
No others published.

Hjelt, Edvard (1855-1921):
1916: Geschichte der organischen Chemie von ältester Zeit bis zur Gegenwart (568 p., Braunschweig; Isis 3, 440-43).

Hoefer, Ferdinand (1811-78):
1866-69: Histoire de la chimie (2 vols., Paris, Didot).—First edition 1842-43.

Jaffe Bernard (1896-   ):
1930: Crucibles.   The lives and achievements of the great chemists (377 p., ill., New York).—Sixth and seventh printings 1936.—New edition under title Crucibles: the story of chemistry from ancient alchemy to nuclear fission (492 p., New York; Isis 41, 133).

Kopp, Hermann (1817-92; Osiris 5, 392-460):
1843-47: Geschichte der Chemie (4 vols.   Braunschweig).
1873: Die Entwickelung der Chemie in der neueren Zeit (876 p., München).
1886: Die Alchemie in älterer und neuerer Zeit (2 vols., Heidelberg).

Ladenburg, Albert (1842-1911):
1900: Lectures on the history of the development of chemistry since the time of LAVOISIER.   (388 p., Edinburgh, Alembic Club).—First German ed. 1869; 2nd ed., 1887; 3rd ed. 1902; 4th ed. 1907—French translation, 1907; 2nd ed. 1911; see COLSON.

Lasswitz, Kurd (1848-1910):
1890: Geschichte der Atomistik vom Mittelalter bis NEWTON (2 vols., Hamburg).

Li Ch'iao-p'ing:
1948: The chemical arts of old China (225 p., ill., Easton, Pennsylvania; Isis 40, 281).

Lieben, Fritz (1890-   ):
1935: Geschichte der physiologischen Chemie (752 p., Leipzig; Isis 25, 164-66).

Lippmann, Edmund O. von (1857-1940; Osiris 3):
1919-31: Entstehung und Ausbreitung der Alchemie.   Mit einem Anhange: Zur älteren Geschichte der Metalle (758 p., 1919; Berlin; Isis 3, 302-05).   Zweiter Band, Ein Lese- und Nachschlage-Buch (266 p., Berlin 1931; Isis 16, 462-63).
1921: Zeittafeln zur Geschichte der organischen Chemie, 1500-1890 (76 p., Berlin; Isis 4, 548).

Lowry, Thomas Martin (1874-1936):
1915: Historical introduction to chemistry (596 p., 57 ill. London).—Third ed. 596 p., 57 ill., 1936.

Lüdy, Fritz, Jr.:
1928: Alchemistische und chemische Zeichen (57 p., 127 pl., Gesellschaft für Geschichte der Pharmazie; Isis 13, 232).

Mabilleau, Léopold (1853-   ):
1895: Histoire de la philosophie atomistique (568 p., Paris).

Meyer, Ernst von (1847-1916):
1891: History of chemistry (578 p., London).—The original German text appeared in Leipzig 1889.—2nd German ed., 1895; 3rd, 1905, 4th, 1914 (630 p., Leipzig; Isis 4, 360-61).—Second ed. of English translation 1898, 3rd, 1906.

Mittasch, Alwin (1869-   ):
1939: Kurze Geschichte der Katalyse in Praxis und Theorie (148 p., Berlin; Isis 32, 389).

Moore, Forris Jewett (1867-1926):
1918: History of chemistry (306 p., New York; Isis 4, 193).—Second ed. 1931. 3rd ed. 1939 (Isis 32, 384).

Ostwald, Wilhelm (1853-1932):
  1896: Elektrochemie, ihre Geschichte und Lehre (1166 p., ill., Leipzig).
  1906: Leitlinien der Chemie (313 p., Leipzig).—French translation (Paris 1909).

Muir, Matthew Moncrieff Pattison (1848-   ):
  1907: History of chemical theories and laws (575 p., New York).

Partington, James Riddick (1886-   ):
  1935: Origins and development of applied chemistry (610 p., London; Isis 25, 504-07).
  1937: A short history of chemistry (400 p., ill., New York; Isis 29, 179-81).

Ramsay, Sir William (1852-1916):
  1896: The gases of the atmosphere, the history of their discovery (248 p., 7 portr., London).—Second ed. 1902; 3rd ed. 309 p., 8 portr., 1905.

Read, John (1884-   ):
  1937: Prelude to chemistry. An outline of alchemy, its literature and relationship (344 p., ill., New York; Isis 27, 528-31).
  1947: The alchemist in life, literature and art (112 p., London).
  1947: Humour and humanism in chemistry (411 p., ill., London).

Schmieder, Karl Christoph (1778-1850):
  1832: Geschichte der Alchemie (623 p., Halle).
  Facsimile reprint with preface by FRANZ STRUNZ, München-Planegg 1927.

Singer, Charles:
  1948: The earliest chemical industry. An essay in the historical relations of economics and technology illustrated from the alum trade (folio 352 p., ill., London; Isis 41, 128-31).

Smith, Henry Monmouth
  1949: Torchbearers of chemistry (270 p., 253 ill., New York; Isis 41, 90).

Soddy, Frederick (1877-   ):
  1949: The story of atomic energy (144 p., London).

Stillman, John Maxon (1852-1923; Isis 34, 142-46):
  1924: The story of early chemistry (580 p., New York; Isis 7, 295).

Taylor, Frank Sherwood (1897-   ):
  1949: The alchemists. Founders of modern chemistry (256 p., ill., New York; Isis 41, 237).

Testi, Gino (1892-   ):
  1950: Dizionario di alchimia e di chimica antiquaria (202 p., Roma).

Thorpe, Sir (Thomas) Edward (1845-1925):
  1894: Essays in historical chemistry (392 p. London).—Second ed. 1902, 3rd ed. 1911, reprinted 1923 (614 p.).
  1909-10: History of chemistry (2 small vols., New York).

Venable, Francis Preston (1856-1934):
  1894: Short history of chemistry (172 p., Boston). 2nd ed. 1896, 3rd 1901, reprinted 1909.

Weeks, Mary Elvira (1892-   ):
  1945: Discovery of the elements. Fifth edition (592 p., Journal of chemical education, Easton, Pennsylvania; Isis 36, 227).—First edition 1933 (366 p.; Isis 21, 455); 2nd ed., 1934; 3rd ed., 1935; 4th ed. 1939 (Isis 32, 386-89).

White, John Henry:
1932: History of the phlogiston theory (192 p., London; Isis 19, 593).
See the Critical Bibliographies of Isis, section 25. Chemistry.

TECHNOLOGY, "INVENTIONS"

Beckmann, Johann (1739-1811):
1797-180?: History of inventions and discoveries (4 vols., London).—Second
ed., 4 vols., 1814; 3rd ed., 4 vols., 1817; 4th ed., 2 vols., 1846.—German original,
Beiträge zur Geschichte der Erfindungen (5 vols., Leipzig 1780, 1786-1805).

Cressy, Edward:
1937: A hundred years of mechanical engineering (340 p., 64 pl., New York;
Isis 31, 94-95).

Ducassé, Pierre:
1945: Histoire des techniques (136 p., Paris; Isis 36, 228).

Feldhaus, Franz Maria (1874-   ):
1910: Ruhmesblätter der Technik von den Urfindungen bis zur Gegenwart
(639 p., 232 fig., Leipzig).
1914: Die Technik der Vorzeit, der geschichtlichen Zeit und der Naturvölker.
(xvi p., 1400 col., 873 ill., Leipzig).
1931: Die Technik der Antike und des Mittelalters (442 p., 452 ill., 15 pl., Potsdam; Isis 16, 167-69).

Fleming, Arthur Percy Morris; Brocklehurst, Harold John Stanley:
1925: History of engineering (320 p., London).

Forbes, Robert James:
1950: Man the maker. History of technology and engineering (376 p., ill., New
York; Isis 42, 79).

Gilfillan, Seabury Columba (1889-   ):
1935: Inventing the ship. Study of the inventions made in her history between floating log and rotorship (294 p., 80 fig., Chicago; Isis 24, 450-53).
1935: The sociology of invention (204 p., Chicago; Isis 25, 166-67).

Kaempffert, Waldemar (1877-   ):
1924: Popular history of American inventions (2 vols., New York).

Karmarsch, Karl:
1872: Geschichte der Technologie seit der Mitte des 18. Jahrhunderts (940 p.,
Munich).

Knight, Edward Henry (1824-83):
1874-77: American mechanical dictionary. A description of tools, instruments,
machines, processes and engineering; history of inventions, general technological
vocabulary (3 vols., 2831 p., 7000 ill., New York).
1882-84: New Mechanical dictionary. A supplement to the former work (1 vol.
in 4 parts, 968 p., 2549 ill., 56 pl., Boston).
These almost forgotten volumes contain an immense amount of valuable information. The author was a patent attorney of English birth (DAB 10, 464).

Kraemer, Hans (1870-   ) (editor):
1902-04: Weltall und Menschheit. Geschichte der Erforschung der Natur und
der Verwertung der Naturkräfte im Dienste der Völker (5 vols., Berlin).

Mason, Otis Tufton (1838-1908):
1895: The origins of invention. A study of industry among primitive peoples
(419 p., ill., London).

Neuburger, Albert (1867-   ):
1930: The technical arts and sciences of the ancients (550 p., 676 ill., London).
—German original, Leipzig 1919; 2nd ed. 1921 (Isis 4, 423; 6, 129-31).

Neudeck, Georg (1866-   ):
1923: Geschichte der Technik (496 p., 550 ill., Stuttgart; Isis 6, 129-31).

Parsons, William Barclay (1859-1932):
1939: Engineers and engineering in the Renaissance (681 p., ill., Baltimore; Isis 32, 354-56).

Rogers, Agnes (1893-   ):
1941: From man to machine. A pictorial history of invention (quarto, 160 p., ill., Boston).

Straub, Hans (1892-   ):
1949: Die Geschichte der Bauingenieurkunst (300 p., 78 fig., 32 pl., Basel).

Thompson, Holland (1873-1940):
1921: The age of invention; a chronicle of mechanical conquest (280 p., ill., New Haven, Yale; Isis 4, 517-19).

Thurston, Robert Henry (1839-1903):
1939: History of the growth of the steam engine. Centennial edition. With a supplementary chapter by WILLIAM NICHOLS BARNARD (568 p., 181 figures, Ithaca; Isis 32, 473).—First published in 1878; 2nd ed. 1884; 3rd ed. 1893; 4th ed. 1897.

Uccelli, Arturo (1889-   ) (*editor*):
1944: Storia della tecnica dal medio evo ai nostri giorni (946 p., 30.5 cm., 2717 ill., Milano; Isis 41, 91).—Reprinted in 1945.
1946: Scienza e tecnica del tempo nostro nei principii e nelle applicazioni (30.5 cm., 846 p., 2137 ill., 6 pl. Milano; Isis 41, 85).

Usher, Abbot Payson (1883-   ):
1929: History of mechanical inventions (412 p., New York; Isis 24, 177-80).—Spanish translation (Mexico 1941; Isis 34, 272).
See Critical Bibliographies of Isis, section 26. Technology.

NAVIGATION

Köster, August (1873-   ):
1923: Das antike Seewesen (254 p., 104 ill., Berlin).
1934: Studien zur Geschichte des antiken Seewesens (Klio, Beiheft 32; 156 p., 1 pl., 16 fig., Leipzig).

Lefebvre des Noëttes, Richard (1856-   ):
1935: De la marine antique à la marine moderne. La révolution du gouvernail. Contribution à l'histoire de l'esclavage (152 p., Paris; Isis 26, 484-86).

Marguet, Frédéric (1874-1951):
1931: Histoire générale de la navigation du XV° au XX° siècle (306 p., ill., Paris; Isis 19, 235-37).

Stevenson, William (1772-1829):
1824: Historical sketch of the progress of discovery, navigation and commerce, from the earliest records to the beginning of the nineteenth century (644 p., Edinburgh).

METROLOGY

A few older books in chronological order:—

Pasi, Bartolommeo di:
1540: Tariffa de i pesi e misure correspondenti dal levante all ponente (200 f., Venice).

Cappel, Jacques (1570-1624):
1606-07: De ponderibus nummis et mensuris libri V (Frankfurt a. M.).

Roberts, Lewes (1596-1640):
1638: The merchants mappe of commerce (London).

Paucton, Alexis Jean Pierre (1732-98):
1780: Métrologie (970 p., tables, 26 cm., Paris).

More recent books in alphabetical order:—

Bigourdan, Guillaume (1851-1932):
1901: Le système métrique des poids et mesures (464 p., ill., Paris).

Decourdemanche, Jean Adolphe (1844-1914?):
1909: Traité pratique des poids et mesures des peuples anciens et des Arabes (152 p., Paris).
1913: Traité des monnaies, mesures et poids anciens et modernes de l'Inde et de la Chine (172 p., Paris).

Döring, Eduard:
1862: Handbuch der Münz-, Wechsel-, Mass- und Gewichtskunde (2. verm. Aufl., 543 p., Coblenz).

Doursther, Horace:
1840: Dictionnaire universel des poids et mesures anciens et modernes (610 p., Bruxelles).

Favre, Adrien:
1931: Les origines du système métrique (252 p., Paris; Isis 16, 449-50).

Hultsch, Friedrich (1833-1906):
1862: Griechische und römische Metrologie (328 p., Berlin).—Second ed. much enlarged (760 p., Berlin 1882).

Kennelly, Arthur Edwin (1861-1939):
1928: Vestiges of pre-metric weights and measures persisting in metric Europa (200 p., New York; Isis 24, 272).

Klimpert, Richard (1847-   ):
1896: Lexikon der Münzen, Masse, Gewichte, Zählarten und Zeitgrössen aller Länder der Erde (2. verm. Aufl., Berlin).—First ed., Berlin 1885.

Lemale, Alexis Guislain:
1875: Monnaies, poids, mesures et usages commerciaux de tous les états du monde (2nd ed. ref., 394 p., Paris).

Miles, George Carpenter (1904-):
1948: Early Arabic glass weights and stamps (176 p., American Numismatic Society, New York; Isis 40, 381).

Nicholson, Edward:
1912: Men and measures. A history of weights and measures (325 p., London).

Petrie, Sir Flinders (1853-1942):
1877: Inductive metrology, or, The recovery of ancient measures from the monuments (166 p., London).

Robertson, Eben William (1815-74):
1872: Historical essays in connection with the land, the church, etc. (342 p. Edinburgh).—Deals with standards of the past in weight and currency, land measurements in Great Britain and Ireland.

Thomas, Edward (1813-86):
1874: Ancient Indian weights (82 p., London).

Vázquez Queipo, Vicente (1804-93):
1859: Essai sur les systèmes métriques et monétaires des anciens peuples depuis les premiers temps historiques jusqu'à la fin du Khalifat d'Orient (3 vol. in 4, 24 cm., Paris).

Viedebantt, Oskar (1883-   ):
1923: Antike Gewichtsnormen und Münzfüsse (172 p., Berlin).

Woolhouse, Wesley Stoker Barker (1809-93):
1890: Measures, weights and moneys of all nations (7th ed. rev., 300 p., London) 2nd ed. 1859, 6th 1881.

CHRONOMETRY AND HOROLOGY

Archer, Peter (S. J.):
1941: The Christian calendar and the Gregorian reform (135 p., New York).

Bassermann-Jordan, Ernst von (1876-   ) (editor):
1920-25: Die Geschichte der Zeitmessung und der Uhren (folio, Berlin). This work is listed here though it remained very incomplete. As far as I know, only three volumes were published.—B I, B, LUDWIG BORCHARDT: Altägyptische Zeitmessung (70 p., 18 pl., 25 fig., 1920; Isis 4, 612).—B I, E, JOSEPH DRECKER: Theorie der Sonnenuhren (112 p., 140 ill., 1925; Isis 11, 241.—B I, F, KARL SCHOY: Gnomonik der Araber (95 p., 30 fig., 1923; Isis 5, 534).

Cunynghame, Sir Henry Hardinge (1848-1935):
1906: Time and clocks. (200 p., 82 ill., New York).

Ginzel, Friedrich Karl (1850-1926):
1906-14: Handbuch der mathematischen und technischen Chronologie. Das Zeitrechnungswesen der Völker (3 vols. Leipzig).
1906: Vol. 1, Zeitrechnung der Babylonier, Ägypter, Mohammedaner, Perser, Inder, Südostasiaten, Chinesen, Japaner und Zentralamerikaner (596 p., 6 fig., tables and map).
1911: Vol. 2, Zeitrechnung der Juden, der Naturvölker, der Römer und Griechen, sowie Nachträge zum 1. Bande (604 p.).
1914: Vol. 3, Zeitrechnung der Makedonier, Kleinasier und Syrier, der Germanen und Kelten, des Mittelalters, der Byzantiner (und Russen), Armenier, Kopten, Abessinier, Zeitrechnung der neureren Zeit, sowie Nachträge zu den drei Bänden (452 p., 6 fig., 1 pl., chronological tables).

Gould, Rupert Thomas (1890-   ):
1923: The marine chronometer, its history and development (304 p., 39 pl., 85 fig., London; Isis 6, 122-29).

Milham, Willis Isbister (1874-   ):
1923: Time and timekeepers (629 p., 339 fig. New York; Isis 7, 347).—Reprinted 1941.

Robertson, John Drummond (1857-   ):
1931: The evolution of clockwork, with a special section on the clocks of Japan (374 p., 101 ill., London; Isis 27, 179).

Saunier, Claudius (1816-1896):
1902-04: Die Geschichte der Zeitmesskunst (1118 p., 216 ill., Bautzen).—
Translated from the French.

Ungerer, Alfred:
1931: Les horloges astronomiques et monumentales les plus remarquables
(514 p., ill., Strasbourg).

PHOTOGRAPHY

Eder, Josef Maria (1855-   ):
1945: History of photography. Translated by EDWARD EPSTEAN (880 p., New
York, Columbia University; Isis 37, 103-04).—Translated from the German,
Geschichte der Photographie, 3rd ed. 1905; 4th 1932.

Moholy, Lucia:
1939: A hundred years of photography (182 p., 40 ill., Harmondsworth, Pelican;
Isis 32, 471).

Newhall, Beaumont:
1938: Photography. A short critical history (220 p., incl. 95 pl., New York,
Museum of Modern Art; Isis 30, 127-128).—First ed. 1937.

Potonniée, Georges:
1925: Histoire de la découverte de la photographie (322 p., ill., Paris; Isis 8,
511-13).
1936: English translation by EDWARD EPSTEAN (282 p., New York).

Rohr, Moritz von (1868-1940):
1899: Theorie und Geschichte des photographischen Objectivs (455 p., 148 fig.,
Berlin).

GENERAL BIOLOGY AND NATURAL HISTORY

Almquist, Ernst Bernhard (1852-   ):
1931: Grosse Biologen, eine Geschichte der Biologie und ihrer Erforscher (143 p.,
23 port., Munich; Isis 18, 206-07).

Anker, Jean; Dahl, Svend:
1938: Werdegang der Biologie (312 p., 8 pl., Leipzig).—The original Danish
edition appeared in 1934.

Aschoff, Ludwig (1866-1942); **Küster, E.; Schmidt, W. J.:**
1938: Hundert Jahre Zellforschung (296 p., Berlin; Isis 32, 393-94).

Bates, Marston (1906-   ):
1950: The nature of natural history (310 p., New York; Isis 42, 164).

Blainville, Henri de (1777-1850):
1845: Histoire des sciences de l'organisation et de leurs progrès comme base de
la philosophie (3 vols., Paris).

Böhner, Konrad:
1933-35: Geschichte der Cecidologie. Mit einer Vorgeschichte von FELIX VON
ÖFELE (2 vols., Gesellschaft für Geschichte der Pharmazie, Mittenwald, Bayern;
Isis 24, 180-83).

Brewster, Edwin Tenney (1866-   ):
1927: Creation. History of non-evolutionary theories (295 p., ill., Indianapolis;
Isis 9, 462-65).

Clay, Reginald S.; Court, Thomas H.:
1932: History of the microscope up to the introduction of the achromatic microscope (280 p., 164 fig. London; Isis 21, 227-30).

Clodd, Edward (1840-1930):
1897: Pioneers of evolution from THALES to HUXLEY (260 p., London).

Conn, Harold Joel (*editor*) (1886-   ):
1933: History of staining (141 p., Geneva, N. Y.; Isis 22, 403).

Daudin, Henri (1881-1947):
1926: Etudes d'histoire des sciences naturelles.—I. De LINNÉ à JUSSIEU. Méthodes de la classification et idée de série en botanique et en zoologie, 1740-90 (266 p.).—II. CUVIER et LAMARCK. Les classes zoologiques et l'idée de série animale (2 vols., 811 p., in all 3 vols., Paris; Isis 10, 502-05).

Disney, Alfred N.; with Hill, Cyril F. and Baker, Wilfred F. Watson:
1928: Origin and development of the microscope (303 p., 30 pl., 36 fig. Royal Microscopical Society, London; Isis 20, 495-97).

Guyénot, Emile (1885-   ):
1941:L'évolution de la pensée scientifique. Les sciences de la vie au XVIIe et XVIIIe siècles. L'idée d'évolution (484 p., Paris).

Locy, William Albert (1857-1924):
1908: Biology and its makers (495 p., ill., New York).—Third ed. rev. (504 p., ill., London, 1915).
1925: The growth of biology. Zoology from ARISTOTLE to CUVIER. Botany from THEOPHRASTOS to HOFMEISTER. Physiology from HARVEY to CLAUDE BERNARD (496 p., ill., London; Isis 8, 513-14).

Meyer-Abich, Adolf:
1934: Ideen und Ideale der biologischen Erkenntnis (Bios 1; 215 p.; Leipzig; Isis 22, 546-48).

Miall, Louis Compton (1842-1921)
1912: The early naturalists. Their lives and work, 1530-1789 (408 p., London).

Nordenskiöld, Erik (1872-1933) (Isis 38, 103-06, portr.)
1928: History of biology (656 p., ill., New York; Isis 12, 336-40).—Reprinted 1932, 1935. First published in Swedish (3 vols., Stockholm 1920-24), then in German (661 p., Jena 1926).

Osborn, Henry Fairfield:
1896: From the Greeks to DARWIN. Outline of the development of the evolution idea (269 p., Columbia University Press, New York).— First printing 1894.
1929: Second ed. (414 p., New York; Isis 13, 386-88).

Peattie, Donald Culross:
1936: Green laurels. The lives and achievements of the great naturalists (392 p., 30 pl., New York; Isis 27, 95).

Pemberton, Henry (1826-1911):
1902: The path of evolution through ancient thought and modern science (403 p., Philadelphia).

Rádl, Emanuel (1873-1942):
1905-1909. Geschichte der biologischen Theorien (2 vols., Leipzig).—Revised ed. of vol. 1, 1913.
1930: History of biological theories (420 p., New York; Isis 15, 195-96).—This is an English translation and adaptation of the German text in vol. 2 (107-580).

Schmidt, Eduard Oscar (1823-86):
1875: The doctrine of descent and Darwinism (340 p., ill., London).—German

original ed. Leipzig 1873. The English translation was reprinted in 1877, 1882, 1888, 1896.

Singer, Charles (1876-   ):
1931: The story of living things. A short account of the evolution of the biological sciences (607 p., ill., New York; Isis 22, 298-300).—The English edition of the same book was entitled:—
1931: A short history of biology. A general introduction to the study of living things (607 p., ill., Oxford, Clarendon).
The two editions are otherwise identical.
1950: History of biology (Revised edition of same work under third title, 579 p., 194 figs., New York; Isis 42, 82).

Zirkle, Conway (1895-   ):
1941: Natural selection before the "Origin of Species" (Proc., American Philosophical Society 84, 71-123; Isis 33, 403).
1946: Early history of the idea of inheritance of acquired characters and of pangenesis (Trans., American Philosophical Society 35, 91-151; Isis 37, 259).
See the Critical Bibliographies of Isis, section 27. Biology.

BOTANY AND AGRICULTURE

Arber, Agnes (Mrs. E. A. Newell Arber; Agnes Robertson) (1879-   ):
1938: Herbals, their origin and evolution, 1470-1670. New edition rewritten (360 p., 27 pl., 131 fig., Cambridge University Press; Isis 30, 131-32).—The first edition, much smaller, appeared in 1912 (Isis 1, 281-82).
1950: The natural philosophy of plant form (260 p., ill., Cambridge University; Isis 41, 322-23).

Aslin, Mary S.:
1926: Catalogue of the printed books on agriculture 1471-1840. Rothamsted Experimental Station Library (332 p., Rothamsted, England; Isis 9, 578).

Fischer, Hermann (1884-   ):
1929: Mittelalterliche Pflanzenkunde (334 p., 70 ill., München; Isis 15, 367-70).

Gager, Charles Stuart (1872-1943):
1937: Botanic gardens in the world. Materials for a history. Brooklyn Botanic Garden Record (26, 149-353; Isis 29, 185).

Gibault, Georges:
1912: Histoire des légumes (412 p., Paris).

Gras, Norman Scott Brien (1884-   ):
1940: History of agriculture in Europe and America (2nd ed., 496 p., New York; Isis 33, 81).—First ed. 1925, 461 p.
Deals only with the economic, not the botanic, aspects of agriculture.

Green, Joseph Reynolds (1848-1914):
1909: History of botany, 1860-1900, being a continuation of SACHS' History (543 p., Oxford, Clarendon).

Greene, Edward Lee (1843-1915):
1909: Landmarks of botanical history. Vol. 1 to 1562. (330 p., Washington, Smithsonian Institution).
No others published, though much was ready in MS when GREENE died.

Guérin, L.
1869: Précis de l'histoire de la botanique par L. G. (535 p., Paris).
Volume 17 of Le règne végétal edited by ARISTIDE DUPUIS, FRÉDÉRIC GÉRARD, OSCAR RÉVEIL, etc. (17 vols., ill., Paris 1864-69). About authorship, see SARTON, Query 124 (Isis 41, 54); the author is not LOUIS GÉRARD.

Haller, Albrecht v. (1708-77):
1771-72: Bibliotheca botanica. Quae scripta ad rem herbariam facientia a rerum initiis recensentur (2 vols., London).
1908: *Idem.* Index emendatus. Perfecit J. CHRISTIAN BAY. Ad diem natalem Alberti de Haller ante hos ducentos annos Bernae nati celebrandum . . . edidit Societas bernensis rerum naturae peritorum (57 p., Bern). With preface in German.

Harvey-Gibson, Robert John (1860-   ):
1919: Outlines of the history of botany (284 p., London; Isis 3, 297-99).

Jessen, Karl Friedrich Wilhelm (1821-89):
1864: Botanik der Gegenwart und Vorzeit in culturhistorischer Entwicklung (517 p., Leipzig).
Photographic reprint by Chronica Botanica, Waltham, Massachusetts, 1948 (Isis 40, 82).

Joret, Charles (1839-1914):
1897-1904: Les plantes dans l'antiquité et au moyen âge; histoire, usages et symbolisme (vol. 1, 520 p., Paris 1897; vol. 2, 672 p., 1904).
Not completed. The parts published deal only with classical antiquity, the ancient Near East, Iran and India.

Large, Ernest Charles:
1940: The advance of the fungi. (488 p., ill., New York; Isis 34, 231-32).

Lotsy, Johannes Paulus (1867-   ):
1906-08: Vorlesungen über Descendenztheorien mit besonderer Berücksichtigung der botanischen Seite der Frage (2 vols., ill., Jena).

Lütjeharms, Wilhelm Jan:
1936: Zur Geschichte der Mykologie. Das XVIII. Jahrhundert (284 p., 2 pl., Gouda; Isis 34, 78).
The book deals with a larger field than the title suggests; it is not restricted to the eighteenth century.

Marzell, Heinrich (1885-   ):
1922: Unsere Heilpflanzen, ihre Geschichte und ihre Stellung in der Volkskunde (268 p., 38 ill., Freiburg im Breisgau; Isis 5, 456-57).

Meyer, Ernst Heinrich Friedrich (1791-1858):
1854-57: Geschichte der Botanik (4 vols., Königsberg).

Möbius, Martin (1859-   ):
1937: Geschichte der Botanik (464 p., Jena; Isis 30, 304-06).

Pickering, Charles (1805-78):
1879: Chronological history of plants. Man's record of his own existence illustrated through their names, uses and companionship (quarto, 1238 p., Boston).
PICKERING devoted the last 16 years of his life to this immense and fantastic compilation which is quoted here, because it may possibly be of some use to certain scholars.

Pritzel, Georg August (1815-74):
1851: Thesaurus literaturae botanicae omnium gentium, inde a rerum botanicorum initiis ad nostra usque tempora quindecim millia operum recensens (555 p., Leipzig).
Editio nova reformata (580 p., Leipzig 1872-77). The second part of the book was edited after the author's death by KARL JESSEN. The Editio nova was reprinted in 1924 and again recently in Milan.

Reed, Howard Sprague (1876-1950):
   1942: Short history of the plant sciences (325 p., ill., Waltham, Mass.; Isis 34, 36).

Roberts, Herbert Fuller (1870-   ):
   1929: Plant hybridization before Mendel (390 p., ill., Princeton University).

Sachs, Julius von (1832-97):
   1890: History of botany, 1530-1860.   (583 p., Oxford, Clarendon).
   The original German ed. was published in Munich 1875.   The English translation was reprinted in 1906.   For continuation, see GREEN.

Salaman, Redcliffe Nathan (1874-   ):
   1949: History and social influence of the potato (710 p., 32 pl., Cambridge University; Isis 42, 85).

Sprengel, Kurt Polycarp Joachim (1766-1833):
   1817-18: Geschichte der Botanik (2 vols., Altenburg).
   Revised edition of his work first published in Latin, Historia rei herbariae (Amsterdam 1807-08).

Tolkowsky, Samuel (1886-   ):
   1938: Hesperides.   History of the culture and use of citrus fruits (391 p., 113 pl., 10 fig. London; Isis 31, 249).

Weevers, Theodorus (1875-   ):
   1949: Fifty years of plant physiology (320 p., Amsterdam; Isis 42, 165).

Whetzel, Herbert Hice (1877-1945):
   1918: Outline of the history of phytopathology (130 p., ill., Philadelphia; Isis 5, 461-64).

Zirkle, Conway:
   1935: The beginnings of plant hybridization (244 p., ill., Philadelphia; Isis 25, 507-08).
   See the Critical Bibliographies of Isis, section 28. Botany.

ZOOLOGY

Anker, Jean (1892-   ):
   1938: Bird books and bird art.   Outline of the literary history and iconography of descriptive ornithology (Quarto 270 p., ill., Copenhagen; Isis 33, 155).

Bodenheimer, Friedrich Simon (1897-   ):
   1928-29: Materialien zur Geschichte der Entomologie (2 vols., 1000 p., ill., Berlin; Isis 13, 388-92; 14, 454-56).

Boubier, Maurice:
   1925: L'évolution de l'ornithologie (310 p., Paris; Isis 8, 515-17).

Carus, Julius Victor (1823-1903):
   1872: Geschichte der Zoologie bis auf JOH. MÜLLER und CHARL. DARWIN (752 p., Munich).
   1880: Histoire de la zoologie (632 p., Paris).

Cole, Francis Joseph (1872-   ):
   1926: History of protozoology (64 p., London; Isis 9, 198).
   1930: Early theories of sexual generation (240 p., ill., Oxford, Clarendon; Isis 16, 463-65).

Dean, Bashford (1867-1928):
   1916-23: Bibliography of fishes (3 vols., American Museum of Natural History, New York; Isis 6, 456-59).

Vol. 3 contains pre-Linnaean literature compiled by EUGENE WILLIS GUDGER, and an elaborate index.

Essig, Edward Oliver (1884-   ):
    1931: History of entomology (1039 p., 263 fig., New York; Isis 17, 447-50).
    1936: Sketch history of entomology (Osiris 2, 80-123).

Gubernatis, Angelo de (1840-1913):
    1872: Zoological mythology (2 vols., London).

Gudger, Eugene Willis (1866-   ):
    See DEAN, B.

Gurney, John Henry (1848-1922):
    1921: Early annals of ornithology (244 p., ill., London; Isis 4, 646).

Howard, Leland Ossian (1857-1950):
    1930: History of applied entomology, somewhat anecdotal (572 p., 51 pl.; Washington, Smithsonian Institution; Isis 16, 169-73).

Loisel, Gustave (1864-   ):
    1912: Histoire des ménageries de l'antiquité à nos jours (3 vols., Paris).

Oudemans, Anthonie Cornelius (1858-1943):[96]
    1926-37: Kritisch-historisch overzicht der acarologie (to 1850; in Dutch, 9 parts, 4797 p., ill., The Hague; Isis 15, 381-86; 27, 182; 28, 206, 271).

Pellett, Frank Chapman (1879-   ):
    1938: History of American beekeeping (222 p., Ames, Iowa).

Perrier, Edmond (1844-1921):
    1896: La philosophie zoologique avant Darwin (3rd ed., 304 p., Paris).—First ed., 1884.

Radcliffe, William (1856-   ):
    1921: Fishing from the earliest times (496 p., ill.; Isis 4, 568-71).

Ransome, Hilda M.:
    1937: The sacred bee in ancient times and folklore (308 p., 12 pl., 35 fig., London; Isis 28, 271).

Romanoff (Alexis Lawrence and Anastasia J.):
    1949: The avian egg (932 p., 424 ill., New York; Isis 41, 134).

Ruch, Theodore Cedric (1906-   ):
    1941: Bibliographia primatologica, a classified bibliography of primates other than man (268 p., Yale Medical Library no. 4; Springfield, Illinois, Isis 34, 79).

Strong, Reuben Myron (1872-   ):
    1939-46: Bibliography of birds (3 vols., Chicago, Field Museum; Isis 39, 23).

Wood, Casey Albert (1856-1942):
    1931: Introduction to the literature of vertebrate zoology. Based chiefly on the titles of various libraries in McGill University, Montreal (quarto, 663 p., London; Isis 18, 207).

Zimmer, John Todd (1889-   ):
    1926: Catalogue of the EDWARD E. AYER ornithological library (2 vols., 716 p., 12 pl., Chicago Field Museum; Isis 10, 94).
    See the Critical Bibliographies of Isis, section 29. Zoology.

---

[96] The dates given in Isis (21, 577), 1831-95, are wrong. They refer to his namesake (I believe, his father).

GEODESY AND GEOGRAPHY

Baker, John Norman Leonard:
1931: History of geographical discovery and exploration (544 p., ill., London; Isis 19, 601).

Beazley, Sir Charles Raymond (1868-   ):
1897-1906: The dawn of modern geography (3 vols., London).

Brown, Lloyd Arnold:
1949: The story of maps (417 p., ill.; Boston; Isis 41, 243).

Dickinson, Robert Eric (1905-   ); **Howarth, O. J. R.:**
1933: The making of geography (268 p., 5 pl., 30 fig., Oxford, Clarendon; Isis 23, 294-95).

Dussieux, Louis (1815-94) (*editor*):
1882-83: Les grands faits de l'histoire de la géographie. Recueil de documents (5 vols., Paris).

Günther, Siegmund (1848-1923):
1904: Geschichte der Erdkunde (355 p., Leipzig).

Heawood, Edward (1863-1949):
1912: History of geographical discovery in the seventeenth and eighteenth centuries (488 p., ill., Cambridge University Press).

Hennig, Richard (1874-   ):
1936-39: Terrae incognitae. Eine Zusammenstellung und kritische Bewertung der wichtigsten vorcolumbischen Entdeckungsreisen an Hand der darüber vorliegenden Originalberichte (4 vols., Leiden; Isis 29, 188-89, 537).

Herdman, Sir William Abbott (1858-1924):
1923: Founders of oceanography. An introduction to the science of the sea (352 p., ill., London; Isis 6, 91-95).

Hugues, Luigi (1836-   ):
1903: Cronologia delle scoperte e delle esplorazioni geografiche dall' anno 1492 a tutto il secolo XIX (496 p., Milano).

Keltie, John Scott (1840-1927); **Howarth, Osbert John Radcliffe** (1877-   ):
1913: History of geography (215 p., ill., New York).

Kimble, George Herbert Tinley (1908-   ):
1938: Geography in the Middle Ages (284 p., 20 pl., London; Isis 30, 540-42).

La Roncière, Charles de (1870-1941):
1939: Histoire de la découverte de la terre, explorateurs et conquérants (312 p., 586 photos., 8 pl., Paris).

Markham, Sir Clements Robert (1830-1916):
1921: The lands of silence. History of Arctic and Antarctic exploration (551 p., ill., Cambridge University Press; Isis 4, 365-67).

Mirsky, Jeannette (1903-   ):
1934: To the North! The story of Arctic exploration (306 p., 16 pl., 13 maps, 9 fig. New York; Isis 33, 483-85).
The English edition of the same book was entitled Northern conquest (406 p., ill., London 1934).—Revised edition under the title To the Arctic! (374 p., ill., New York, 1948).

Nansen, Fridtjof (1861-1930):
1911: In northern mists. History of Arctic exploration in early times (2 vols., ill., London).

Nordenskiöld, Adolf Erik (1832-1901):
1897: Periplus. Early history of charts and sailing directions (folio 218 p., 100 ill., 60 maps, Stockholm).

Olsen, Ørjan (1855-   ):
1933-37: La conquête de la terre (6 vols., Paris).—Original Norwegian edition (6 vols., Oslo 1929-31; Isis 27, 532-34).

Perrier, Georges (1872-1946):
1939: Petite histoire de la géodésie. Comment l'homme a mesuré et pesé la Terre (188 p., Paris; Isis 36, 231).

Peschel, Oscar (1826-75):
1877: Geschichte der Geographie bis auf ALEXANDER VON HUMBOLDT und CARL RITTER (854 p., ill., Munich).—First ed. 1865 (726 p.).

Phillips, Philip Lee (1857-1924):
1909-20: A list of geographical atlases in the Library of Congress. 4 vols. U. S. Government Printing Office, Washington.—1909: Vol. 1, Atlases, xiv + 1208 p.— 1909: Vol. 2, Author list; index, p. 1209-1659.—1914: Vol. 3, Supplement, titles 3266-4087, cxxxvii + 1030 p.—1920: Vol. 4, Second supplement, titles 4088-5324, clviii + 639 p.
Vol. 4 includes author list and index to the whole work, all the titles listed being numbered consecutively from 1 to 5324.

Segal, Louis (1887-   ):
1939: The conquest of the Arctic (284 p., London; Isis 32, 398).

Stefansson, Vilhjalmur (*editor*):
1947: Great adventures and explorations, as told by the explorers themselves. With the collaboration of OLIVE RATHBUN WILCOX (788 p., ill., maps, New York; Isis 39, 124).

Stevenson, Edward Luther (1859-1944):
1921: Terrestrial and celestial globes (2 vols., New Haven, Yale; Isis 4, 549-53).

Sykes, Sir Percy Molesworth (1867-1945):
1950: History of exploration from the earliest times to the present day (3rd ed., 440 p., New York).
1st ed., 388 p., 25 pl., London 1934; Isis 26, 580; 2nd ed., 1936.

Thomson, James Oliver:
1948: History of ancient geography (438 p., Cambridge University; Isis 41, 244).

Tozer, Henry Fanshawe (1829-1916):
1897: History of ancient geography (406 p., 10 maps, Cambridge University Press).
1935: Second ed. with notes by MAX CARY (same text plus 34 p. of notes).

Vivien de Saint Martin, Louis (1802-97):
1873-74: Histoire de la géographie et des découvertes géographiques (632 p., atlas of 13 pl., Paris).

Weule, Karl (1864-1926):
1904: Geschichte der Erdkenntnis und der geographischen Forschung (448 p., 40 pl., 190 ill., Berlin).

See the Critical Bibliographies of Isis, sections 30. Geodesy, 31. Geography and Oceanography.

GEOLOGY, MINERALOGY, PALAEONTOLOGY

Adams, Frank Dawson (1859-1942):
1938: The birth and development of the geological sciences (510 p., 14 pl., Baltimore; Isis 32, 218-20).

Brewster, Edwin Tenney (1866-   ):
1928: This puzzling planet. The earth's unfinished story; How men have read it in the past and the wayfarer may read it now (328 p., ill., Indianapolis; Isis 12, 341-43).

Cline, Walter:
1937: Mining and metallurgy in Negro Africa (155 p., Menasha, Wisconsin; Isis 28, 522-28).

Davison, Charles (1858-1940):
1927: The founders of seismology (254 p., Cambridge University; Isis 11, 254).

Geikie, Sir Archibald (1835-1924):
1905: The founders of geology. (2. ed. much increased, 498 p.; London).—
First edition (307 p., London 1897; Baltimore 1901).

Groth, Paul von (1843-1927):
1926: Entwicklungsgeschichte der mineralogischen Wissenschaften (266 p., 5 fig., Berlin).

Kobell, Franz von (1803-82):
1864: Geschichte der Mineralogie, 1650-1860 (720 p., 50 fig., Munich).

Launay, Louis de (1860-1938):
1905: La science géologique. Ses méthodes, ses résultats, ses problèmes, son histoire (750 p., Paris).
1908: La conquête minérale (390 p., Paris).

Mather, Kirtley F.; Mason, Shirley L.:
1939: A source book in geology (724 p., New York; Isis 31, 578).

Margerie, Emmanuel de (1862-   ):
1896: Catalogue des bibliographies géologiques (754 p., Paris).
1943-48: Critique et géologie. Contribution à l'histoire des sciences de la terre (4 vols. Paris; Isis 36, 74-75; 38, 263; 40, 390).

Metzger, Hélène (1889-1944):
1918: La genèse de la science des cristaux (248 p., Paris; Isis 3, 445-46).

Meunier, Stanislas (1843-1925):
1911: L'évolution des théories géologiques (364 p., Paris).

Montessus de Ballore, Fernand de (1851-1923):
1923: Ethnographie sismique et volcanique, ou Les tremblements de terre et les volcans dans la religion la mythologie et le folklore de tous les peuples (214 p., Paris).

Rickard, Thomas Arthur (1864-   ):
1932: Man and metals. History of mining in relation to the development of civilization (2 vols., 1080 p., ill., New York; Isis 21, 334-36).

Tertsch, Hermann (1880-   ):
1947: Das Geheimnis der Kristallwelt (391 p., 12 pl., 48 fig., Wien).

Zittel, Karl Alfred von (1839-1904):
1901: History of geology and palaeontology to the end of the nineteenth century (575 p., 13 port., London).
Translation of the German original text (Munich 1899).
See the Critical Bibliographies of Isis, section 32. Geology.

METEOROLOGY

Gilbert, Otto (1839-   ):
1907: Die meteorologischen Theorien des griechischen Altertums (750 p., Leipzig).

Hellmann, Gustav (1854-1934):
1883: Reportorium der deutschen Meteorologie (22 p., 996 col., Leipzig).
1921: Die Meteorologie in den deutschen Flugschriften und Flugblättern des 16. Jahrhunderts (96 p., Berlin; Isis 5, 224).
1914-22: Beiträge zur Geschichte der Meteorologie (15 parts in 3 vols., Berlin; Isis, vols. 4 and 7, passim).

Shaw, Sir William Napier (1854-1945):
1926: Manual of meteorology. Vol. 1. Meteorology in history (359 p., 18 pl., Cambridge University Press).—New edition in 1932, reprinted in 1942.
See Critical Bibliographies of Isis, section 33. Meteorology.

ANATOMY AND PHYSIOLOGY

Bastholm, E.:
1950: History of muscle physiology (Acta historica scientiarum naturalium, vol. 7,257 p. Copenhagen; Isis 42).

Choulant, Ludwig (1791-1861):
1920: History and bibliography of anatomic illustration in its relation to anatomic science and the graphic arts. Translated and edited by MORTIMER FRANK (quarto, 463 p., ill., Chicago; Isis 4, 357-59).
The original German edition appeared in 1852.

Cole, Francis Joseph (1872-   ):
1944: History of comparative anatomy from ARISTOTLE to the eighteenth century. (532 p., ill., London; Isis 37, 112-14; 38, 264-66).

Curtis-Bennett, Sir Noel:
1949: The food of the people (320 p., 30 fig., London).

Duval, Mathias (1844-1907):
1898: Histoire de l'anatomie plastique. Les maîtres, les livres et les écorchés (364 p., 118 ill., Paris).

Foster, Sir Michael (1836-1907):
1901: Lectures on the history of physiology during the sixteenth, seventeenth, and eighteenth centuries (310 p., Cambridge University).
These lectures were first delivered at the Cooper Medical College, San Francisco, 1900.

Franklin, Kenneth James (1897-   ):
1949: Short history of physiology (140 p., 16 ill., London; Isis 41, 404). First edition 1933 (Isis 24, 283).

Fulton, John Farquhar (1899-   ):
1930: Selected readings in the history of physiology (337 p., Springfield, Illinois; Isis 15, 386-88).
1931: Physiology (Clio Medica 5, 158 p., 8 ill., New York; Isis 16, 174-76).

Haller, Albrecht von (1708-77):
1774-77: Bibliotheca anatomica. Quae scripta ad anatomen et physiologiam facientia a rerum initiis recensentur (2 vols., Zürich).

Holländer, Eugen (1867-   ):
1921: Wunder, Wundergeburt und Wundergestalt in Einblattdrucken des 15. bis 18. Jahrhunderts (quarto, 390 p., 202 ill., Stuttgart; Isis 4, 506-07).

Hyrtl, Joseph (1811-94):
1835: Antiquitates anatomicae rariores (121 p., Wien).

Meyer, Arthur William (1873-   ):
1939: The rise of embryology (384 p., Stanford University; Isis 32, 396-98, 478).

Mondor, Henri (1885-   ):
1949: Anatomistes et chirurgiens (546 p., Paris).

Needham, Joseph (1900-   ):
1934: History of embryology (292 p., ill., Cambridge; Isis 27, 98-102).

Neuburger, Max (1868-   ):
1897: Die historische Entwicklung der experimentellen Gehirn- und Rücken-marksphysiologie vor FLOURENS (387 p., Stuttgart).

Schmidt, Eduard Oscar (1823-1886):
1855: Die Entwicklung der vergleichenden Anatomie (146 p., Jena).

Singer, Charles (1876-   ):
1926: Evolution of anatomy. Short history of anatomical and physiological discovery to HARVEY (New York; Isis 10, 521-24).

Wegner, Richard N.:
1939: Das Anatomenbildnis. Seine Entwicklung im Zusammenhang mit der anatomischen Abbildung (199 p., 105 fig., Basel).

Weindler, Fritz:
1908: Geschichte der gynäkologisch-anatomischen Abbildung (202 p., 122 ill., Dresden).

Willius, Frederick Arthur; Dry, Thomas J.:
1948: History of the heart and the circulation (474 p., ill., Philadelphia; Isis 40,392).
See Critical Bibliographies of Isis, sections 34. Anatomy, 35. Physiology.

ANTHROPOLOGY, ETHNOLOGY, FOLKLORE

For books dealing with the beginnings of definite sciences, say, astronomy or medicine, see the bibliographies relative to those sciences.

Casson, Stanley (1889-1944):
1939: The discovery of man. The story of the inquiry into human origins (339 p., ill., London; Isis 33, 302-03).

Count, Earl Wendel (1899-   ):
1950: This is race, an anthology selected from the international literature on the races of man (775 p., New York; Isis 41, 403).

Dieserud, Juul:
1908: Scope and content of the science of anthropology. Historical review, library classification and select, annotated bibliography (200 p., Chicago).

Haddon, Alfred Cort (1855-1940; Isis 35, 36-37):
1910: History of anthropology (226 p., ill., London).
1934: Revised edition in the Thinker's Library, no. 42 (158 p., ill., London; Isis 25, 291).

Kroeber, Alfred Louis (1876-   ):
1944: Configurations of culture growth (892 p., Berkeley, Calif.; Isis 37, 118-19).

Lowie, Robert Harry (1883-   ):
1937: History of ethnological theory (308 p., New York; Isis 29, 475-77).

Muehlmann, Wilhelm Emil (1904-   ):
1948: Geschichte der Anthropologie (274 p., Bonn; Isis 41, 403).

Penniman, Thomas Kenneth:
1935: A hundred years of anthropology (400 p., London; Isis 26, 229-32)

Quatrefages, Armand de (1810-92):
1867: Rapport sur les progrès de l'anthropologie (574 p., Paris).

Thompson, Stith (1885-   ):
1932-36: Motif-index of folk-literature. A classification of narrative elements in folktales, ballads, myths, fables, mediaeval romances, examples, fabliaux, jest-books and local legends (6 vols. Indiana University, Bloomington, Indiana; Isis 20, 607; 28. 602).
1946: The folktale (520 p., New York; Isis 37, 267).

See the Critical Bibliographies of Isis, sections 35. Physical Anthropology, 39. Prehistory, 40. Ethnology, 41. Superstition and Occultism.

PSYCHOLOGY

Baldwin, James Mark (1861-1934):
1913: History of psychology (2 small vols. New York).

Boring, Edwin Garrigues (1886-   ):
1929: History of experimental psychology (715 p., New York). Revised ed. (777 p., New York 1950).
1942: Sensation and perception in the history of experimental psychology (660 p., New York).

Brett, George Sidney (1879-1944; Isis 36, 110-14):
1912-21: History of psychology (3 vols., London; Isis 4, 376-78).

Dennis, Wayne (1905-   ) (*editor*):
1948: Readings in the history of psychology (598 p., tables, New York).

Dessoir, Max (1867-   ):
1912: Outlines of the history of psychology (308 p., New York).—German original (Heidelberg 1911).

Flügel, John Carl (1884-   ):
1933: A hundred years of psychology, 1833-1933 (384 p., New York; Isis 23, 597).

Hall, Granville Stanley (1844-1924):
1912: Founders of modern psychology (475 p., New York).—Reprinted 1924.

Hulin, Wilbur Schofield (1899-   ):
1934: Short history of psychology (195 p., New York).

Klemm, Otto (1884-   ):
1914: History of psychology (394 p., New York).—German original edition (398 p., Berlin 1911).

Mercier, Désiré (cardinal, 1851-1926):
1918: Origins of contemporary psychology (New York).—French original ed. (498 p., Louvain 1897); 2nd ed. 1908.

Müller-Freienfels, Richard (1882-   ):
1935: Evolution of modern psychology (New Haven, Yale).—German original ed. (Leipzig 1929).

Murphy, Gardner (1895-   ):
1929: Historical introduction to modern psychology (New York).—Rev. ed. 1949 (480 p., New York).

Pillsbury, Walter Bowers (1872-   ):
1929: History of psychology (326 p., New York).
See the Critical Bibliographies of Isis, section 37. Psychology.

PHILOSOPHY

Out of a great many books only a few could be listed here for the convenience not of the historian of philosophy but rather of the historian of science.

Alexander, Archibald Browning Drysdale (1855-1931):
1907: Short history of philosophy (624 p., Glasgow).—Second enlarged ed. (664 p., Glasgow 1922), reprinted 1934.

Bréhier, Emile (1876-   ):
1926-38: Histoire de la philosophie (8 parts, Paris; Isis 19, 557, etc.).

De Wulf, Maurice (1867-1947):
1909: History of medieval philosophy (532 p., London).—New ed., 2 vol. 1926, 3rd ed. 1935-38.—Original French ed. Louvain (488 p., 1900), 6th ed. 3 vols. Louvain 1934-47.

Fischer, Kuno (1824-1907):
1854-77: Geschichte der neuern Philosophie (6 vols., Mannheim). Second ed. (6 vols., Heidelberg 1865-77). Later ed. (10 vols., Heidelberg 1897-1911).

Fuller, Benjamin Apthorp Gould (1879-   ):
1938: History of philosophy (2 pts. 1105 p., New York).—Rev. ed. 1945 (1000 p.).

Gilson, Etienne (1884-   ):
1922: La philosophie au Moyen âge (2 small vols. 326 p., Paris; Isis 5, 537).—Second ed. revised and much increased (782 p., Paris 1944).
1936: The spirit of mediaeval philosophy (Gifford Lectures 1931-32, 500 p., New York).—Original French ed. (299 p., Paris 1932); 2nd ed. (450 p., Paris 1944).

Høffding, Harald (1843-1931):
1900-8: History of modern philosophy (2 vols. London).—Reprinted 1915, 1924.
—First published in Danish (2 vols. Copenhagen 1894-95).
1915: Modern philosophers (320 p., London).—Lectures delivered in Copenhagen in 1902, 1913.

Masson-Oursel, Paul (1882-   ):
1926: Comparative philosophy (218 p., London).—French original, Paris 1923 (Isis 6, 99-104).

Papillon, Fernand (1847-74):
1876: Histoire de la philosophie moderne dans ses rapports avec le développement des sciences de la nature. Ouvrage posthume, publié par CHARLES LÉVÊQUE, avec une notice biographique (2 vols., 830 p., Paris).
Remarkable work written by a very young man under the influence of LEIBNIZ.

Picavet, François (1851-1921):
1905: Esquisse d'une histoire générale et comparée des philosophies médiévales (400 p., Paris).

Russell, Bertrand Arthur William (1872-   ):
1945: History of Western philosophy (918 p., New York; Isis 38, 268-70).

Sortais, Gaston (S. J.):
1912: Histoire de la philosophie ancienne (645 p., Paris).
Extends to the Renaissance, included.
1920-22: La philosophie moderne depuis BACON jusqu'à LEIBNIZ (2 vols. Paris).

Incomplete.   The author deals with the sixteenth century then with BACON, GAS-
SENDI and HOBBES.

Ueberweg, Friedrich (1826-71):
    1863-66: Grundriss der Geschichte der Philosophie von Thales bis auf die Gegen-
wart (3 vols., Berlin).
    Many editions more and more elaborate.   12th ed. in 5 vols. 1923-28.   The 4th
ed. was translated into English (2 vols., New York 1871-73; reprinted 1903).   For
up-to-date information, one must refer to the German text.

Weber, Alfred (1835-1914):
    1896: History of philosophy.   Translated from the 5th French ed.   (642 p., New
York).—New edition of that translation completed by RALPH BARTON PERRY (628
p., New York 1925).—First French ed. (610 p., Paris 1872); 9th ed. 1925.
    See the Critical Bibliographies of Isis, section 48. Philosophy.

MEDICINE

    History of general medicine and also of a few medical branches, except Dentis-
try, Epidemics, Gynaecology and Obstetrics, Pharmacy, Veterinary Medicine, dealt
with separately below.

Artelt, Walter (1906-   ):
    1949: Einführung in die Medizinhistorisk.   Ihr Wesen, ihre Arbeitsweise und
ihre Hilfsmittel.   (248 p., Stuttgart; Isis 42).

Baas, Johann Hermann (1838-1909):
    1889: Outlines of the history of medicine and the medical profession (1183 p.,
New York).
    The original German edition appeared in Stuttgart, 1876.
    1896: Die geschichtliche Entwicklung des ärztlichen Standes und der medizini-
schen Wissenschaften (492 p., ill., Berlin).

Bartels, Max (1843-1904):
    1893: Die Medizin der Naturvölker (373 p., 175 ill., Leipzig).

Buck, Albert Henry (1842-1922):
    1917: The growth of medicine to 1800 (600 p., ill., New Haven).
    1920: The dawn of modern medicine (308 p., ill., New Haven).—Deals with
XVIII (2), XIX (1).

Bullock, William (1868-1941):
    1938: History of bacteriology (434 p., ill., London; Isis 31, 480-82).

Castiglioni, Arturo (1874-   ; Isis 36, 61; 38, 131):
    1927: Storia della medicina (972 p., 389 fig., Milano; Isis 13, 251).
    1931: Histoire de la médecine (781 p., 279 fig., Paris; Isis 16, 468-71).
    1936: Storia della medicina (857 p., ill., Milano; Isis 27, 536-38).
    1941: History of medicine (1036 p., 40 pl., New York).—Revised edition (1283
p., New York 1947).
    1948: Storia della medicina (revised ed. in 2 vols., 1018 p., 516 fig., 10 col. pl.,
Verona).

Choulant, Johann Ludwig (1791-1861):
    1828: Handbuch der Bücherkunde für die ältere Medizin (212 p., Leipzig), 2nd
ed. (455 p., Leipzig 1841).   Anastatic reprint of that edition (München 1926).
    1842: Bibliotheca medico-historica; sive, Catalogus librorum historicum de re
medica et scientia naturali systematicus (279 p., Leipzig).

Cumston, Charles Greene (1868-1928):
    1926: Introduction to the history of medicine to the end of the eighteenth cen-
tury (422 p., 24 pl., London; Isis 10, 303).

Cushing, Harvey (1869-1939; Isis 37, 92-93):
1943: The Harvey Cushing Collection of books and manuscripts (223 p., New York; Isis 35, 338-41).

Daremberg, Charles Victor (1817-72):
1865: La médecine, histoire et doctrines. Second ed. (516 p., Paris).
1870. Histoire des sciences médicales (2 vols., Paris).

Desnos, Ernest (1852-   ):
1914: Histoire de l'urologie (Encyclopédie française d'urologie, tome 1, 294 p., ill., Paris; Isis 2, 466).

Diepgen, Paul (1878-   ):
1913-28: Geschichte der Medizin (5 little vols. of the Sammlung Göschen, Berlin).
1949: Geschichte der Medizin. Die historische Entwicklung der Heilkunde und des ärztlichen Lebens. 1. Band. Von den Anfängen bis zur Mitte des 18. Jahrhunderts (355 p., 29 fig., Berlin 1949; Isis 42, 166).

Dock, Lavinia L.:
1920: Short history of nursing (New York).—Second ed. 1925; 3rd ed. 1931 (418 p.; Isis 4, 635).
Abridgment of the history of nursing by NUTTING and DOCK.

Dumesnil, René (1879-   ); **Bonnet-Roy, Flavien** (editors):
1947: Les médecins célèbres (quarto, 372 p., ill., Genève).

Duncum, Barbara M.:
1947: Development of inhalation anaesthesia (656 p., ill., Wellcome Museum, London; Isis 38, 131-33).

Freind, John (1675-1728) (Isis 27, 453-71; 29, 100):
1725-26: History of physick to the beginning of the sixteenth century (2 vols., London).—Vol. 1, 1725 is a 2nd ed. corrected; 4th ed. (2 vols. 1750).

Galdston, Iago (editor):
1949: Social medicine (310 p., New York; Isis 40, 397).

Garrison, Fielding Hudson (1870-1935):
1913: Introduction to the history of medicine (763 p., Philadelphia).—Third ed. 1921 (942 p., 237 fig., Philadelphia; Isis 4, 554-56); 4th ed. 1929 (996 p., 286 fig., Philadelphia; Isis 13, 137-38).

Graham, Harvey:
1939: The story of surgery (425 p., 23 pl., New York; Isis 32, 489).
GRAHAM is the pseudonym of an English physician ISAAC HARVEY FLACK (1912-   ).

Grasset, Hector:
1911: La médecine naturiste à travers les siècles. Histoire de la physiothérapie (468 p., Paris).

Gurlt, Ernst Julius (1825-1899):
1898: Geschichte der Chirurgie (3 vols., Berlin).

Guthrie, Douglas (1885-   ):
1945: History of medicine (464 p., 72 pl., London).

Haagensen, Cushman Davis (1900-   ); **Lloyd, Wyndham Edward Buckley:**
1943: A hundred years of medicine. New edition (456 p., New York).—First ed. 1936, by LLOYD alone.

Haeser, Heinrich (1811-84):
1845: Lehrbuch der Geschichte der Medizin und der Volkskrankheiten (955 p.,

Jena).—Second ed. (2 vols. Jena 1853-65); 3rd ed. (3 vols. Jena 1875-82).   Vol. 1, 1875, antiquity and middle ages; vol. 2, 1881, modern times; vol. 3, 1882 epidemics.

Haller, Albrecht von (1708-77):
1774-75: Bibliotheca chirurgica.   Quae scripta ad artem chirurgicam facientia a rerum initiis recensentur (2 vols. Bern).   Vol. 1, to 1710; vol. 2, 1710 to 1774.
1776-88: Bibliotheca medicinae practicae, Quae scripta ad partem medicinae practicam facientia a rerum initiis . . . recensentur (4 vols., Bern).

Harley, George Way:
1941: Native African medicine (310 p., Cambridge, Mass.; Isis 34, 187-89).

Hemmeter, John Conrad (1864-1931):
1927: Master minds in medicine (794 p., ill., New York).

Herrick, James Bryan (1861-   ):
1942: Short history of cardiology (274 p., 48 pl., Springfield, Illinois; Isis 34, 530).

Hirschberg, Julius (1843-1925):
1899-1915: Geschichte der Augenheilkunde (Leipzig).
Published passim in the Graefe-Saemisch Handbuch der gesamten Augenheilkunde.

Höfler, Max (1848-1914):
1908: Die volksmedizinische Organotherapie und ihr Verhältnis zum Kultopfer (310 p., Stuttgart).

Holländer, Eugen (1867-   ):
1903: Die Medizin in der klassischen Malerei (288 p., 165 ill., 30 cm., Stuttgart).
—Second ed. 1913 (497 p., ill., Stuttgart); 3rd ed. 1923 (502 p., 307 ill. Stuttgart).
1905: Die Karikatur und Satire in der Medizin.   Mediko-kunsthistorische Studie (370 p., 223 ill., 30 cm., Stuttgart).—Second ed. 1921 (420 p., 11 pl., 251 fig., Stuttgart; Isis 4, 370).
1912: Plastik und Medizin (584 p., 434 ill., Stuttgart).
1928: Äskulap und Venus (495 p., 330 ill., Berlin; Isis 11, 560).

Hovorka, Oskar von (1866-   ):
1915: Geist der Medizin.   Analytische Studien über die Grundideen der Vormedizin, Urmedizin, Volksmedizin, Zaubermedizin, Berufsmedizin (372 p., Wien; Isis 4, 202).

Hovorka, Oskar von; Kronfeld, A. (*editors*):
1908-9: Vergleichende Volksmedizin (2 vols., Stuttgart).

Hübotter, Franz:
1920: 3000 Jahre Medizin (Quarto, 536 p., ill. handwriting mimeographed, Berlin; Isis 4, 369-70).

Keys, Thomas Edward (1908-   ):
1945: The history of surgical anesthesia (221 p., New York; Isis 37, 122).

Laignel-Lavastine, Maxime (1875-   ) (*editor*):
1936-49: Histoire générale de la médecine, de la pharmacie, de l'art dentaire et de l'art véterinaire (quarto, 3 vols., richly ill., Paris).

Libby, Walter (1867-   ):
1922: History of medicine in its salient features (438 p., 9 pl., Boston; Isis 5, 478-79).

Long, Esmond Ray (1890-   ):
1928: History of pathology (315 p., Baltimore; Isis 12, 436).
1929: Selected readings in pathology from HIPPOCRATES to VIRCHOW (315 p., 25 pl., Springfield, Illinois; Isis 15, 490).

Major, Ralph Hermon (1884-   ):
1932: Classic descriptions of disease (660 p., 127 ill., Springfield, Illinois; Isis 19, 518-20).—Third ed. (711 p., 1945; Isis 36, 237).

Mettler, Cecilia Charlotte (1909-43):
1947: History of medicine. A correlative text arranged according to subjects (1244 p., 16 ill., Philadelphia; Isis 40, 88-90).

Meunier, Louis (1870-   ):
1911: Histoire de la médecine (648 p., Paris).

Meyer-Steineg, Theodor (1873-   ); **Sudhoff, Karl:**
1921: Geschichte der Medizin im Überblick mit Abbildungen (444 p., 208 ill., Jena; Isis 4, 368).—Second ed. 1922 (450 p., ill., Jena; Isis 5, 188). 3rd ed., 1928.

Neuburger, Max (1868-   ):
1901-5: (editor with JULIUS PAGEL). Handbuch der Geschichte der Medizin (3 vols., Jena).
Elaborate textbook of medical history founded by THEODOR PUSCHMANN (1847-99). Vol. 1, 1902. Antiquity and Middle Ages, vols. 2-3, 1903-5. Modern times.
1906-11: Geschichte der Medizin (2 vols., Stuttgart).—To the fifteenth century, no others published.
1910-25: History of medicine (2 vols., London; Isis 9, 486-89).—Partial and revised translation of the German text.

Nutting, Mary Adelaide (1858-   ); **Dock, Lavinia L.:**
1907-12: History of nursing (4 vols., New York).

Osler, Sir William (1849-1919; Isis 8, 358-61):
1921: The evolution of modern medicine. Yale lectures (260 p., ill., New Haven; Isis 4, 556-57).
1929: Bibliotheca Osleriana, a catalogue of books illustrating the history of medicine and of science (822 p., Oxford).

Pagel, Julius Leopold (1851-1912):
1898: Geschichte der Medizin (2 vols., Berlin).
1908: Zeittafeln zur Geschichte der Medizin (Berlin).
1915: Einführung in die Geschichte der Medizin. 2te. Aufl. durchgesehen durch KARL SUDHOFF (632 p., Berlin; Isis 4, 202).
1922: Third ed. appearing under SUDHOFF's name (542 p., Berlin; Isis 5, 188).
See NEUBURGER, above.

Pazzini, Adalberto:
1947: Storia della medicina (2 vols., ill., Milano).

Politzer, Adam (1835-1920):
1907-13: Geschichte der Ohrenheilkunde (2 vols., Stuttgart).

Power, Sir D'Arcy (1855-1941):
1923: Chronologia medica (282 p., ill., London).

Pusey, William Allen (1865-1940):
1933: History of dermatology (240 p., ill., Springfield, Illinois; Isis 20, 504-05).

Rosen, George:
1943: History of miners' diseases (490 p., ill., New York; Isis 36, 239).
1947 (with BEATE CASPARI-ROSEN): 400 Years of a doctor's life (446 p., New York; Isis 39, 130).

Ruhräh, John (1872-1935):
1925: Pediatrics of the past (617 p., 18 pl. 54 fig., New York; Isis 8, 386-88).

Sand, René:
    1948: Vers la médecine sociale (672 p., Paris; Isis 40, 90).

Schullian, Dorothy M.; Schoen, Max (editors):
    1948: Music and medicine (509 p., 18 ill., New York; Isis 40, 299).

Schwalbe, Ernst:
    1905: Vorlesungen über Geschichte der Medizin (Jena).—Second ed. 1909; 3rd
ed. 1920 (191 p.; Isis 4, 557).—Very simplified account.

Scott, Henry Harold:
    1939: History of tropical medicine (2 vols., London; Isis 32, 490).

Shryock, Richard Harrison (1893-   ):
    1936: The development of modern medicine, an interpretation of the social and
scientific factors involved (458 p., 7 ill., Philadelphia; Isis 27, 538-39).
    1947: American medical research, past and present (364 p., New York; Isis 39,
201-02).

Sigerist, Henry Ernest (1891-   ):
    1933: The great doctors (436 p., New York).—Translated from the German
(München 1932).
    1951: History of medicine (vol. 1, 586 p., 104 ill., New York; Isis 42).
    Work to be completed in 8 volumes. Vol. 1 deals with primitive and archaic
(Egyptian, Mesopotamian) medicine.

Singer, Charles (1876-   ):
    1928: Short history of medicine (392 p., 142 ill., Oxford, Clarendon Press; Isis
13, 254).

Sprengel, Kurt Polykarp Joachim (1766-1833):
    1821-37: Versuch einer pragmatischen Geschichte der Arzneykunde (3rd ed.,
6 vols. in 7, Halle). 4th ed. of vol. 1 (662 p., Leipzig 1846).

Sudhoff, Karl (1853-1938):
    1922: Kurzes Handbuch der Geschichte der Medizin. 3. und 4. Auflage von
J. L. PAGELS Einführung (542 p., Berlin; Isis 5, 188).
    Wrote two treatises on the history of medicine, the first in collaboration with
MEYER-STEINEG, the second in the form of a revised edition of PAGEL's treatise. *See*
notes on MEYER-STEINEG and PAGEL.

Thompson, Charles John Samuel (1862-1943):
    1928: The quacks of old London (356 p., London).

Vierordt, Hermann (1853-1943):
    1916: Medizin-geschichtliches Hilfsbuch mit besonderer Berücksichtigung der
Entdeckungsgeschichte und der Biographie (469 p., Tübingen; Isis 3, 365).

Walsh, James Joseph (1865-1942):
    1912: Psychotherapy, including the history of the use of mental influence . . .
in healing . . . (821 p., New York).—Revised ed. (875 p., New York, 1923).

Weyl, Theodor (1851-1913):
    1904: Zur Geschichte der sozialen Hygiene (Handbuch der Hygiene, 4. Supp.
Bd., 791-1046, 8 ill., 2 pl., Jena).
    1910: Histoire de l'hygiène sociale (480 p., 8 ill., 2 pl., Paris).—French transla-
tion of the German work.

Willius, Frederick Arthur:
    1941 (with THOMAS E. KEYES): Cardiac classics. A collection of classic works
on the heart and circulation (878 p., St. Louis).
    1948 (with THOMAS J. DRY): History of the heart and the circulation (456 p.,
170 ill., Philadelphia).

Wise, Thomas Alexander (1801-89):
1867: Review of the history of medicine (2 vols., London).
Running title: History of medicine among the Asiatics.

Withington, Edward Theodore:
1894: Medical history from the earliest times (432 p., London).

Wright, Jonathan (1860-1928):
1914: History of laryngology and rhinology.—Second ed. revised (358 p., Philadelphia).

DENTISTRY

Geist-Jacobi, George Pierce:
1896: Geschichte der Zahnheilkunde (262 p., ill., Tübingen).

Guerini, Vincenzo:
1909: A history of dentistry until the end of the eighteenth century (355 p., 104 fig., 20 pl., Philadelphia).

Koch, Charles Rudolph Edward (*editor*):
1909: History of dental surgery (2 vols., Chicago).

Lufkin, Arthur Ward:
1948: History of dentistry (*2nd* ed. rev., 367 p., 104 ill., Philadelphia).—First ed. 1938 (255 p., 90 ill.).

Sudhoff, Karl (1853-1938):
1926: Geschichte der Zahnheilkunde (*2nd* ed., 230 p., 134 fig., Leipzig; Isis 9, 599). First ed., 1921.

Weinberger, Bernhard Wolf:
1948: Introduction to the history of dentistry (2 vols., 922 p., 430 ill., St. Louis; Isis 40, 299-301).—Vol. 2 deals with the history of dentistry in America.

EPIDEMIOLOGY

Creighton, Charles (1847-1927):
1891-94: History of epidemics in Great Britain (2 vols., Cambridge).

Haeser, Heinrich (1811-84):
1862: Bibliotheca epidemiographica, sive, Catalogus librorum de historia morborum epidemicorum cum generali tum speciali conscriptorum. Editio altera aucta et prorsus recognita (245 p., Greifswald).—First ed. Jena 1843.
1882: Geschichte der epidemischen Krankheiten (Third vol. of his Lehrbuch der Geschichte der Medizin, 1875-82; 911 p., Jena).

Hecker, Justus Friedrich Karl (1795-1850):
1835: Epidemics of the Middle Ages (London, Sydenham Society).—Reprinted 1837, 1844, 1846, 1849.—German edition by August Hirsch, Berlin 1865.

Newsholme, Sir Arthur (1857-   ):
1927: The evolution of preventive medicine (242 p., Baltimore).
1929: The story of modern preventive medicine (308 p., Baltimore). Continuation of the preceding work.

Prinzing, Friedrich (1859-   ):
1916: Epidemics resulting from wars (352 p., *edited by* Harald Westergaard. Oxford, Clarendon Press; Isis 5, 297).

Proksch, Johann Karl (1840-   ):
1895: Die Geschichte der venerischen Krankheiten (2 vols., Bonn).

Stearn, Esther (Wagner); Stearn, Allen Edwin:
1945: The effect of smallpox on the destiny of the Amerindian (153 p., Boston; Isis 37, 124).

Sticker, Georg (1860-   ):
1908-12: Abhandlungen aus der Seuchengeschichte und Seuchenlehre (2 vol. in 3, Giessen).—Vol. 1 in 2 parts, 1908-10, History of the plague.—Vol. 2, 596 p., 1912. History of cholera.

Winslow, Charles Edward Amory (1877-   ):
1943: The conquest of epidemic disease (424 p., Princeton, N. J., Isis 35, 347).

Zinsser, Hans (1878-1940):
1935: Rats, lice and history (312 p., Boston). History of typhus fever.

GYNAECOLOGY AND OBSTETRICS

Diepgen, Paul (1878-   ):
1937: Geschichte der Frauenheilkunde (Handbuch der Gynäkologie, hrg. v. W. STOECKEL; vol. 12, München).—1. Teil, Die Frauenheilkunde der alten Welt (358 p., ill.; Isis 28, 123-26).

Engelmann, Georg Julius (1847-1903):
1883: Labor among primitive peoples (2nd ed. rev. 246 p., St. Louis).—German transl. (212 p., Wien 1884).

Fasbender, Heinrich (1843-1914):
1906: Geschichte der Geburtshilfe (1044 p., Jena).—Very elaborate history.

Findley, Palmer (1868-   ):
1939: Priests of Lucina (436 p., ill., Boston; Isis 32, 489).

La Torre, Felice (1846-1923):
1917: L'utero attraverso i secoli (852 p., ill., Città di Castello; Isis 5, 279).

Leonardo, Richard A.:
1944: History of gynecology (454 p., 25 pl., New York; Isis 37, 123).

Ricci, James Vincent (1890-   ):
1949: The development of gynaecological surgery and instruments (604 p., Philadelphia; Isis 42).
1950: The genealogy of gynaecology. History of the development of gynaecology (599 p., Philadelphia; Isis 42).

Siebold, Eduard Kaspar Jakob v. (1801-61):
1839-45: Versuch einer Geschichte der Geburtshülfe (2 vols. Berlin).—Revised ed. (2 vols. Tübingen 1901-2).—Continuation by RUDOLF DOHRN, for the period 1840-80, forming vol. 3 (in 2 parts, Tübingen 1903-4).

Thoms, Herbert (1885-   ):
1935: Classical contributions to obstetrics and gynecology (289 p., ill., Springfield, Illinois; Isis 25, 174-75).

Weindler, Fritz:
1908: Geschichte der gynäkologisch-anatomischen Abbildungen (202 p., ill., Dresden).

Witkowski, Gustave Joseph (1844-   ):
1887: Histoire des accouchements chez tous les peuples (728 p., 1584 fig. Paris).
The author wrote many other books dealing with obstetrics and medicine from the anecdotic and iconographic points of view.

PHARMACY AND TOXICOLOGY

André-Pontier, L.:
1900: Histoire de la pharmacie (750 p., Paris).

Benedicenti, Alberico:
1924-25: Malati, medici e farmacisti. Storia dei remedi traverso i secoli e delle teorie che ne spiegano l'azione sull'organismo (2 vols., Milano; Isis 8, 650; 13, 257). 2nd ed., 1946.

Berendes, Julius (1836-1914):
1891: Die Pharmacie bei den alten Culturvölkern (2 vols., Halle a. S.).
1907: Das Apothekenwesen (378 p., Stuttgart).

Kremers, Edward (1865-1941); Urdang, George:
1940: History of pharmacy (476 p., 30 ill., Philadelphia; Isis 33, 307-08).

Lewin, Louis (1850-   ):
1920: Die Gifte in der Weltgeschichte (612 p., Berlin; Isis 4, 371-73).
1931: Phantastica, narcotic and stimulating drugs (346 p., New York).—German original ed. (Berlin 1924).

Peters, Hermann (1847-1920):
1886-89: Aus pharmazeutischer Vorzeit (2 vols., 532 p., Berlin).—Third ed., vol. 1, Berlin 1910.—Partial English translation of vol. 1 by WILLIAM NETTER: Pictorial history of ancient pharmacy (200 p., Chicago 1889).

Phillippe, Adrien (1801-58):
1853: Histoire des apothicaires chez les principaux peuples du monde (460 p., Paris).

Schelenz, Hermann (1848-1922):
1904: Geschichte der Pharmazie (944 p., Berlin).

Wootton, A. C.:
1910: Chronicles of pharmacy (2 vols., ill., London).

VETERINARY MEDICINE

Eichbaum, Friedrich:
1885: Grundriss der Geschichte der Thierheilkunde (336 p., Berlin).—Mostly bibliography.

Leclainche, Emmanuel (1861-   ):
1936: Histoire de la médecine vétérinaire (828 p., Toulouse; Isis 27, 360-63).

Moulé, Léon (1849-1922):
1891-1911: Histoire de la médecine vétérinaire jusqu'au XVI. siècle (in 4 parts, 684 p., Paris).

Postolka, August:
1887: Geschichte der Thierheilkunde (2nd ed., 409 p., Wien).

Smith, Sir Frederick (1857-   ):
1919-30: Early history of veterinary literature and its British development to 1700 (vol. 1, 378 p., 27 fig., London, Isis 3, 307).—Vol. 1 goes to the seventeenth century, inclusive. 3 vols. published.

See the Critical Bibliographies of Isis, sections 50 to 53.

EDUCATION

There are many recent textbooks on the history of education, too many to be quoted here. Those listed will be more than sufficient for the reader's general purpose. For the history of universities, *see* RASHDALL and IRSAY. A great many books are devoted to the history of each separate university. Scholars studying the life and work of a man of science are advised to consult the histories of the universities and academies of which he was a member.

Boyd, William:
1921: History of western education (454 p., London).—Fourth ed., 1947.

Cubberley, Ellwood Patterson (1868-   ):
1920: History of education (873 p., ill., Boston).
1920: Readings in the history of education (710 p., ill., Boston).
1922: Brief history of education (484 p., ill., Boston).

De Hovre, Frans (1884-   ); Breckx, Léon:
1936: Les maîtres de la pédagogie contemporaine (590 p., ill., Bruges).

Graves, Frank Pierrepont (1869-   ):
1909: History of education before the Middle Ages (318 p., New York).
1910: History of education during the Middle Ages and the transition to modern times (343 p., New York).
1913: History of education in modern times (425 p., New York).
1915: A student's history of education (478 p., New York).

Hambly, Wilfrid Dyson (1886-   ):
1926: Origins of education among primitive peoples, a comparative study in racial development (London).

Irsay, Stephen d' (1894-1934; Isis 24, 370-74):
1933-35: Histoire des universités françaises et étrangères des origines à nos jours. (2 vols., Paris).
1933: Vol. 1, Moyen Age et Renaissance.
1935: Vol. 2, Du XVIe siècle à 1860.

Monroe, Paul (1869-1947):
1905: Textbook in the history of education (795 p., ill., New York).—Often reprinted.
1907: A brief course in the history of education (431 p., ill., New York).—Often reprinted.

Rashdall, Hastings (1858-1924):
1936: The universities of Europe in the Middle Ages. New ed. in 3 vols. by F. M. POWICKE and A. B. EMDEN (Clarendon Press, Oxford).
Vol. 1, Salerno, Bologna, Paris. Vol. 2, Italy, Spain, France, Germany, Scotland, etc. Vol. 3, English universities. Student life.—First edition 1895, 2 vols. in 3.

Schröteler, Joseph (1886-   ) (*editor*):
1934: Die Pädagogik der nichtchristlichen Kulturvölker (399 p., München).

Ulich, Robert (1890-   ):
1945: History of educational thought (424 p., New York).
1947: Three thousand years of educational wisdom. Selections from great documents (624 p., Cambridge, Harvard University; Isis 38, 272).

Woody, Thomas (1897-   ):
1949: Life and education in early societies (825 p., ill., New York).
See the Critical Bibliographies of Isis, sections 54 to 57.

SOCIOLOGY

Ayala, Francisco (1906-   ):
1947: Historia de la sociologia (3 vols., Buenos Aires).

Barnes, Harry Elmer (1889-   ) (*editor*):
1938: Social thought from lore to science (2 vols. Boston).
1948: Introduction to the history of sociology (976 p., Chicago).

Bogardus, Emery Stephen (1882-   ):
1940: Development of social thought (572 p., New York; 2d ed. 608 p., 1949).

De Greef, Guillaume (1842-1924):
1895: Evolution des croyances et des doctrines politiques (330 p., Bruxelles).

Ellwood, Charles Abram (1873-1946):
1938: Story of social philosophy (592 p., New York).—Reprinted 1947.

Furfey, Paul Hanly (1896-   ):
1942: History of social thought (480 p., New York).

Lichtenberger, James Pendleton (1870-   ):
1923: Development of social theory (495 p., New York).—Reprinted 1925, 1938.

Müller-Lyer, Franz (1857-1916):
1920: History of social development (362 p., London).—Reprinted 1935.

Sarkar, Benoy Kumar (1887-   ):
1922: The political institutions and theories of the Hindus, a study in comparative politics (266 p., Leipzig).
1928: The political philosophies [in India] since 1905 (404 p., Madras).

Todd, Arthur James (1878-1948):
1918: Theories of social progress (592 p., New York).—Reprinted in 1922.
See the Critical Bibliographies of Isis, section 43.   Sociology.

PREHISTORIC ARCHAEOLOGY
Daniel, Glyn E.:
1950: A hundred years of archaeology (344 p., New York; Isis 41, 405).
See the Critical Bibliographies of Isis, section 39.   Prehistory.

20. JOURNALS AND SERIALS CONCERNING THE HISTORY (AND PHILOSOPHY) OF SCIENCE

(by George Sarton and Claudius F. Mayer)

This is an edition revised and considerably extended of the Bibliographie synthétique des revues et des collections de livres (Isis 2, 125-61, 1914). The arrangement is different: the items were subdivided by general subjects in the list of 1914; in the present list they are put in alphabetical order of titles. The items described are called journals and serials, not periodicals; indeed, though some of them appeared periodically, many others were aperiodic, or their periodicity was very irregular.

The reader may be astonished by the great number of items recorded in this list, yet it is almost certainly incomplete. We are confident that the most important items have been included (almost all of them have been examined by one of us); it is probable that in spite of every effort some items have eluded the authors' attention; it is highly probable that those unmentioned are not very important, at any rate, as far as the international reader is concerned (indeed, the omitted items are very likely to be written in languages which do not enjoy any international currency).

Such a list should be used critically. The author does not wish to separate the important items from the unimportant ones, or the more important from the less important, because such a distinction is always somewhat subjective. The reader must be warned that the length of a description is independent of the merit of an item. Poor items often require a longer description than rich ones. The edition and publication of journals or series often implied many irregularities (changes of title or subtitle, editors, publishers, purpose, scope, periodicity); it would require much space to indicate these irregularities even in an abbreviated and imperfect manner; to describe them completely would be endless.

The list includes only (with few exceptions) series exclusively devoted to the history of science; other series whose scope is wider are not included in spite of the fact that they may be richer in studies on the history of science than some other series which are included. For example, the Carnegie Institution of Washington has published many worthwhile books on the history of science, but as those books were not grouped together in a special collection they could not be mentioned here (see list of them in Osiris 9, 634-38, 1950).

The bibliography of series of books is more difficult than that of periodicals. All the numbers of each periodical are classified together, while in most libraries the books of each series are scattered, each book being classified with other books (wherever published) dealing with the same subjects. The matter is simplified when the books of a series are well numbered and no. k of the series bears a list of books no. 1 to (k-1); unfortunately, that precaution is often neglected.

Many series of books are purely commercial undertakings and represent only the personal fancy of a publisher or editor. When success does not reward their efforts, when the series "does not pay," it is stopped. Nevertheless, we must recognize its existence. Such abortive series may contain important books.

In the following list the title of each journal or serial is preceded by the date of its birth; if publication has come to an end, the title is preceded by two dates, those of birth and death. The first of these dates is always known, the second is sometimes uncertain. A series may be resurrected after a long interval.[97] No attempt has been made to describe completely each item, but for living journals we have tried to quote the present editor and publisher and their address. The purpose of the journal is generally indicated in its title or subtitle; further indications have been added whenever necessary, also references to Isis where more information is available.

---

[97] The best example known to me is that of the Memoirs of the Philadelphia Society for promoting Agriculture. Vols. 1 to 5 appeared from 1808 to 1826; vol. 6, in 1939 after an interval of 113 years; vol. 7 has not yet appeared (Isis 32, 476).

Many of the journals published in or after 1912 have been analyzed in the Critical Bibliographies of Isis. It is possible that those Bibliographies include occasional references to other journals which might have been listed below but were accidentally omitted.

References to Isis have been added to many items; when no such reference occurs it does not by any means follow that the item has not been reviewed or listed in Isis.

After having completed my task, I submitted the notes assembled by me to Dr. CLAUDIUS F. MAYER, Editor of the Index-Catalogue (Isis 40, 119; 1949), Chief Medical Officer, Army Medical Library, Washington, D. C. Dr. MAYER was kind enough to revise them. He not only corrected or brought up to date many of the items mentioned by me, but he added many more which I had omitted. As his efforts have doubled the list, it is fair to consider him as co-author. His initials are put at the end of items entirely or chiefly contributed by him, but it should be understood that the other items may have been revised and partly rewritten by him.

Dr. MAYER was able to add many items partly because of his superior bibliographical knowledge, partly because of his greater catholicity. On the other hand, his long experience has enabled him to discard many items, the title of which suggests that they concern the history of science, but which are nevertheless irrelevant. A list of these discarded items being in itself very instructive has been printed in the appendix at the end of this chapter.

G. S.

1925-1936: Abhandlungen aus der Geschichte der Veterinärmedizin.
Edited by the Gesellschaft für Geschichte und Literatur der Veterinärmedizin; published in Leipzig-Mölkau by W. RICHTER.
Numbered serial of monographs devoted to the history of veterinary medicine. Heft 30 was never published. Heft 31 (1935) is the last one recorded; it is a work on the development of veterinary services in a German town, written by K. UNTEUTSCH.
Other serials issued by the German Society of veterinary historians and listed below are: Beiträge zur Geschichte der Veterinärmedizin, Cheiron, Veterinärhistorisches Jahrbuch, and Veterinärhistorische Mitteilungen. (C. F. M.)

1929- : Abhandlungen und Berichte des Deutschen Museums. Edited by E. SÖRENSEN (Augsburg) and J. ZENNECK (München); published first by the Verein deutscher Ingenieure at Berlin, later by the Leibniz Verlag in München.
Irregularly issued little books (21cm × 15cm) containing articles related to the history of technics such as on the development of telescopes (1931), biographies of physicists and industrialists, etc., the chief source of the material being the Deutsches Museum von Meisterwerken der Naturwissenschaft und Technik (German Museum of masterpieces of science and technic). Some 28 volumes had appeared by the end of 1932. The last Jahrgang recorded is that of 1948. (C. F. M.)

1904-1929: Abhandlungen zur Didaktik und Philosophie der Naturwissenschaften.
Edited by F. POSKE (et al.); published in Berlin.
Irregularly issued numbered serial forming supplements to the Zeitschrift für den physikalischen und chemischen Unterricht; devoted to the philosophy of natural sciences. It was not published from 1912 to 1926. The serial seems to end with Heft 14. Heft 1 to Heft 11 are arranged in two volumes. (C. F. M.)

1877-1913: Abhandlungen zur Geschichte der mathematischen Wissenschaften mit Einschluss ihrer Anwendungen. Edited by MORITZ CANTOR, and published by Teubner, Leipzig.
See Isis 2: 134, 205.
Parts 1 to 10 were published as supplements to the Zeitschrift für Mathematik und Physik, vols. 22 (1877) to 45 (1900). Parts 11 to 30 were published independently from 1901 to 1913. Part 29 (Festschrift for the centenary of EDUARD KUMMER) appeared in 1910. Part 30, the last (1913) was the work of a Japanese historian, YOSHIO MIKAMI, in English version.

1902-1906: **Abhandlungen zur Geschichte der Medizin.** 18 parts edited by Hugo Magnus (1842-1907), with the assistance of Max Neuburger and Karl Sudhoff. Breslau, J. U. Kern's Verlag (Max Müller).
See Isis 2: 147.

1934-1940: **Abhandlungen zur Geschichte der Medizin und Naturwissenschaften.** Edited by Paul Diepgen, Julius Ruska, Julius Schuster. Verlag Emil Ebering, Berlin.
A serial of medico-historical and biographical monographs. It ends with Heft 36 (1940).

1922-25: **Abhandlungen zur Geschichte der Naturwissenschaften und der Medizin.** Eight parts edited by Oskar Schulz (Erlangen) and published by Max Mencke, Erlangen.
See Isis 5: 563; 8: 743.

1942- : **Acta historica scientiarum naturalium et medicinalium.** Edited by the University Library of Copenhagen and published by Ejnar Munksgaard in that city, 6, Nörregade.
Monographs issued at irregular intervals; written in Danish, German, English or other languages. Each volume is devoted to a special topic. Vol. 1: Oldtidens laere om hjerte (etc.); by E. Gotfredsen (see Isis 37, 247). Vol. 2: Otto Friderich Müller (pt. 1); by J. Anker (Isis 35, 356). Vol. 3: Middelalderens laegekunst i Danmark; by V. Møller-Christensen (Isis 37, 234). Vol. 4 (1948): Ktesibios, Philon and Heron; by A. G. Drachmann. Vol. 5-6 (1950): Thomas Bartholin; by A. Garboe. Vol. 7 (1950): The history of muscle physiology from the natural philosophers to Albrecht von Haller; by E. Bastholm (257 p.).

1930-32: **Acta Paracelsica.** Edited for the Paracelsus-Gesellschaft by Ernst Darmstädter, Richard Koch and Manfred Schroeter. München, Paracelsus-Gesellschaft.
5 parts (Heft) published, 142 p.; plus Beilage: Nachweise zur Paracelsus-Literatur Nr. 1-1089, by Karl Sudhoff, 68 p.; separately paginated (Isis 15: 230).
For the Paracelsus-Gesellschaft see undated circular reprinted in Isis (13: 361-62).
See also Nova Acta Paracelsica.

1934- : **Actas Ciba.** Published by the Brazilian branch of the Ciba Co.; edited by G. A. de Lima Torres, Avenida Venezuela 110, Rio de Janeiro; printed in the same city by the Irmãos Barthel.
Monthly issues with similar contents as that of the Ciba Zeitschrift. Latest issue on record: vol. 13, 1946. (C. F. M.)

1947- : **Actas Ciba.** Published in Spanish by the Productos químicos Ciba in Buenos Aires; printed in the same city by Platt, S. A.
Monthly serial containing medico-historical, anthropological and pharmaco-historical articles; resembling the English issues of Ciba Symposia (q.v.). Latest issue seen: Nov. 1948. Independent from other Ciba publications.
See also Ciba.

1911- : **Aesculape; revue mensuelle illustrée.** Published by the Société internationale d'histoire de la médecine since 1923; edited by Benjamin Bord; issued by M. Avalon, Paris (old series published by A. Rouzaud, Paris).
See Isis 2: 150.
Vol. 1 (1911) to vol. 4 (1914) is also mentioned as the first (or old) series; of folio size (35 cm × 28 cm). Vol. 5 to vol. 12 do not exist. Vol. 13 (1923) to vol. 30 (1940) is also known as the new series; of quarto size. The new series was the official organ of the Société internationale d'histoire de la médecine which was established in 1921 in Paris. Published monthly; the last issue is No. 4, May 1940.
Aesculape is published again under the editorship of Jean Avalon, 89 Avenue Denfert-Rochereau, Paris 14. No. 1-2 of vol. 30 (new series) was issued in Nov.-

Dec. 1949. This was the first post-war issue; it is strange that the pagination of no. 1 begins with p. 97.

The nature of the serial is expressed by its subtitles. The old series calls itself "latéro-médicale" while the new series reads: "revue . . . des lettres et des arts dans leurs rapports avec les sciences et la médecine." It is especially valued for its illustrative material: reproductions of art objects to serve as source material for history. Its articles are more or less in the easy style of feuilletons on such topics as health and medicine in old and contemporary art, artistic hobbies of physicians, diseases in history and art, numismatics, patron saints, history of balneography, of dentistry, etc. (C. F. M.)

1908-1909: **The Aesculapian:** a quarterly journal of medical history, literature and art. Edited by ALBERT TRACY HUNTINGTON. 1 vol. Brooklyn, New York.

Only 4 nos. issued between December 1908 and September 1909. Continuation of Medical Library and Historical Journal. See Isis 2: 149.

1927-   : **Agricultural history.** Published by the Agricultural History Society. Chicago & Baltimore.

The first volume of 1927 was preceded by the Papers of the Agricultural History Society; it was issued from Washington, vol. 1 (1918) to vol. 3 (1920), and contained articles reprinted from the Annual Report of the American Historical Society. (C. F. M.)

Vol. 25 appeared in 1950. For subscriptions apply to Agricultural History Society, Room 3906, South Agriculture Building, U. S. Bureau of Agricultural Economics, Washington 25, D. C. An abbreviated table of contents of vols. 1 to 25 can be obtained from that office.

1947-   : **Akademiia nauk SSSR. Institut istorii estestvoznaniia. Trudy.**

Thanks to the gracious collaboration of DAVID A. JONAH, Librarian of Brown University, Providence, R. I., vols. 1 to 3 (1947-49) of those Trudy will be analyzed in the 77th Critical Bibliography (Isis 42), and subsequent volumes in the following bibliographies.

These volumes contain many memoirs on the history of science in Russia and elsewhere. Vol. 1 has a bibliography of Russian works on the history of science published in 1939-44; that bibliography is continued in the following volumes.

1938-1945: **Alcmeone;** revista trimestrale di storia della medicina. Edited by GIOVANNI P. ARCIERI; published in New York.

Vol. 1 was published in 1938-39, and vol. 2 in 1940. The publication as well as the editor met with some difficulties, and, after no. 3 of vol. 2 (July/September) the serial was forced to rest. In 1945, on No. 1 of vol. 7, its title reads: Alcmeone, journal of history of medicine. It was issued as an annex of the first volume of the newly founded Journal of Cardiorespiratory Diseases, a bilingual quarterly. Latest no. seen, Vol. 9, no. 1, 1947. (C. F. M.)

1898-1933: **Alembic Club Reprints.** Published for the Alembic Club by JAMES THIN. 55 South Bridge, Edinburgh.

Collection of booklets (18 cm × 12 cm) each of which contains the reprint of a short classic of physical or chemical science. No. 1 (JOSEPH BLACK) appeared in 1898; last number seen, No. 21 (ARCHIBALD SCOTT COUPER) in 1933. List of nos. 1 to 17 in Isis 2: 168. Publication was suspended from 1912 to 1928.

No. 21 was really the last no.; the list of all the items 1 to 21 is included in DENIS I. DUVEEN: Bibliotheca alchemica (p. 14, 1949; Isis 40, 387).

The whole series has been recently reprinted.

1747-1774: **Allgemeine Historie der Reisen zu Wasser und zu Lande.** Published by Arkstee, in Amsterdam.

Twenty-one volumes in quarto; contains source material for the history of geography. (C. F. M.)

1910-12: **Alte Meister der Medizin und Naturkunde in Facsimile-Ausgaben und Neudrucken.** Edited by Prof. Dr. Gustav Klein. München, Kuhn, 1910. Only five vols. published; for vols. 4-5 *see* Isis 1, 271-73. Gustav Klein (1863-1920), obituary by Karl Sudhoff (Mitt. 19: 224). Facsimile reprints of early books by Ortolff von Bayerland, Eucharius Rösslin, Hieronymus Brunschwig, early writers on syphilis (Sudhoff), Thomas of Cantimpré.

1937-   : **Ambix**; being the Journal of the Society for the study of alchemy and early chemistry. Quarterly. Edited by F. Sherwood Taylor. Published by Taylor and Francis, London.
See Isis 28: 262.   Vol. 1 in 3 parts (202 p., 1937-38); vol. 2 in 4 parts (198 p., 1938-46); vol. 3 in 2 parts called 1-2, 3-4 (156 p., 1948-49).

1919-1921: **Analecta Ambrosiana.** Issued by the Biblioteca Ambrosiana and edited by Luigi Gramatica, the director of the Library. Published by Alfieri and Lacroix, Milano.
Numbered series of monographs dealing with Leonardo da Vinci. Complete in seven numbers.   No. 1: Le memorie di Leonardo da Vinci (A. Mazenta); No. 3: Il cenacolo di L. da Vinci (G. Galbiati).   (C. F. M.)

1939-   : **Anales de la Sociedad Peruana de Historia de la Medicina.** Lima.
Journal dealing with the history of medicine in general and more particularly with South American, Peruvian medicine.
Vol. 1, 1939, 96 p.   Vol. 2, 1940, 182 + lx p., 1942.   Vol. 3, 1941, 92 p.   Vol. 4, 1942 (Periodo 1942-44) 140 p.   First page bears the mention Vol. IV.   Lima 1942.   Fasc. 1; the cover, wrongly, 1943 (Fasc. 1).   The following book Juan B. Lastres: Vida y obras de Miguel Tafur (xxxvi + 136 p., Lima 1943; Isis 37: 216) served as fasc. 2 of that year.   Vol. 5, 1942-43, 48 p. Vol. 6, 1944, 138 p. Vol. 7, 1945, 200 p.   Vol. 8, 1946, 80 p.   Vol. 9, 1947, 70 + xliv p.   This latest no. was printed by Casa Editorial Emp. Edit. Rimac, Padre Jerónimo 427, Lima (no other address being given).

1804-1870: **Annales des voyages, de la géographie et de l'histoire; ou,** Collection des voyages nouveaux . . . et des mémoires historiques sur l'origine, la langue, les moeurs et les arts des peuples, Paris.
The older set under the above title makes 24 volumes which were published from 1804 to 1814 under the editorship of Malte-Brun (1775-1826).   A general index to the first 20 volumes was issued in 1813.   Publication was suspended from 1815 to 1818.   Under the title "Nouvelles annales des voyages" publication was resumed in 1819 and continued through several series until 1870.   The new title runs through 188 volumes, with slight variations of the subtitle and with many changes in the editorial chair (Eyriès, Larénaudière, Klaproth, Humboldt, Arago, Marmier, Malte-Brun, etc.)   (C. F. M.)

1927: **Annali del Istituto di storia della medicina.**   Napoli.   Only the first volume was issued; contains medico-historical studies by the staff of the institute. (C. F. M.)

1917-42: **Annals of medical history.**   Edited by Francis R. Packard, published by Paul B. Hoeber, New York.
Vol. 1 appeared in 1917-1919; 24 volumes were published between April 1917 and Nov. 1942.   These volumes are numbered First series 1 to 10, Second series 1 to 10, Third series 1 to 4.
A general index to the 24 vols., compiled by Hilda C. Lipkin, was published in 1946 by Henry Schuman, New York.

1936-   : **Annals of science:** a quarterly review of the history of science since the Renaissance.   Edited by Douglas McKie, Harcourt Brown and Henry W. Robinson.   Published by Taylor and Francis, London.
Vol. 1, No. 1: Jan. 15, 1936 (Isis 25: 488); that vol. was completed in the same year.   Vol. 5, 1941-47.   Vol. 6 began to appear in October 1948.

1919-1923: **Antichi scrittori d'idraulica veneta.** Issued by the R. Magistrato alle acque, Ufficio idrografico, of Venezia. Edited by G. FERRARI.

Large size (32 cm × 22 cm) numbered volumes, being the reprints of early monographs related to engineering problems in Venice. Vol. 1 (1919): Scritture sulla laguna; written by M. CORNARO (1412-1469) and edited by G. PAVANELLO. The latest volume on record is vol. 4: Discorso sopra l'aere di Venezia, written by A. MARINI about 1566. Vol. 4 was issued in 1923 (not in 1930). (C. F. M.)

1924-1926: **Arbeiten aus dem Institut für Geschichte der Naturwissenschaften.** Edited by J. RUSKA in Heidelberg, and published in the same city by C. Winter.

There were four numbered volumes published within the framework of another series (Heidelberger Akten der von-Portheim Stiftung). The activities of the institute ceased when RUSKA moved to Berlin. No. 3 (1925): Ein Astrolab aus dem Indischen Mogulreiche (J. FRANK & M. MEYERHOF; Isis 8: 612). (C. F. M.)

1930-1932: **Arbeiten des Instituts für Geschichte der Medizin an der Universität Leipzig.** Edited by HENRY E. SIGERIST and published by Georg Thieme, Leipzig.

Monographs of 21 cm × 14 cm numbered volumes. Only two volumes were published. The serial ceased when its editor moved to Baltimore. Bd. 1 (1930): ALBRECHT VON HALLER (ST. D'IRSAY; Isis 16, 501). Bd. 2 (1932): Die Embryologie im Zeitalter des Barock und des Rokoko (T. BILIKIEWICZ; Isis 20, 604). (C. F. M.)

1929-33: **Arbeiten zur Kenntnis der Geschichte der Medizin im Rheinland und in Westphalen.** Edited by PAUL KRAUSE; published by Fischer in Jena.

Issued in numbered octavo pamphlets, at irregular intervals. The first no. bears the title: Arbeiten (etc.) Geschichte der westfälischen Medizin. The last no. was no. 12 (1933): Die Gesundheitspflege in . . . Westfalen, by R. RUMPE (136 p.) (C. F. M.)

1928- : **Archeion.**
See 1919 Archivio di storia della scienza.

1823: **Archiv for laegevidenskabens historie i Danmark.** Edited by J. D. HERHOLDT. Published by Andreas Seidelin in Copenhagen.

The first number of the first volume, an octavo volume of 192 p., is the only one published. It contains biographies of old physicians and medical professors, articles on medical history, hospital history, old statutes of surgeons, a finding list of portraits, etc., chiefly of the period of 1478 to 1588. Continued as Samlinger(?) (C. F. M.)

1790: **Archiv für die Geschichte der Arzneykunde in ihrem ganzen Umfange.** I. Bd., 1. St. hrg. von PHILLIP LUDWIG WITTWER [1752-92]. Published by Ernst Christoph Grattenauer in Nürnberg.

Vol. 1, part 1 was the only part to appear because of the editor's premature death (BL 5, 976). Contents in Isis 2: 152. The purpose of the serial was to publish historical, biographical and bibliographical data, also articles on medical travel, on art objects of medical interest, on numismatics etc.

1907-1943: **Archiv für die Geschichte der Medizin.** Edited by KARL SUDHOFF. Published by the Puschmann-Stiftung an der Universität Leipzig. Leipzig, Johann Ambrosius Barth.
Cf. Isis 2: 148.

Six numbers were issued a year. Vols. 18 to 20 were edited by KARL SUDHOFF and HENRY E. SIGERIST. Vol. 21 (1925) to 26 bore the title Sudhoffs Archiv für Geschichte der Medizin and were edited by SIGERIST alone. From vol. 27, 1934-35, on the title was changed to Sudhoffs Archiv für Geschichte der Medizin und der Naturwissenschaften, zugleich Fortsetzung der Zoologischen Annalen. Edited by I. D. ACHELIS, AD. MEYER, K. SUDHOFF. The editors of vol. 28 were AD. MEYER and K. SUDHOFF; those of vol. 29, W. V. BRUNN and AD. MEYER; those of vol. 30,

1938, etc. W. v. Brunn and R. Zaunick. Last no. published was vol. 36 (1-2, June 1943).

1909-31: Archiv für die Geschichte der Naturwissenschaften und der Technik.
Vol. 1 edited by Karl von Buchker, Hermann Stadler, Karl Sudhoff. Published by F. C. W. Vogel, Leipzig 1909; vol. 8, 1918, edited by Siegmund Gunther, Arthur Haas, Georg Lockeman, Sudhoff and Stadler; vol. 9, 1920, only 126 p.
Beginning with vol. 10 in 1927 the title was changed to Archiv für Geschichte der Mathematik, der Naturwissenschaften und der Technik. Edited by Julius Schuster, same publisher. Last volume, 13, 1930-31, same editor and publisher. For the earlier volumes *see* Isis 2: 154.
With the change in title, vol. 10 to vol. 13 is also numbered as "neue Folge" vol. 1 to vol. 4. Continued as Quellen und Studien zur Geschichte der Naturwissenschaften und der Medizin (*q.v.*).

1913-1931: Archiv für Fischereigeschichte; Darstellungen und Quellen. Edited by E. Uhles; published by the Deutscher Fischerei-Verein in Berlin.
Numbered monographs of octavo size devoted to the history of fishing and history of the right of fishing. The last number on record is Heft 16, 1931. (C. F. M.)

1927-1931: Archiv für Geschichte der Mathematik, der Naturwissenschaften und der Technik.
See Archiv für die Geschichte der Naturwissenschaften und der Technik.

1911: Archiv für Geschichte der Pharmazie. Hrsg. von H. Güntzel.
Isis 2, 152. The first no. of this monthly journal was to appear on 1 Jan. 1911. Was it actually published, and were other nos. published? (The journal remained just an idea. No trace of it can be found in any library. C. F. M.)

1888-1932: Archiv für Geschichte der Philosophie. Edited by Ludwig Stein (1859-1930) and others. Published by C. Heymann in Berlin.
In 1894 it became the Abteilung 1 of Archiv für Philosophie (und Soziologie); as such it is considered a "neue Folge" to the first set of seven volumes. Publication ceased with vol. 41 (n. F. 34) 1932. (C. F. M.)

1947- : Archives internationales d'histoire des sciences. Publication trimestrielle de l'Union internationale des sciences. Nouvelle série d'Archeion. Vol. 1, no. 1, October 1947.
Edited by Aldo Mieli and Pierre Brunet, aided by an international committee the most active member of which is Pierre Sergescu of Bucureşti, now in Paris. Published by the Académie internationale d'histoire des sciences, 12 rue Colbert, Paris 2. On part 3 of vol. 1, the address of another publisher was added Hermann, Paris, and this vol. 1 was also called vol. XXVII of Archeion. This is puzzling, because the last part of Archeion was vol. XXV, no. 2/3. I do not know of any vol. XXVI.
Vol. 2 is being published in 1949.
For the earlier avatars of this journal *see* 1919 Archivio di storia della scienza. It was explained by Prof. Sergescu to me that the no. 1 of Oct. 1947 would count as vol. 26 (1947); the rest published in 1948 would count as vol. 27 (1948); vols. 26 and 27 have but one pagination between them.

1896-1941: Archives internationales pour l'histoire de la médecine et pour la géographie médicale.
Subtitle of Janus (*q.v.*)

1919-1943: Archivio di storia delle scienze. Edited by Aldo Mieli, Roma; published by Attilio Nardecchia.
Part 1 appeared in April 1919, part 4, completing vol. 1, in August 1920. It became the organ of the International Academy of science in 1928 (vol. 9, fasc. 4,

Jan. 1929) when that Academy was founded by the editor of the Archivio. With vol. 8, fasc. 3, Oct. 1927, the journal assumed the title Archeion, the original title becoming a subtitle.

Vol. 10, fasc. 1 (Dec. 1929) is an index to the years 1919-29 (Indice undecennale). That volume was completed in April 1937 by a second fasc. called "vol. X et XX. Index des vingt premiers volumes de la revue, 1919-37." This whole volume (X and XX) covers 132 p. Beginning with vol. XXII Archeion was published by the Universidad nacional del litoral in Santa Fe, Republica Argentina. The last number of the Argentine series was "vol. XXV, 1943 N. 2/3. Nueva serie T. IV," dated 3 Sept. 1943. Further publication was forbidden by the Universidad nacional del litoral. But in some copies of that number it was possible to add a general index for the year covering XII supplementary pages. The no. itself covers p. 101-292. (Information kindly given by Dr. A. MIELI, in a letter dated Florida, Prov. Buenos Aires, 22 Dec. 1948).

Archeion has been revived in 1947 under a new title Archives internationales d'histoire des sciences.

1926-1927: **Archivio per gli studi storici della medicina e delle scienze naturali.** Editor-in-chief: DEMETRIO B. RONCALI; edited by MAURIZIO MASTRORILLI. Published in Napoli.

Short-lived publication of 33.5 cm × 24 cm size. Its first number was issued April 21, 1926 or "2679 ab Urbe condita." Its last issue was No. 1/3, of vol. 2, April-August, 1927 (or "2680 ab Urbe condita"). The publication was dedicated to MUSSOLINI and to fascism; "una pubblicazione bluffistica" as ALDO MIELI called it (cf. Archeion, 1926, 7: 201). (C. F. M.)

1944-   : **Archivos argentinos de historia de la medicina.** Published in La Plata. Journal issued by the Sociedad de historia de la medicina de La Plata, Calle 50, No. 374, La Plata, Argentina, according to CHEVALIER L. JACKSON (Bull. Hist. Med., 22, 838, 1948). Editor: ENRIQUE LUIS CARRI.

1886-1923: **Archivos de história de medicina portuguésa.** Periodico bi-mensal. Edited by MAXIMIANO LEMOS. Published in Porto by Lemos.

Journal devoted to the history of Portuguese medicine. Vol. 1 (1886-87) 1887; vol. 2 (1887-88) 1888; vol. 3 (1888-89) 1889; vol. 4, 1894; vol. 5, 1895; vol. 6, 1896. Each volume has 192 p., except vol. 1, 116 p. Note the five year gap between vol. 3, 1889 and vol. 4, 1894. A longer gap occurred after the publication of vol. 6.

A new series bearing the same title began with a new vol. 1 in 1910. It was edited by M. LEMOS and JOÃO DE MEIRA. In 1912 it became Arquivos. After the 14th volume in 1923 it ceased publication.

1934-1935: **Archivos de historia médica de Venezuela.** Caracas. Only two volumes have been published. (C. F. M.)

1924-1932: **Archiwum historij i filozofij medycyny.** Published by the Polish Science History Society in Poznan.

The latest volume on record is vol. 12, 1932. Apparently its publication ended with that volume. (C. F. M.)

1933-   : **Arkhiv istorii nauki i tekhniki.** *See* Trudy Instituta istorii nauki i tekhniki.

1926-1938: **Argonaut Press Publications,** London.

A publisher's numbered series of de-luxe reprints related to the history of geography. No. 1 (1926): The world encompassed (Sir F. DRAKE); No. 2 (1927): A new voyage round the world (W. DAMPIER). The last is No. 16 (1938): Northern Najd; a journey from Jerusalem to Anaiza in Qasim (C. GUARMANI). (C. F. M.)

1926-   : **Aristote; science et médecine; revue réservée au corps médical.** Edited by J. RAVILY; published by G. de Malherbe & cie, Paris.

Monthly publication with much irregularity in issue; vol. 6, 1931; vol. 7, 1932, contains numbers 59 to 63. Last volume on my record is vol. 8, 1933. It is a serial devoted to curiosities in medicine, and in medical history; it resembles Aesculape in contents, with its "paramedical" tendencies, articles on Mme Sévigné, Rousseau, the Chevalier (or Chevalière) d'Eon, etc. (C. F. M.)

1912-1923: **Arquivos de história de medicina portuguésa.**
    See Archivos . . . (C. F. M.)

1907-   : **Atti della riunione; Società italiana di storia critica delle scienze mediche e naturali.**
    Vol. 1 contains the proceedings of the meetings of Perugia (1907) and Faenza (1908), published in Faenza 1909. The proceedings of the meeting of Venezia (1909) were published in Venezia 1909. Atti del I Congresso nazionale, Roma 1912, general secretary V. Pensuti, Grottaferrata, Tipografia S. Nilo 1913.
    Atti del III Congresso nazionale (Venezia 1925), general secretary A. Corsini, Siena, Tipog. S. Bernardino 1926.
    See also 1910 Rivista. *Cf.* Isis 2: 154.

1935-   : **Atti e memorie dell' Accademia di storia dell'arte sanitaria.**   Roma.
    The Accademia was founded in 1920 under the name Istituto storico italiano dell'arte sanitaria. It assumed its present name in 1935. The publication of the institute was a Bollettino (*q.v.*), vol. 1-14, 1921-1934; with the new name of the institute the title of the publication also changed to Atti which is considered the second series; vol. 1 was published in 1935; last volume on record is vol. 46 (fasc. 4, Oct.-Dec.) 1947. Edited in 1947 by Silvestro Baglioni.
    See Bollettino dell'Istituto storico dell'arte sanitaria. ((C. F. M.)

1937/38-   : **Atti e memorie del Istituto italiano di storia della chimica.**   Edited by Giulio Provenzal and Gino Testi in Rome.
    A numbered series of volumes containing reprints from the journal La Chimica. Vol. 1 to 4 called also series no. 1. The latest is vol. 6. (C. F. M.)

1947-   : **Beihefte zur Zeitschrift Elemente der Mathematik.**   Verlag Birkhäuser, Basel.
    Under the editorship of L. Locher-Ernst each of these Beihefte, beginning with no. 2 (1947) contains the biography of a mathematician. Have thus far appeared, or will appear shortly, the biographies of Steiner, Euler, Ludwig Schläfli, Bürgi, Johann and Jakob Bernoulli, Galois, Abel, Monge, Fermat. Each Heft covers 24 pages and costs Sw. Fr. 3.50.

1903-1925: **Beiträge aus dem Grenzgebiet zwischen Medizingeschichte und Kunst, Kultur, Literatur.**   Published by Ferdinand Enke in Stuttgart.
    Richly illustrated quarto volumes, all being the works of the single author Eugen Holländer. Several volumes were re-issued repeatedly. Vol. 1: Die Medizin in der klassischen Malerei (1st ed. 1903; 2nd ed. 1913; 3rd ed. 1923). Vol. 2: Die Karikatur und Satire in der Medizin (1st ed. 1905; 2nd ed. 1921). Vol. 3: Plastik und Medizin. Vol. 4: Wunder, Wundergeburt (etc.). (1st ed. 1921; 2nd ed. 1922). Vol. 5: Anekdoten aus der medizinischen Weltgeschichte (1925). (C. F. M.)

1873-1881: **Beiträge zur Entdeckungsgeschichte Afrikas.**   Issued by the Gesellschaft für Erdkunde in Berlin; published by D. Reimer in the same city.
    Numbered series of monographs related to the geographical history of Africa. Only four numbers were issued. No. 1: Erläuterungen (H. Kiepert); No. 3: Tagebuch (P. Pogge); No. 4: Reisen (Schutt). (C. F. M.)

1935-   : **Beiträge zur Geschichte der Astrologie.**   Published in Heidelberg.
    Only one volume is known to be on record. (C. F. M.)

1794-96: **Beiträge zur Geschichte der Medizin.** Edited by KURT SPRENGEL (1766-1837). Only one volume published, in 3 parts: 1, 239 p., 1794; 2, 244 p., 1795; 3, 270 p., 1796. Halle a. S., Rengersche Buchhandlung. *See* Isis 2: 142. Each fascicle is dedicated to a scholar: No. 1 to HENSLER, No. 2 to BÖTTIGER and No. 3 to WEIGEL. The first fascicle contains many of the editor's unpublished writings (history of smallpox in Western Europe, the Black Death of 1349-1350, letters on GALEN's philosophical system, anecdotes from the times of LOUIS XI, etc.) The 2nd fascicle contains an article of HELLMUTH on the yellow fever in Philadelphia. The third number deals with the alleged southwestern African origin of syphilis, contains a treatise of IBN SĪNĀ on nerves in Arabic original with German translation, also an essay of G. F. HARLESS on the history of physiology of the blood in classical antiquity. (C. F. M.)

1911-1927: **Beiträge zur Geschichte der Medizin.** Edited by ADOLF KRONFELD. Published by M. Perles in Wien. Irregularly published numbers, being reprints of single or several medico-historical articles originally issued in the Wiener medizinische Wochenschrift. No. 1 (1911): Zur Geschichte der Syphilis; ein antikes Votivbild; eine Poliklinik aus dem V. Jahrhundert (A. KRONFELD); No. 2 (1912): Die Entwicklung des Anatomiebildes seit 1632 (A. KRONFELD); Dr. PASQUAL JOSEF FERRO (O. STEINHAUS); No. 3 (1923): Erinnerungen an LEOPOLD V. DIETL. The last number is No. 4 (1927). (C. F. M.).

1925-1926: **Beiträge zur Geschichte der Medizin.** Edited by HENRY E. SIGERIST; published by Orell Füssli in Zürich. A short series of monographs, 25 cm × 16 cm, comprising only 3 nos. issued for the Institut für Geschichte der Medizin in Leipzig. No. 1 (1925): Frühmittelalterliche Rezeptarien (J. JÖRIMANN); No. 2 (1925): Die lateinischen Handschriften Pseudogalens (H. LEISINGER); No. 3 (1926): Zur Kenntnis der Medizinhistorie in der deutschen Romantik (H. V. SEEMEN). (C. F. M.)

1948- : **Beiträge zur Geschichte der Medizin.** Edited by L. SCHÖNBAUER, and published by F. Deuticke in Wien. Numbered and illustrated monographs, 23 cm, issued from the Institut für Geschichte der Medizin in Wien. Nos. 1-4 were written by the editor on such topics as the importance of Austrian surgery, the Austrian military medicine, history of anesthesia, wound treatment (history of antisepsis and asepsis). Hefte 5 and 6 are M. JANTSCH on history of goiter, and history of malaria. Latest no. on record Heft 6 (1948). (C. F. M.)

1902-1929: **Beiträge zur Geschichte der Naturwissenschaften,** by EILHARD WIEDEMANN, Erlangen. *See* Sitzungsberichte der Physikalisch-medizinischen Sozietät zu Erlangen.

1891- : **Beiträge zur Geschichte der Philosophie (und Theologie) des Mittelalters;** Texte und Untersuchungen. Established by CLEMENT BÄUMKER; edited by MARTIN GRABMANN. Published in Münster by Aschendorff. A series of numbered monographs, 24 cm × 16 cm, of great importance for the history of medieval sciences though it is chiefly devoted to philosophy (and theology). No. 15 and No. 16 (1916-1920): De animalibus (text of ALBERTUS MAGNUS). Band 31, No. 2 (1934): Die Quaestiones naturales des ADELARDUS VON BATH (M. Müller). Last volume on record is Bd. 36, No. 1, 1940. There are also supplements, vol. 1 being from 1913. (C. F. M.)

1923: **Beiträge zur Geschichte der Syphilis.** Tokyo. The serial ended with its first number. (Since the publication was not in my hand, it is questionable whether it is a true serial or a monograph). (C.F.M.).

1909- : **Beiträge zur Geschichte der Technik und Industrie.** Jahrbuch des Vereines Deutscher Ingenieure. Edited by CONRAD MATSCHOSS, Berlin. Annual publication containing papers on the history of technology and industry.

Vols. 1 to 5 (1909-13) briefly described in Isis 2: 140. Vol. 21 concerned the year 1931-32. Vol. 22 (1933) appeared with a new title Technik-Geschichte, the old title becoming a subtitle. Latest volume on record vol. 30 (1941), 1943.

1909: Beiträge zur Geschichte der Tierheilkunde. Ed. by FRIEDRICH FREYTAG. H. 1, 72 p., Magdeburg, Verlag Erika.
This is the only published part, including a single memoir (Isis 2: 152).

1905- : Beiträge zur Geschichte der Universität Jena. Issued within the Zeitschrift des Vereins für thüringische Geschichte und Altertumskunde. Published by Fischer in Jena.
Numbered volumes of monographs forming supplements to the above mentioned periodical. No. 6 (1937): Die Geschichtswissenschaften an der Universität Jena in der Zeit der Polyhistorie (1674-1763) (L. HILLER), which is Beiheft 18 of the Zeitschrift. No. 7: Astronomie an der Universität Jena (O. KNOPF). No. 8: ERNST ABBE (M. ROHR), issued as Beiheft 21. This is the latest issue known to me. (C. F. M.)

1938- : Beiträge zur Geschichte der Veterinärmedizin. For the Reichsärztekammer edited by REINHARD FROEHNER, W. RIECK and E. WEBER. Published by R. Schoetz in Berlin.
Six numbers form an annual volume. The serial is the direct continuation of Cheiron (q.v.). Vol. 1, 1938; it is also considered the 18th vol. of Veterinärhistorische Mitteilungen. Vol. 2, 1939/40; vol. 3, for 1940/41, was issued in 1941. Latest vol. on record is vol. 6, 1943/44. (C. F. M.)

1943- : Berner Beiträge zur Geschichte der Medizin und der Naturwissenschaften. Edited by E. HINTZSCHE, W. RYTZ and A. SCHMID. Published by P. Haupt in Bern.
Numbered short monographs. No. 2: Ein deutscher anatomischer Text (E. HINTZSCHE). No. 3 (1944): ALFONSO CORTI (1822-1876) (E. HINTZSCHE), also Das medizinische Institut in Bern (1797-1805) (R. JAUSSI). The latest on record is No. 6, 1946. (C. F. M.)

1929-1933: Biblioteca hebraico-catalana. Barcelona.
Numbered monographic series of Hebrew-Catalan critical editions of 22 cm × 14 cm format. No. 1 (1929): Llibre revelador; Meguillat ha-megalle of ABRAHAM BAR HIJA; No. 2 (1931) a work of JOSEPH BEN MEIR; No. 3 (1931): Llibre de geometria; Hibbur hameixiha uehatixbóret by ABRAHAM BAR HIJA. The latest issue known is No. 4, 1933: Tractat de l'assafea d'Azarquiel (by DON PROFEIT TIBBON). (C. F. M.).

1926- : Biblioteca medico-istorica. Edited by JULES GUIART and VALERIU L. BOLOGA; published by the Institutul de istoria medicinii şi farmaciei in Cluj (Kolozsvár).
Series in Romanian language, of size 23.5 cm × 16 cm. Two items only are known to us, JULES GUIART: Medicine in the age of the Pharaos (51 p. in Romanian 1926; Isis 23, 545). VALERIU L. BOLOGA: Contributions to the history of medicine in Transylvania (102 p. in Romanian, 1927; Isis 23, 603).

1925-1930: Biblioteca Scientia. Edited by J. REY PASTOR and published by A. MEDINA in Madrid, later in Toledo.
Publisher's numbered series, 19 cm × 12.5 cm. No. 2 (1926): Los matemáticos españoles del siglo XVI (J. R. Pastor). (C. F. M.)

1944- : Biblioteca Teoria e historia de las ciencias. Published by the Editorial Losada in Buenos Aires.
Unnumbered publisher's series containing histories of the theory of science, biographies of scientists, etc. F. VERA: Puntos críticos de la matemática contemporanea (1944); E. T. BELL: La reina de las ciencias (1944); G. SCHIAPARELLI: La astronomia en el antiguo Testamento (1945); also life of GALILEI (1945), of HUYGHENS (1945). (C. F. M.)

1923-   : **Biblioteka puteshestvii.** Published in Moskva and Leningrad.
This series contains descriptions of expeditions and monographs related to the history of geography. There are several series. No. 1 of the *3rd* series was issued in 1923. It is N. K. LEBEDEV's Zavoevanie zemli, popularnaia istoria geograficheskikh okrytii i puteshestvii. (Is it still current? C. F. M.)

1936-   : **Bibliotheca humanitatis historica.** Issued by the Hungarian National Museum (Magyar Nemzeti Muzeum), and edited by Count ISTVÁN ZICHY. Budapest.
No. 1 is history of the Dance of Death (A haláltáncok története) by KOZÁKY. Was the series continued? (C. F. M.)

1884-1914: **Bibliotheca mathematica.** Edited by GUSTAV ENESTRÖM [1852-1923].
Three series have appeared. First series, 3 vols. quarto printed in 2 columns, as supplement to Acta mathematica, Stockholm, Berlin, Paris, 1884-86.
Second series, 13 vols. octavo, Stockholm, Berlin, Paris, 1887-99. Subtitle in German and French, Zeitschrift für Geschichte der Mathematik.
Third series, 14 vols. octavo, subtitle in German only, Zeitschrift für Geschichte der mathematischen Wissenschaften. Leipzig, Teubner, 1900-14.
In all, thirty volumes have appeared which are a mine of information on the history of mathematics. They include practically the whole literature ad hoc from 1884 to 1914; the bibliography was continued in Isis. For more details *see* Isis 2: 135-36, and the biography of ENESTRÖM (Isis 8, 313-20, 1926).
Not to be confused with the Bibliotheca mathematica of A. ERLECKE (307 p., Halle 1872-73) which is a German mathematical bibliography up to 1870.

1937-   : **Bibliotheca medica Americana.** Baltimore.
This is the title of the *4th* series of the Publications of the Institute of History of Medicine, of Baltimore. *Cf.* Publications (etc.) (C. F. M.)

1868-1881: **Bibliothek geographischer Reisen und Entdeckungen älterer und neuerer Zeit.** Published by the Griesbach Verlag in Gera, later by Costenoble in Jena.
Numbered series of monographs of octavo size. Complete in 12 numbers. It contains description of expeditions (chiefly contemporary). No. 1 (1868): Das offene Polar-Meer (J. J. HAYES). No. 2: Abenteuerliche Reise durch China (by PINTO). (C. F. M.)

1894: **Bibliothek medizinischer Klassiker.** Edited by J. C. HUBERT; published by J. F. Lehmann in München.
It ceased publication after No. 1 which is: Die Gynäkologie des SORANUS VON EPHESUS. (C. F. M.)

1895-1898: **Bibliothèque de voyages anciens.** Paris, Ernest Leroux.
Only three volumes: vol. 1 (ALVISE CÀ DA MOSTO 1895); vol. 3 (HENRI CORDIER: Centenaire de MARCO POLO 1896). (C. F. M.).

1932-   : **Bibliothèque d'histoire de la philosophie.** Published by J. Vrin in Paris.
Unnumbered series of the publisher, of size 25.5 cm by 16 cm. It first comes upon the record in 1932 with R. POIRIER's Essai sur quelques caractères des notions d'espace et de temps. Is it still current? (C. F. M.)

1909: **Bibliothèque d'histoire scientifique.** Published by Guilmoto in Paris.
Only two volumes were published, both of them written by E. T. HAMY. Tome 1: Correspondance d'A. DE HUMBOLDT avec FR. ARAGO; tome 2: Les débuts de LAMARCK. (C. F. M.)

1901-1914: **Bibliothèque historique de La France Médicale.** Edited by the editor of the France médicale; published by Champion in Paris.
It is an unnumbered series of octavo monographs. The set is complete in 51 volumes. It contains such works as the following: D. R. NEVEU: Le culte d'Esculape dans l'Afrique romaine (1910); E. BELUZE: La Crèche Saint-Gervais (1911); BOIS-MOREAU: Coutûmes médicales . . . (1911). (C. F. M.)

19 ? -   : Bibliothèque de philosophie scientifique, dirigée par le Dr. GUSTAVE LE BON (1841-1931). Paris, Ernest Flammarion.

1921-   : Bijdragen tot de geschiedenis der geneeskunde. Edited by G. VAN RIJNBERK. Published by the Nederlandsch Tijdschrift voor Geneeskunde, Amsterdam.

Published originally in the Nederlandsch tijdschrift voor geneeskunde, then irregularly issued also as a separate publication. Present publisher: Heirs of F. Bohn N. V., Haarlem.

Octavo serial with 4 irregularly issued numbers to a year. It contains original studies, book reviews, feuilletons, and archival material prepared by members of the Genootschap voor Geschiedenis der Geneeskunde, Wiskunde en Natuurwetenschappen. Volume 1 was issued in 1921. Latest volume, published in 1949, includes two years' material: v. 27 for 1947 and v. 28 for 1948. (Also published in vol. 91 and vol. 92 of the journal mentioned above.)

See also 1907 Opuscula selecta Neerlandicorum de arte medica.

1927-   : Les Biographies médicales; notes pour servir à l'histoire de la médecine et des grands médecins. Founded by P. BUSQUET and A. GILBERT; published by J. B. Baillière et fils, in Paris.

An illustrated monthly review issued in a "simple" and a "de-luxe" edition; each number contains a biography, with portraits, of a famous 18th or 19th century physician. Vol. 1 (1927) includes the lives of ALIBERT, DOUBLE, CHAUSSIER, BROUSSAIS, LAËNNEC, CORVISART, BOURDOIS, DUMÉRIL, DESGENETTES, ESQUIROL, etc. The latest issue seen is No. 5 (June-July) of vol. 13, 1939. (C. F. M.)

1947-   : Biologia, an International Year-Book devoted to the pure and applied plant and animal sciences is now being issued, once a year, as a special number of CHRONICA BOTANICA, under the auspices of the International Union of Biological Sciences.

It contains: (1) An Annotated list of all international organizations concerned with the plant and animal sciences, followed by: (2) The Forum—articles and discussions on international relations, historical and methodological subjects; (3) Florilegium Biologicum (Quotations); (4) Reviews, Notes, Queries, etc.; (5) Many illustrations, both modern and old, often on special plates or in a 'portfolio.'

Edited by FRANS VERDOORN and published by the Chronica Botanica Co., Waltham, Mass.

BIOLOGIA I (1947) was issued as a newsletter and consists of six issues.

1932-1939: Blätter für Technikgeschichte. Edited by LUDWIG ERHARD; published by Springer in Wien.

Numbered series of octavo pamphlets issued for the Forschungsinstitut für Technikgeschichte in Wien. Seven numbers make a complete set. No. 1 to No. 5 have the title: Geschichte der Technik. (C. F. M.)

1937-   : Boletín bibliográfico de antropología americana. Founded by ALFONSO CASO; edited by WIGBERTO JIMÉNEZ MORENO. Published by the Instituto panamericano de geografía e historia in México, D. F.

Irregular serial publication containing progress reports on existing research rather than original articles; yet, it contains much material and revelation of sources for the history of precolumbian science or the history of colonial period as they exist in Spanish and Portuguese libraries and archives. (C. F. M.)

1921-   : Bollettino dell'Istituto storico italiano dell'arte sanitaria. Edited by G. CARBONELLI and PIETRO CAPPARONI, later by G. BILANCIONI, Roma.

The Istituto storico was established in 1920. Its Bollettino was published six times a year as a supplement to Rassegna di clinica, terapia e scienze affini. In this form it ended with volume 14 in 1934. Then, the Istituto was renamed as Accademia di storia dell'arte sanitaria. The newly named institution began to publish its Atti e Memorie in 1935 (known as series 2). The latest issue of the Atti on record is from 1945. (C. F. M.)

1898-1921: **Bollettino di bibliografia e storia delle scienze matematiche.** Edited by GINO LORIA, 21 vols. (in two series, series 1, vols. 1-19, 1898-1917; series 2, 3 vols., 1918-21). Torino & Palermo.

After 1921 LORIA's Bollettino lost its independence and became a section of the new series of Bollettino di matematica (v. 1, 1922) edited by ALBERTO CONTI in Roma and Bologna. That section (sezione storico-bibliografica) continued to be edited by GINO LORIA. It was smaller than the original Bollettino but not essentially different.

See Isis 2: 138. GINO LORIA: Guido allo studio della storia delle matematiche (*2nd* ed., p. 84-86, Milano 1946; Isis 37: 254).

1892-1897: **Bollettino di storia e bibliografia matematica.** Napoli.

Six volumes published as supplements to the Giornale de matematiche, edited by G. BATTAGLINI and published in Napoli. This serial is considered as a predecessor of the Bollettino of LORIA (*cf. above*).

See also Bullettino. (C. F. M.)

1881- : **Botanische Jahrbücher für Systematik, Pflanzengeschichte und Pflanzengeographie.** Edited by ADOLF ENGLER; published by Wilhelm Engelmann in Leipzig.

Vol. 57, 1920; vol. 72, 1942. Index to v. 1-30, 1880-1900, and to v. 31-66, 1901-34. (C. F. M.)

1950- : **British journal for the philosophy of science.** Edinburgh, Thomas Nelson & Sons, Parkside Works.

Quarterly to be issued February, May, August and November; small octavo serial containing original articles and the summaries of proceedings of the Philosophy and Science Group of the British Society for the History of Science. Its general editor is A. C. CROMBIE, University College, Gower St., London W. C. I. Vol. 1, no. 1, was issued in May 1950. (C. F. M.)

1852-1862: **Bulletin de bibliographie, d'histoire et de biographie mathématiques.** Edited by OLRY TERQUEM (1782-1862), as a supplement to the Nouvelles annales de mathématiques, journal des candidats aux écoles polytechnique et normale. (Founded in 1842, edited by TERQUEM and CAMILLE CHRISTOPHE GÉRONO). The Bulletin began to appear in vol. 14, 1855 and continued to vol. 20, 1861, then in *2nd* series, vol. 1, 1862, published by Mallet-Bachelier, Paris.

After 8 volumes, the Bulletin stopped in 1862 because of TERQUEM's death. *See* Isis 2: 133.

1926-1930: **Bulletin de la Section de synthèse historique.** Published by the Centre international de synthèse in Paris.

Complete in 10 volumes which form supplements to the Revue de synthèse historique. *Cf.* Revue. (C. F. M.)

1913-1930: **Bulletin de la Société d'histoire de la pharmacie.** Paris, 7, rue de Jouy. Edited by the secretary of the society, EUGÈNE-HUMBERT GUITARD.

The Society was founded in 1913 (Isis 1, 250; 2, 152). The complete set of the bulletin consists of 17 volumes. After 1930 the Society began to publish its Revue (*q.v.*) and the serial Dionysos (*q.v.*). (C. F. M.)

1902-1942: **Bulletin de la Société française d'histoire de la médecine.** Edited by ALBERT PRIEUR.

Vol. 1, no. 1, 1902. ALPHONSE PICARD, Paris. Last no. published, no. 1 of vol. 36, January-June 1942. Description of early volumes in Isis 2, 147.

Continued under the title Mémoires de la Société française d'histoire de la médecine. *See* also Publications.

1910: **Bulletin de la Société médico-historique.** 1 vol. Paris, Ch. Boulangé, 1910.

One volume published (271 p.) including the works of that Society during 1909-10. (Isis 2, 150.) This is a single volume for years 1909-1910. The society was

208 Journals and Serials

founded on 2 March, 1908, at the initiative of Dr. CABANÈS. The small octavo volume contains 19 articles which relate chiefly to French medicine. (I do not know of further volumes; neither is any recorded in catalogs.)

1870-   : **Bulletin des sciences mathématiques.** Edited by GASTON DARBOUX [1842-1917] and EMILE PICARD [1856-1941]. Paris, Gauthier-Villars.
Vols. 1-19 (1870-84) were entitled Bulletin des sciences mathématiques et astronomiques; after that the astronomical part was published separately in the Bulletin astronomique. The latest volume seen was that of 1948. General tables for 1870-76, 1877-1906. *See* Isis 2, 134.
Vol. 1-11, 1870-1876, form series No. 1; series 2, begins with vol. 1, 1877. The serial is issued from the Ecole pratique des hautes études in Paris.

1939-   : **Bulletin of the history of medicine.** Baltimore.
From vol. 7, 1939, on, this is the current title of the Bulletin of the Institute of the History of Medicine. (C. F. M.)

1933-(1938): **Bulletin of the Institute of the History of Medicine.** Edited by HENRY E. SIGERIST. Baltimore, The Johns Hopkins Press.
Vol. 1 appeared in 1933. Latest no. seen vol. 24, 6 (December 1950). Supplements to the Bulletin began to appear in 1943, also edited by SIGERIST. These supplements dealing with special subjects were reviewed or listed in Isis under their authors' names. *E.g.*, no. 1, LUDWIG EDELSTEIN, Baltimore 1943 (Isis 33, 53), no. 9, BENJAMIN SPECTOR, 1947 (Isis 40).
The title of the publication was changed to Bulletin of the History of Medicine in 1939 (with vol. 7).

1900-1912: **Bulletin of the Lloyd Library of botany, pharmacy and materia medica.** Cincinnati.
Complete in 20 numbers of octavo size. Edited by JOHN URI LLOYD, and related to the history of botany and pharmacy. No. 11 (1909): Life and discoveries of SAM. THOMSON; No. 12: The eclectic alkaloids; No. 13: History of the vegetable drugs of the U.S.P. (J. U. LLOYD): No. 19 (1912): Biographies (H. W. FELTER). (C. F. M.)

1941-1943: **Bulletin of the Medical Library Association.** Menasha, Wisconsin.
According to its editors the character of this publication changed. It usually contains association affairs. In vol. 30 and vol. 31 (1941-1943), under the management of CLAUDIUS F. MAYER, its associate and managing editor, the journal was also publishing "contributions of value to . . . the history of medicine in its bibliographical aspect." A special section was devoted to rare books and exhibits, and another to medical bibliography. (C. F. M.)

1911-   : **Bulletin of the Society of Medical History of Chicago.** Published in Chicago.
This is a very irregularly issued medico-historical journal containing the papers of the Society (founded February 1910). It has a few general articles, and many biographies, local (Chicago and Illinois) histories.
An unusual example of slow motion publishing. Vol. 1 includes four numbers which were issued as follows: No. 1, Oct. 1911; No. 2, Aug. 1912; No. 3, March 1913; No. 4. Jan. 1916. Five nos. of vol. 2 were published from Jan. 1917 to March 1922. Vol. 3 in 4 Nos., Jan. 1923 to Sept. 1925. Vol. 4 from April 1928 on. Vol. 5, from Jan. 1937 to June 1946. The latest is No. 5 of vol. 5. There is an Index to vol 1 to 4. (C. F. M.)

1868-1887: **Bullettino di bibliografia e di storia delle scienze matematiche e fisiche.** Edited by BALDASSARE BONCOMPAGNI [1821-94]. 20 vols. folio. Roma.
At the end of vol. 20 (p. 697-748), elaborate tables to the 20 vols. I have a separate copy of these tables dated Roma 1890. The Index was also separately reprinted in the Serie di Indici generali di Opere periodiche italiane estinte; edited by ATTILIO NARDECCHIA (Roma, 1915).

This is a very rich collection, a model of its kind, indispensable in any library of mathematical history. There are variations in the text of different copies; this is explained in Isis 2: 133.

See also Bollettino above.

1933(?)- : **The Carus mathematical monographs.** Chicago, Open Court Publishing Company.
Numbered series of 19 cm by 13 cm volumes; some of them dealing with history of mathematics. No. 5 (1934): A history of mathematics in America before 1900 (D. E. SMITH & J. GINSBURG). (C. F. M.)

1945- : **Castalia; rivista di storia della medicina.** Edited by NICOLA LATTRONICO; published in Milano (Via Gran Sasso 5).
Bimonthly publication from July 1945 to the end of 1946. Only one number was published in 1947 (*i.e.,* vol. 3). The latest volume on record is vol. 4, 1948. It contains publications from the medico-historical school of the University of Milano. No. 3-6 (1947): LA CAVA, A. F., Quattro mostruosità fetali inedite osservate nei sec. XIV e XV. (*N. B. Castalia* was the name of the sacred spring of the Delphi oracle at the foot of Parnassus. Its water would give inspiration to poets.) (C. F. M.)

1950- : **Centaurus.** International magazine of the history of science and medicine. Edited by JEAN ANKER, Director, University Library (Scientific and medical department) and published by Ejnar Munksgaard, Copenhagen.
Quarterly, about 400 p. per year, illustrated, annual subscription 40 Danish crowns ($6). Articles in English, French or German.

1922-1925: **Chapters in the history of science.** Edited by CHARLES SINGER; published by the Oxford University Press in London.
Numbered monographic series, 18 1/2 cm by 12 cm, complete in 4 issues. No. 1: Greek biology and Greek medicine (C. SINGER). No. 2: Mathematical and physical science in classical antiquity (J. L. HEIBERG). No. 3: Chemistry to the time of DALTON (E. J. HOLMYARD). No. 4: The history of mathematics in Europe (J. W. N. SULLIVAN). (C. F. M.)

1936-1938: **Cheiron; veterinärhistorisches Jahrbuch.** Issued by the Gesellschaft für Geschichte und Literatur der Veterinärmedizin; edited by REINHARD FROEHNER (*et al.*); published by W. RICHTER in Mölkau, and by R. SCHOETZ in Berlin.
This is the direct continuation of Veterinärhistorisches Jahrbuch (*q.v.*) which had its vol. 1-7 from 1925 to 1935. With volume 8, 1936, the change in title occurred. Vol. 9, 1937 and vol. 10, 1938, were published in Berlin. Vol. 10 includes such articles as History of rabies, Discussion of DEGLI ALBERTIS' De equo animante libellus, the Hippiatrica of ALBERTUS MAGNUS, etc.
Continued as Beiträge zur Geschichte der Veterinärmedizin (*q.v.*). (C. F. M.)

1930- : **La Chimica.** Edited by ARGEO ANGIOLANI; published in Rome.
Includes also a historical section which is edited by GIULIO PROVENZAL; related to the Società italiana di storia della chimica pura ed applicata which was founded in 1931. It contains also the original articles which make up the Atti e Memorie del Istituto italiano di storia della chimica (*q.v.*). (C. F. M.)

1947- : **Chinese Journal of Medical History.** Published quarterly by the Chinese Medical History Society, 41 Tze ki Road, Shanghai 9.
Summary of vol. 2, 1948 in Archives internationales d'histoire des sciences (no. 6, 542-43, Jan. 1949).

1935- : **Chronica Botanica, an International Collection of Studies in the Method and History of Biology and Agriculture,** founded and edited by FRANS and JOHANNA G. VERDOORN, Waltham, Mass., U. S. A.
Aims primarily at the promotion of: (1) International relations and coöperation in the biological sciences, (2) studies in the method, philosophy, and history of pure

and applied biology, (3) a better understanding among specialists in the various branches of biology and agriculture, and the improvement of their relations with the world at large.

The first volumes of CHRONICA BOTANICA (1935-1937) were published as annual records and reviews of current research, activities and events in the plant sciences. They constitute the first international census of current research in any field of the natural sciences.—Vols. 4-7 (1938-1942) were published as an 'international plant science newsmagazine.' From Vol. 8 (1944) to the present, CHRONICA BOTANICA contains more material than formerly, dealing with the basic humaniora of the plant sciences: history, methodology, and philosophy.

An annual volume of CHRONICA BOTANICA consists of six numbers (3 or more issues) with memoirs, international directories, reprints of classical papers, BIOLOGIA (q.v.), and smaller issues dealing with timely subjects.

The current volume is Vol. 14 (1950-1951).

See also Pallas.

1894-1938: **La chronique médicale.** Revue bimensuelle de médecine historique, littéraire et anecdotique. Founded and edited by AUGUSTIN CABANÈS [1862-1928]. Paris, 15 rue Lacépède.

Published twice a month (not every two months), see Isis, 2, 146. Dr. CABANÈS was a master of anecdotic medicine, and his journal was anecdotic rather than historical in a deeper sense. Publication ceased with volume 45, 1938.

1948-   : **Chymia: annual studies in the history of chemistry.** Published by the Edgar F. Smith Memorial Collection, University of Pennsylvania. Edited by TENNEY L. DAVIS (1890-1949): University of Pennsylvania Press, Philadelphia. Vol. 1 (204 p., illust., 1948); vol. 2, 1949; vol. 3, 1950.

After DAVIS' death HENRY M. LEICESTER, of San Francisco, was appointed editor, and JOHN READ, of St. Andrews, associate editor.

1939-   : **Ciba symposia.** Monthly publication in English of the Ciba Pharmaceutical Products, Lafayette Park, Summit, New Jersey.

It began in September 1939 and is a companion journal to the Swiss-German monthly Ciba Zeitschrift listed below and to several others. Deals with the history of medicine and science, also with medical anthropology and ethnology. In 1948, it was edited by B. CASPARI-ROSEN.

See also Actas Ciba.

1938-   : **Ciba-tijdschrift.** Published by the Ciba Pharmaceutical Products in Basel.

Companion journal of Ciba Zeitschrift; in Dutch language. No. 1 was issued in 1938; latest number on record: No. 29 Feb. 1948. (C. F. M.)

1933-   : **Ciba Zeitschrift.** Published monthly since 1933 by the Society of the Chemical Industry (Ciba pharmaceutical products), in Basel, Switzerland.

Though the main purpose of this journal is to advertise the Society publishing it, it is very well edited and contains a number of valuable studies, richly illustrated, on the history of medicine and science. This journal was not known to the editor of Isis until very late (end of 1948) and therefore the contents of only the latest nos. were listed in Isis.

Latest volume seen is volume 8, 1942. There are several companion journals issued by various national branches of the same manufacturing company in Brazil, Argentina, U. S., the Netherlands. For these see Actas Ciba, Ciba symposia, Ciba-tijdschrift. (C. F. M.)

1946-   : **Clásicos de la medicina.** Edited by PEDRO LAIN ENTRALGO in Madrid, according to HENRY E. SIGERIST (cf. his History of Medicine, N. Y., 1951, vol. 1, p. 519). (C. F. M.)

1923-   : **Classici della scienza.** Published by the Casa Editrice Leonardo da Vinci in Roma.

This is but a title of a subseries of the monographic series Universitas scriptorum (*q.v.*). (C. F. M.)

1940- : Classici della scienza. Published by the R. Accademia d'Italia. Printed by Bardi, Roma.
This monographic series is in 4° size; it differs from the previous one of the same name. No. 1: CESTONI, G. Epistolario ad ANTONIO VALLISNIERI. (Pt 1: 436 p., 1940; Pt 2: publ. in 1941.) (C.F.M.)

1914: Classici delle Scienze e della Filosofia. Edited by ALDO MIELI and ERMINIO TROILO. Serie scientifica. Bari, Società tipografica editrice Barese, 1914 (1913).
The three volumes announced in Isis (1, 99-100, 246) were actually published in 1914 (Isis 2, 90-99, 209-13).

1930- : Classici italiani della medicina. Published by the Casa editrice L. Cappelli, Bologna.
Monographic series of large quarto volumes. Vol. 1, MONDINO DE' LIUCCI: Anatomia (1930; Introd. 3, 845). Latest volume on record: No. 3, PUTTI, V.: BERENGARIO DA CARPI (1937).

1924: Classics of medicine. Edited by CHARLES SINGER. London, John Bale, Sons and Danielsson.
Vol. 1: Selections from the works of AMBROISE PARÉ, by DOROTHEA WALEY SINGER (1924; Isis 7, 208). No further volumes on record.

1922: Classics of scientific method. Edited by E. R. THOMAS. London, G. Bell and Sons.
Collection of little volumes each devoted to the history of a definite scientific problem: circulation of the blood (Isis 5, 194), nature of the air, JOULE and the study of energy, composition of water, origin of colors, etc.

1937-1938: Classiques (Les) de la découverte scientifique (Mémoires de chimie). Published by Gauthier-Villars, 55 Quai des Grands-Augustins, Paris (6ᵉ).
Publisher's unnumbered, irregularly issued series of small octavo volumes (19 cm × 13 cm) containing the basic, classical works, lectures and articles of modern chemistry; each (polygraphic) volume is edited by an expert. Under the general direction of A. DAMIENS, professor at the Pharmaceutical Faculty of the Univ. of Paris. Works of AVOGADRO, AMPÈRE, BERTHELOT, GERHARDT, PASTEUR, etc., are included. About 8 volumes have been published both in an ordinary and in a deluxe edition. (C. F. M.)

1913-1923: Classiques de la science. Edited by H. ABRAHAM, H. GAUTIER, H. LE CHATELIER, J. LEMOINE. Paris, Armand Colin.
Collection of books each of them reprinting classical memoirs devoted to a single topic such as air, carbonic acid and water; the speed of light; molecules, etc. The first four volumes were analyzed in Isis (1, 707, 770; 2, 277, 279). Vols. 1-4, 1913; vols. 5-7, 1914; vol. 8, 1923.

1931: Classiques de la science mondiale. Published by the Editions régionales in Leningrad.
Unnumbered monographs, 20 cm by 15 cm, in Russian language; *e.g.*, in 1931 a number on LAVOISIER, edited and translated by E. and N. TROPOVSKY. (When it started and ended is not known to me). (C. F. M.)

1930- : Clio medica; a series of primers on the history of medicine. Edited by E. B. KRUMBHAAR; published by P. B. Hoeber in New York.
Small monographs, 17 cm by 11 cm, in a numbered series. Vol. 1 (1930): The beginnings: Egypt and Assyria (W. R. DAWSON). Vol. 11 (1934): Chinese medicine (W. R. MORSE). The latest volume on record is no. 22. (C. F. M.)

1927-1932: Colección de documentos inéditos para la historia de Hispano-América. 14 vols., Madrid. (C. F. M.)

1864-1932: Colección de documentos inéditos relativos al descubrimiento, conquista
y organización de las antiguas posesiones españoles (etc.) Madrid.
The first set of this monumental series on the history of American and other trans-
marine colonies of Spain was published from 1864 to 1884; it comprises 42 volumes.
The second series includes 25 volumes, 1885-1932. Important for the history of
geography. (C. F. M.)

1945-   : Colección de la ciencia. Published by Emecé Editores in Buenos Aires.
Unnumbered series for reprint of classics of sciences; *e.g.*, SPALLANZANI, L.
Experiencias sobre las generaciones. (C. F. M.)

1920-   : Colección de libros referentes a la ciencia Hispano-Americana. Edited
by H. J. PAOLI; published in Buenos Aires.
Numbered series of reprints of old texts important for the history of science, technology, medicine. No. 1 (1920): BARBA, A. A. Arte de los metales/Madr., 1729/.
No. 2 (1920): MONARDES, N. Primera y secunda y tercera partes de la Historia me-
dicinal/Sevilla 1580/. No. 3 (1920): PERES DE VERGAS. Los nueve libros de re
metallica/Madr. 2. ed., 1569/. Any more? (C. F. M.)

1945-   : Colección de los viajes y descubrimientos que hicieron por mar los Españoles. Published by the Editorial Guarania in Buenos Aires.
Numbered series related to the history of geography; vol. 1, 1945. (C. F. M.)

1922(?)-   : Colección de publicaciones médicas histórico-artísticas de los Labora-
torios de Norte de España. Edited by J. CUSI; published at Figueras and
Masnou.
Richly illustrated numbered monographic studies, 22 cm by 14 cm, with reproduction of rare fragments of manuscripts; of medico-historical contents. No. 1:
JOHANNES DE CARSO: Tractus de conservatione visus. No. 2: ARNALDUS DE
VILLANOVA: Libellus regiminis de confortatione visus. No. 3: Anonymus: Tractatus
de egritudinibus oculorum. No. 4 (1924): Arte y humor en medicina. No. 5
(1928): J. FABRICIO AB AQUAPENDENTE: De la sufusión o cataracta. Latest number
known to me: No. 9, Las viejas antiparras (1934). (C. F. M.)

1945-   : Colección historia y filosofía de la ciencia. Edited by JULIO REY
PASTOR. Espasa-Calpe Argentina, Buenos Aires-México.
Two series are published. Smaller volumes called Serie menor, the first being
ALDO MIELI: El mundo antiguo (1945), and larger volumes called Serie mayor, the
first of these being DESIDERIO PAPP: Historia de la fisica (1945).

1945-   : Collana di studi di storia della medicina. Edited by N. LATRONICO, of
Milano; published by U. Hoepli, Milano.
Numbered monographs issued irregularly. Vol. 1 (1945): La chirurgia del
pulmone attraverso i tempi, by A. BOTTERO. The latest issue is vol. 8 (1947):
GEROLAMO CARDANO, by A. BELLINI. (C. F. M.)

1947-   : Collana di vite medici e naturalisti celebri. Edited by ANDREA CORSINI
and LORIS PREMUDA. Published by Floriano Zigiotti, in Trieste, Galleria del
Corso No. 4.
Irregularly published, numbered series of the publisher; it contains small octavo
monographs. The set also carries the title: Series I Monografia. No. 1: GIOVANNI
ALFONSO BORELLI, by E. BARBENSI. No. 2: PAOLO ASSALINI, by F. LA CAVA
(1947). No. 3 (1948): FRACASTORO, by F. PELLEGRINI. No. 4: BERNARDINO
RAMAZZINI, by PAZZINI. No. 5: MARCELLO MALPIGHI, by N. LATRONICO. No. 6:
ASCLEPIADE, by L. PREMUDA. (C. F. M.)

1942-   : Collana storica di storia della chimica. Edited by ANGELO TARCHI,
Director of the Istituto Italiano di Storia della Chimica. Published by Casa-
Editrice Mediterranea Tipogr. Castaldi, Roma.
Irregular octavo series of monographs. No. 3 (1942): TESTI G., PARACELSO.
(C. F. M.)

1903-1933: **Collectio ophtalmologica veterum auctorum.** Edited by P. PANSIER; published by J. B. Baillière in Paris.
Reprints of ophthalmological classics in numbered fascicles of 25 cm by 16 cm size. Seven fascicles make the set. Fasc. 1 includes *a*) ARNALDUS DE VILLANOVA: Libellus regiminis de confortatione visus, and *b*) JOHANNES DE CARSO: Tractatus de conservatione visus. Fasc. 2: ALCOATIM: Congregatio sive liber de oculis. Fasc. 7 (1933): CONSTANTINUS AFRICANUS: Liber de oculis (Isis 24, 198, 212). (C. F. M.)

1884-   : **Collection de mémoires sur la physique.** Paris, Gauthier Villars.
First series, 8 vols. 1884-91. Second series, vol. 1 (ions, électrons, corpuscules) (1154 p., 1905). List of these six volumes in Isis 1, 706-07.
Other books appeared in the same collection, second series, without serial number: Les idées modernes de la constitution de la matière (1913), Le progrès de la physique moléculaire (1914).

1948-   : **Collection de travaux de l' Académie internationale d'histoire des sciences.** Published for the Academy, 12 rue Colbert, Paris 2, by Hermann et Cie.
Vol. 1. PAUL VER EECKE: Proclus de Lycie (1948; Isis 40, 256).
Vol. 2. Actes de V*e* congrès international d'histoire des sciences, Lausanne 1947 (288 p.).
See 1947 Archives internationales.

1920-1925: **Collection des maîtres de la pensée scientifique.** Paris.
See Maîtres de la pensée scientifique.

1902-1910: **Collezione storica Villari.** Published by U. Hoepli, in Milano.
This is a so-called publisher's series. Only the following member of the collection could be 'excavated': CARLO ERRERA: L'epoca delle grandi scoperte geografiche (1902; 2*nd* ed. 1910). (C. F. M.)

1947-   : **Connaitre; cahiers de l'humanisme médical; revue bimestrielle.** Founded and edited by E. and H. BIANCANI. Published by Le Concours Médical in Paris.
Bimonthly publications. No. 1 was issued in 1947. Each number is devoted to a special topic such as folklore and medicine (no. 11, 1948) or mysticism and medicine (no. 12, 1948). The serial also contains a section on medical history, and it gives many illustrations of historical interest; it also discusses old medical books. (Not to be confused with another publication of the same title which was issued at Salonica in 1924). (C. F. M.)

1914-   : **Corpus medicorum Graecorum.** Published by Teubner in Leipzig and Berlin.
An undertaking for the critical restoration of the authentic text of classical Greek medical authors. Very irregularly published and very elaborately numbered; vol. 5, no. 9, pt. 1, one of GALEN's commentaries to HIPPOCRATES, was published in 1914 while the issue marked vol. 1 was published in 1927.
There is a main series and a supplemental series. The main series progressed up to vol. 11. The supplemental series started in 1931 with vol. 1, and it reached its vol. 2. (C. F. M.) *See* Isis 42, 150.

1915-1928: **Corpus medicorum Latinorum.** Published in Leipzig for the Puschmannstiftung.
A numbered series of critical reprints of classical Latin authors of medicine. Eight volumes make the series which ends with No. 1, vol. 8. Vol. 2, no. 1-2 and vol. 3, no. 6-7 were never published. The series includes CELSUS (vol. 1, 1915), SERENUS SAMMONICUS (vol. 2, 1916). MARCELLUS EMPIRICUS (vol. 5, 1916), etc. (C. F. M.)

1928-   : **I curiosi della natura.** Edited by GIOVANNI CAU; published by Agnelli in Milano.

A series of unnumbered monographs dealing with the life of great scientists. The booklets are 18 1/2 cm by 13 cm. In the order of their appearance they are: *1.* Cau G: Antonio Pacinotti; la storia della dinamo (1928); *2.* Montalenti, G.: Lazzaro Spallanzani (1928); *3.* Loria, G.: Archimede (1928); *4.* Abetti, G.: Angelo Secchi (1928); *5.* Corsini, A.: Antonio Cocchi (1928); *6.* Di Brazzà, F. S.: Antonio Stoppani (1929). Any more? (C. F. M.)

1934-   : **Dansk veterinaerhistorisk aarbog.** Published in Skive.
Annual volumes for history of veterinary medicine; published by the Dansk veterinaerhistorisk samfund. (C. F. M.)

1878-1885: **Deutsches Archiv für Geschichte der Medizin und medicinische Geographie.** Edited by Heinrich Rohlfs (1827-   ) and Gerhard Rohlfs [1831-96]. Eight volumes published by C. L. Hirschfeld, Leipzig.
Vols. 1, 2, 3 (1876-80) were edited by both brothers: Heinrich, physician and historian of medicine, Gerhard, explorer and geographer. In 1884, Gerhard withdrew. Long extracts from the original program "Was wir wollen," signed by both brothers, were reprinted in Isis 2, 144-45.

Deutsches Museum.
See Abhandlungen und Berichte.

1948-   : **Dialectica.** A quarterly journal devoted to the philosophy of knowledge. Latest volume on record: vol. 2, 1949. Published in Neuchâtel (subscriptions at H. K. Lewis, 136 Gower St., London, W. C. 1). (C. F. M.)

1932-   : **Dionysos;** gazette du praticien, ami des lettres, des arts et du théatre. Supplement to the Revue d'histoire de la pharmacie (*q.v.*). Published by the Société d'histoire de la pharmacie; edited and founded by E. H. Guitard. Published at Paris VI, 14 Ave. de l'Observatoire.
Irregularly issued, first as a separate journal; with No. 10, March 1934, it became a separately numbered part of the original revue. Latest number seen: No. 35, 1940 as supplement to No. 110 of the Revue. (C. F. M.)
See also Bulletin; Revue.

1925-1928: **Documents scientifiques du XV***e* **siècle.** Edited by A. C. Klebs; published by E. Droz in Paris.
Numbered series of facsimile volumes related to the history of various sciences. Four volumes complete the set. Tome 1 (1925): Remèdes contre la peste; taken from various manuscripts and incunabula. Tome 2 (1925): Hélin, M., La clef des songes. Tome 3 (1926): Wickersheimer, E., Anatomies de Mondino dei Luzzi et de Guido de Vigevano. Tome 4 (1928): Smith, D. E., Le comput manuel de Magister Anianus. (C. F. M.)

1884-1887: **Drugs and medicine of North America;** a quarterly devoted to the historical and scientific discussion of the botany, pharmacy, chemistry and therapeutics of the medicinal plants of North America, their constituents, products and sophistications. Edited by John Uri Lloyd and C. G. Lloyd; printed by Robert Clarke and Co. in Cincinnati.
A true journal of quarto size of which the first number was published April 1884. Vol. 1 includes nine numbers, the 9th issued March 1886. The journal progressed to No. 5, vol. 2 (April 1887). As the introduction states: "it will be neither a medical nor a pharmaceutical journal." It is chiefly the work of the Lloyd brothers though other contributors wrote also. The first volume is entirely devoted to the historical description of *Ranunculaceae*. (C. F. M.)

1923-1945: **Early science in Oxford.** Edited by R. T. Gunther (1869-1940). Privately printed in Oxford.
A 14-volume set on history of science in England and on the activities of Oxford men of science. Vol. 1, on chemistry, physics, mathematics and surveying. There are five vols. on Robert Hooke (v. 6, 7, 8, 10, 13). Vol. 9 is a facsimile edition of

RICHARD LOWER's De corde (Lond., 1669) with translation by K. J. FRANKLIN. Vol.
14 (1945) is the life and letters of EDWARD LLWYD (Introd. 3, 1886). (C. F. M.)

1941: **Eudemus.** An international journal devoted to the history of mathematics
and astronomy. Published by Brown University, Providence, Rhode Island,
U. S. A. With assistance from income of the Arnold Buffum Chace Fund of the
Mathematical Association of America. Edited by OTTO NEUGEBAUER and RAY-
MOND CLARE ARCHIBALD.
Vol. 1, 48 p. Published for Brown University by Ejnar Munksgaard, Copenhagen,
1941. No more published (Isis 34, 74).

1922-1925: **Evolución de las ciencias en la República Argentina.** Published by
Editorial Coni in Buenos Aires.
Numbered monographs of 26 cm by 17 cm. The serial started on occasion of
the 50th anniversary of the Sociedad científica argentina. No. 2 (1924): La evolu-
ción de la física (R. G. LOYARTE). No. 6 (1925): Los estúdios botánicos (HICKEN,
C. M.). (C. F. M.)

1920-   : **L'Evolution de l'humanité.** Edited by HENRI BERR; published by La
Renaissance du Livre in Paris.
See Bibliothèque de synthèse historique. (C. F. M.)

1922-   : **Il Facsimile.** Published by SEEBER in Firenze.
A series of texts and documents related to the history of graphic arts and sciences;
25 cm by 17 1/2 cm volumes edited in facsimile, described, transcribed and illustrated. Irregularly published. Most volumes were edited by G. BOFFITO, with the
aid of others. No. 1 (1922): Il quadrante d'Israele (with G. FUMAGALLI); No. 3
(1925): Iniziali istoriate; No. 5 (1929): Gli strumenti della scienza; No. 6 (1931):
Il primo compasso. (C. F. M.)

1926-1940: **Facsimile reproductions of scientific classics.**
This title was given retroactively to a series of papers published in Isis, the first
in vol. 8, 671-84, 1926 (ABRAHAM DE MOIVRE), the twenty-first in vol. 31, 327-79,
1940 (ROEMER). The series was discontinued, because Isis was overcrowded with
other contributions; it is hoped to renew it sooner or later.

1885-1904: **Fiziko-matematicheskaya nauki v ikh nastoyashchem i proshedshem.**
(The physico-mathematical sciences in their present and their past). Journal
edited by V. V. BOBYNIN. Moskva.
VICTOR VICTOROVICH BOBYNIN (1849-   ) was the author of a Russian bibliography of physics and mathematics (Russkaia fiziko-matematicheskaya bibliografia)
published in 13 parts forming 3 vols. Moskva, 1886-1900). Vol. 1 deals with the
period 1587-1763; vol. 2 with 1764-1799; vol. 3 with 1800-98. He wrote many
papers (in Russian and French) on the history of mathematics and contributed to
vol. 4 of CANTOR's Vorlesungen. He founded this Russian journal on the history of
mathematics and physics in 1885; 13 volumes appeared between 1885 and 1898;
from 1899 to 1904, a final volume which might be called vol. 14 or the single vol. of
series 2 appeared under a somewhat different title: Fiziko-matematicheskaya nauki
v khode ikh razvitiya (The physico-mathematical sciences in the course of their
development.).
I wonder whether the Russian bibliography did not first appear in BOBYNIN's
journal; this is suggested by the fact that it appeared in 13 parts and that the journal
filled 13 volumes.
Cf. Isis 2, 136-7.

1928-1940: **Forschungen zur Geschichte der Optik** (Beilagehefte zur Zeitschrift
für Instrumentenkunde). Edited by MORITZ VON ROHR. Published by J.
Springer, Berlin.
Vol. 1, 1 Dec. 1928. Suspended Nov. 1930 to Oct. 1935. Supplements to the
Zeitschrift für Instrumentenkunde which began in 1881. Latest vol. of the Zeit-
schrift: vol. 60, 1940.

1900-1914: **France Médicale;** Revue d'histoire de la médecine. Edited by ALBERT
PRIEUR. Paris, 1 Place des Vosges.
Journal founded in 1854, but before 1900 it dealt with medicine in general.
From 1900 on under the direction of Dr. PRIEUR it became a medico-historical jour-
nal. Isis 2, 146. It ends with vol. 61, 1914.

1938-1939: **Freiburger Forschungen zur Medizingeschichte.** Edited by L. ASCHOFF;
published by Hans Speyer in Freiburg i. B.
Series of medico-historical monographs and reprint of classical texts. Only two
numbers are on record. No. 1: Ueber die Entdeckung des Blutkreislaufes (L.
Aschoff) (1938); No. 2: contains MARCELLO MALPIGHI's De polypo cordis dissertatio
(1939). (C. F. M.)

1940-   : **Gazzetta internazionale di medicina e chirurgia.** Roma.
For its medico-historical supplement *see* Humana studia.

1942-1943: **Geistiges Europa.** Edited by ALBERT ERICH BRINCKMANN; published
by Hoffmann & Campe in Hamburg.
An unnumbered series of the publisher containing books "über geistige
Beziehungen europäischen Nationen." W. LINDEN: ALEXANDER v. HUMBOLDT;
Weltbild der Naturwissenschaft (1942); P. STÖCKLEIN: CARL GUSTAV CARUS (1943).
No later issue could be found. (C. F. M.)

1721-1725: **Das Gelahrte Preussen,** aus neuen und alten, gedruckten und unge-
druckten Schriften, wie auch der gelahrten Männer, welche in Preussen geboren
oder daselbst gelebt . . . Leben, wöchentlich vorgestellt. Published in Thorn.
There are five volumes ("Teil"), the fifth in 4 parts. A weekly biographical
periodical related chiefly to Prussian men of science. Not seen. (C. F. M.)

1932-1937: **Geschichte der Technik.** Wien.
See Blätter für Technikgeschichte. (C. F. M.)

1864-1913: **Geschichte der Wissenschaften in Deutschland.** Edited by the Historische Kommission of the K. Akademie der Wissenschaften in München; published by the Koehler Verlag in Leipzig.
Monumental set on history of German science. Complete in 24 volumes.
(C. F. M.)

1928-1932: **Geschichtliche Einzeldarstellungen aus der Elektrotechnik.** Published
by the Elektrotechnischer Verein. Berlin, v. 1-4 (C. F. M.)

1914-1927: **Geschichtsblätter für Technik, Industrie [und Gewerbe];** illustrierte
Monatschrift. Edited by Count CARL v. KLINCKOWSTROEM, Munich and FRANZ
M. FELDHAUS, Berlin. Berlin -Friedenau, Fr. Zillessen.
Vol. 1, xi + 260 p., 65 fig. (Isis 11, 459); ceases publication with part 4 of vol. 11
(then a quarterly) 1927. Same editors, but published by Verlag Quellenforschungen
zur Geschichte der Technik und Industrie, Berlin-Tempelhof.
This was an annual publication issued by the society called "Geschichte der
Technik." It was not published in 1924-1926.

1943-   : **Gesnerus;** Vierteljahrsschrift für Geschichte der Medizin und der
Naturwissenchaften. Founded by J. STROHL. Edited by H. FISCHER, Zürich,
E. OLIVIER, Lausanne, G. PIOTET, Nyon, ROLIN WAVRE, Genève. Published by
H. R. Sauerländer, Aarau, Aargau.
The first part appeared in 1943, vol. 1 (in 4 parts) was completed in Sept. 1944
(Isis 37, 248). It is the official organ of the Schweizerische Gesellschaft für
Geschichte der Medizin und der Naturwissenschaften. Latest issue: fasc. 3/4
December, vol. 5, 1948.

1793-1800: **Giornale per servire alla storia ragionata della medicina di questo secolo,**
13 vols., Venezia.
This item should not be included in the present list, but having been included

erroneously in the previous list, the present note is meant to correct that error and also to serve as warning.   In the previous list (Isis 2, 142) it was cautiously remarked "I have not seen that journal which I know only by title, and I am not by any means certain that it is a historical journal in our sense of the word.   In the past history and bibliography were often confused.   From that point of view every scientific journal is also a historical journal; their editors are the annalists of contemporary science."

Dr. CLAUDIUS F. MAYER has kindly examined the set and reports as follows (letter of 11 Jan. 1949): "The Giornale is not an organ for the publication of medico-historical articles, but an ordinary medical monthly.   I examined every volume carefully as to its contents.   The journal claims to be the first Italian medical monthly (NB. It was, however, the second) and it was edited by FRANCESCO AGLIETTI, the secretary of the Società medica di Venezia.   It contains abstracts or digests of current medical book and journal literature, such as the transactions of the scientific or medical societies of Paris, Uppsala, London, etc., with many lengthy book-reviews and occasional original letters written to the editor, discussing a few medical case-histories.   The journal is a treasure house of little known Italian pamphlets of the late 18th century.   Its main arrangement includes sections for such subjects as anatomy, theoretical and practical medicine, medical chemistry, surgery, and miscellaneous. I do not want to say much about its publishing history since it should not be included in your list.   Vol. 1 was published in 1783 in Venezia, in the house of Pasquali; the same publishers brought out the other volumes, with some difficulties on account of 'international' troubles.   The latest volume bears the year 1800; it is the 13th volume.   The Army Med. Libr. has vols. 1-12.   (The 13th vol. was recently microfilmed)."

1923(?): **Los grandes viajes clásicos.**   Published by Espasa-Calpe in Madrid.
Only a fragment of this monographic series came to my attention.   In 1923 the reports of CIEZA DE LEÓN were reprinted in a volume.   (C. F. M.)

ca 1940-   : **I Grandi Italiani, collana di biografie.**   Edited by LUIGI FEDER-ZONI, president of the R. Accademia d'Italia.   Published by Unione Tipografica-Editrice Torinese, Torino.
Irregularly issued, numbered series of biographies; octavo.   It includes all branches of science.   No. 14 (1914): GIORDANO, D., GIAMBATTISTA MORGAGNI, 268 p.   No. 15 (1941): PESSION, G., GUGLIELMO MARCONI, 204 p.   No. (?) (1941): CAPPARONI, P., SPALLANZANI, 282 p.   (C. F. M.)

1906-1908: **Grenzfragen der Literatur und Medizin in Einzeldarstellungen.**   Edited by S. RAHMER; published by E. Reinhardt in München.
Numbered octavo monographs discussing the role of medicine in the writings of light literature.   Eight numbers complete the set.   (C. F. M.)

1910-1932: **Grosse Männer;** Studien zur Biologie des Genies.   Founded by WILHELM OSTWALD; published by the Akademische Verlagsbuchhandlung in Leipzig.
Numbered series of mostly biographical material.   No. 1 & 2: DE CANDOLLE, A. Zur Geschichte der Wissenschaften (1910; Isis 1: 132).   Other volumes include the life of JACOBUS HENR. VAN'T HOFF (no. 3), VICTOR MEYER (no. 4), E. ABBÉ (no. 5), E. RATHENAU (no. 6), W. HOFMEISTER (no 7), JOHANNES MÜLLER (no. 8, 1924). The series ended with no. 12 (1932), ROBERT KOCH, part 1, by B. HEYMANN. (C. F. M.)

1919-1928: **Guide "Ics";** profili bibliografici de "L'Italia che scrive."   Edited by FORMIGGINI; published by the Istituto per la propagazione della cultura italiana (Fondazione Leonardo) in Rome.
Numbered series of small, 16° or 24°, volumes related to bibliography and history of various sciences.   There is a series 1, containing 45 nos., published from 1919 to 1928.   No. 1 (1919): ALMAGIA, R., Geografia; No. 3 (1920): BÉGUINOT, A., La botanica; No. 4 (1920): BILANCIONI, G., La storia della medicina.
In 1935 a new series was started by the institute, both the series and the institute

assuming a new title (and a new character): Guide bibliografiche, by the Istituto nazionale di cultura fascista. (C. F. M.)

1847-   : Hakluyt Society Works.   Society established in London in 1846 for the
    publication of original narratives of important voyages, travels, expeditions and
    other geographical works.
    It was named after RICHARD HAKLUYT (1552-1616) who was one of the first
to collect and publish such narratives.   100 volumes (forming series I) were
issued from 1847 to 1898.   A second series was begun in 1899; vols. 97-98 (issued
for 1948) were received in December 1948.   The honorary secretary has his office
in the British Museum; the honorary secretary for the United States, in the Athe-
naeum, Boston, Mass.
    An extra-series of 33 vols. has been published by the Society from 1903 to 1905.
This includes RICHARD HAKLUYT's Principal Navigations (vols. 1-12, Glasgow
1903-5), the texts and versions of JOHN DE PLANO CARPINO and WILLIAM DE
RUBRUQUIS (vol. 13, Cambridge 1903), Hakluytus Posthumus or Purchas His Pil-
grimes (vols. 14-33, Glasgow 1905-7).
    EDWARD LYNAM: RICHARD HAKLUYT and his successors.   A volume issued to
commemorate the centenary of the Hakluyt Society (vol. 93 of second series, London 1946; Isis 38, 130).   This includes a history of the society and a list of all the
HAKLUYT editions and maps, well indexed.

1898-1899: Harper's scientific memoirs.
    See Scientific memoirs.   (C. F. M.)

1922-   : Heidelberger Akten der von-Portheim Stiftung.   Published by C. WIN-
TER in Heidelberg.
    Numbered series of monographs, 26 cm by 18 cm; it includes the Arbeiten aus
dem Institut für Geschichte der Naturwissenschaften, all numbers of the subseries
edited and/or written by J. RUSKA.   No. 6(1924): Arabische Alchemisten; no. 10
(1924): the same topic; no. 16 (1926): Tabula smaragdina.   The latest issue on
record is vol. 25.   (C. F. M.)

1934-   : The Hideyo Noguchi Lectures.
    This is the specific title of the 3rd series of the Publications of the Institute of
Medicine, Baltimore (q.v.).   (C. F. M.)

1898-1899: Hippocrate; revue mensuelle de médecine historique, patriotique, an-
    ecdotique.   Edited by Dr. SOCRATE LAGOUDAKY and HECTOR RAVEAU; pub-
    lished by Pairault & cie in Paris.
    It is a single volume of 416 p., made up of 14 monthly issues.   The first number
was published February 1898, the last issue is no. 13/14, March 1899 ("2. année").
The editor's preface states: "nous publierons des travaux historiques, patriotiques,
littéraires écrits par des Grecs ou par des philhellènes."   And so, it is a mélange of
biography of Greek national heroes, French translation of Hippocratic works (Aphorisms), the Hippocratic Oath, history of Greek medicine, also current medical
articles, and news from Macedonia and Crete, etc.   (C. F. M.)

1935(?)-   : Hippocrate (Collection).   Edited by Prof. LAIGNEL-LAVASTINE.
    Published by Le François, in Paris.
    Unnumbered series of the publisher, including vols. of 24 cm by 15½ cm size;
e.g., P. DELAUNAY: La vie médicale aux 16e, 17e et 18e siècle (1935).   Any more?
(C. F. M.)

1926-1944: Historia medicinae.   Once edited by VICTOR ROBINSON; published by
    the Froben Press, New York.
    This is a publisher's series of unnumbered monographs.   There are autobiogra-
phies, histories of specialties, essays in the history of medicine (MAX NEUBURGER),
medical practice in foreign countries, etc.   Latest issue on record is from 1944.   Up
to that time 24 volumes were published.   Vols. 1, 2, & 4 were also advertised as
Library of medical history.   (C. F. M.)

1936-   : **Historical bulletin.** Issued quarterly by Calgary Associate Clinic as a supplement to its monthly "Historical Nights." Published in Calgary, Alberta, Canada.

Small octavo quarterly with notes and abstracts related to medical history. Latest issue is no. 3, November, vol. 13, 1948/49; it contains articles on the history of Canadian medical schools (W. T. CONNELL), history of gout (A. P. C. CLARK), medical pioneering in Alberta (A. W. PARK), etc. (C. F. M.)

1935-   : **Historical notes and papers.** Communications from the Astronomical Observatory, Lund, Sweden.

These booklets dealing with the history of astronomy are separate numbers of the "Meddelande frän Lunds Astronomiska Observatorium, Ser. II." Nos. 1 to 15 being respectively no. 72, 73, 77, 78, 80, 82-85, 88, 89, 91, 96, 101, 102 of the general series. No. 15 appeared in 1939; no. 22 in 1949.

Each number contains a single memoir.

All these memoirs have been listed in Isis under the author's names: KNUT LUND-MARK (4 items). BJÖRN SVENONIUS (3), PER COLLINDER (3), ÅKE OHLMARKS, ABDEL HAMID SAMAHA (2), LEWIS A. R. WALLACE, D. KOTSAKIS, etc.

1841: **Historical society of science.** 2 vols. Printed for the Society, by R. and J. E. Taylor, London.

Only two volumes were published, both in 1841. *1.* JAMES ORCHARD HALLIWELL (-PHILLIPPS): Collection of letters illustrative of the progress of science in England from the reign of Queen ELIZABETH to that of CHARLES II (144 p.). *2.* THOMAS WRIGHT: Popular treatises on science written during the Middle Ages in Anglo-Saxon, Anglo-Norman and English (156 p.). At the end of volume 1, one may find a list of 12 additional vols. (nos. 3 to 15) suggested for publication. (Isis 18, 127-32).

1929-1938: **Historische bibliotheek voor de exacte wetenschappen.** Published by P. Noordhoff in Groningen.

Six numbered volumes complete the set. No. 1: (1929): De elementen van EUCLIDES (E. J. DIJKSTERHUIS); No. 2 (1929): Inleiding in de niet-Euclidische meetkunde op historischen grondslag (H. J. E. BETH). (C. F. M.)

1889-1896: **Historische Studien aus dem Pharmakologischen Institute der K. Universität zu Dorpat.** vol. 1-5. Published in Halle a. S. (C. F. M.)

1838-1840: **Historisch-literarisches Jahrbuch für die deutsche Medizin.** Published by Voss in Leipzig.

Three octavo volumes chiefly written by LUDWIG CHOULANT; they contain analysis of the German medical bibliography for the years 1837-1839, with many valuable medico-historical notes related to ancient and medieval medicine. (C. F. M.).

1930-   : **History of medicine series.** Published by the New York Academy of Medicine Library in New York.

Vol. 1 was issued in 1930. The series progressed as far as no. 6. It includes also a magnificent folio of Vesalian works with many illustrations from the original woodcuts. (C. F. M.)

1909-   : **A History of the Sciences;** collection of small illustrated volumes published by the Rationalist Press Association, London; G. P. Putnam's Sons, New York.

GEORGE FORBES: History of astronomy (1909).

Sir THOMAS THORPE: History of chemistry (2 vols. 1909-10).

HORACE BOLINGBROKE WOODWARD: History of geology (1911).

JAMES MARK BALDWIN: History of psychology (2 vols. 1913).

JOHN SCOTT KELTIE: History of geography (1913).

History of Science Society Publications.—In addition to Isis, the Society has published many books or patronized their publication. The bibliography of this is even more difficult than that of other series, because the nine works (12 vols.) published from 1928 to 1936, were issued by five different publishers in five different cities. Full list in Isis (34, 411).

The Secretary-Treasurer of the HSS is Mr. FRED. G. KILGOUR (Yale Medical Library, New Haven, Conn.)

1940-   : Humana studia; contributi dell'Istituto di storia della medicina della R. Università di Roma. Edited by ADALBERTO PAZZINI. Published in the Gazzetta internazionale di medicina e chirurgia; Roma, Società anonima Edizioni Scientifiche, via Nomentana 216.

Folio-sized biweekly publication; it appeared first as a special column ('rubrica') of the main journal; now it is an Appendix, without separate pagination but with a title-page of its own. Each issue contains 8-10 pages of original articles, also reproductions of portraits related to history of medicine. Its publication started in vol. 49, 1940, of the Gazzetta. (C. F. M.)

1936-   : Humanior; biblioteca del Americanista moderno. Edited by J. IMBELLONI; published in Buenos Aires.

There are three different series published under this title: ser. A, Propedéutica; ser. B, Razas y migraciones, and ser. C. Patrimonio cultural indiana. The last named series brought forth its vol. 1 in 1936; it deals with cultural history and folklore of science. Vol. 3 (1937): Medicina aborigen Americana (R. PARDAL). (C. F. M.)

1919-1932: L'illustrazione medica italiana. Genova.

Monthly serial rich in illustrative material and in para-medical articles related to history of Italian medicine and Italian art. Vol. 1, 1919; vol. 2, 1920. Last volume: v, 14, 1932. (C. F. M.)

1940: Illustrierte Monographien zur Geschichte der Medizin. Issued by Senkenbergisches Institut für die Geschichte der Medizin an der Universität Frankfurt a.M.; published by J. A. Barth in Leipzig.

There is apparently nothing more than the first volume: No. 1 (1940): CHRISTINA MENTZEL (W. ARTELT). (C. F. M.)

1935-   : Imago mundi. Jahrbuch der alten Kartographie. Edited by LEO BAGROW.

Vol. 1, 84 p., ill., Published by Bibliographikon, Berlin 1935 (Isis 26, 285). Vol. 2, 111 p., ill., 1937 (Isis 30, 181). Vol. 3, 117 p., ill., 1939. Vol. 2 and 3 were edited with the help of EDWARD LYNAM and published by HENRY STEVENS, London. Latest volume: Vol. 5, 110 p., ill., Kartografiska Sällskapet, Stockholm, 1948.

1950-   : Impact of Science on Society. Paris.

Published by UNESCO, 19 Avenue Kléber, Paris 16. Vol. 1, no. 1, April-June 1950; no 2, July-September 1950.

1880-   : Index-Catalogue of the Library of the Surgeon General's Office. United States Army (Army Medical Library), Government Printing Office, Washington, D. C.

It may seem odd to include a catalogue among serials, but the inclusion of this one is fully justified because of its intrinsic importance and of its periodicity. This Index-Catalogue contains fairly complete lists by authors and subjects of every kind of medical literature, the historical kind as well as the others.

First Series, vols. 1-16, 1880-95, edited by ROBERT FLETCHER.

Second Series, vols. 1-17, 1896-1912, edited by FLETCHER, vol. 18-21, 1913-16, edited by FIELDING H. GARRISON.

Third Series, vols. 1-2, 1918-20, edited by GARRISON; vols 3-10 edited by ALBERT ALLEMANN.

Fourth Series, vols. 1-10, 1936-48, edited by CLAUDIUS F. MAYER. The latter began in vol. 6 a Bio-bibliography of XVI. century medical authors (67 p., 1941);

first half of letter **A.** Vol. 10 of the Fourth Series is vol. 57 of the whole collection, the largest of its kind in existence.
See description of the AML and its Index-Catalogue by Maj. Gen. EDGAR ERSKINE HUME (Isis 26, 423-27, 2 portraits, 1936). *See* also Isis 33, 726-27; 40, 119.

1921: **Invenzioni, scoperte.** Published by G. Barbera in Firenze.
Series of octavo volumes. No. 1 (1921): Il volo in Italia; storia documentata (etc.) (G. BOFFITO). Any more? (C. F. M.)

1913- : **Isis.** Revue consacrée à l'histoire de la science, publiée par GEORGE SARTON. Wondelgem-lez-Gand, Belgique. The first article (SARTON's program) written in Nov. 1912, appeared before the end of that year. First no., March 1913, first vol. completed in 1914. The subtitle of Isis has been changed repeatedly, the general meaning remaining the same. It now is (vol. 40, 1949) "an international review devoted to the history of science and civilization, official quarterly of the History of Science Society." The editor is still SARTON, the managing editor I. BERNARD COHEN (Harvard Library 189, Cambridge 38, Massachusetts, U. S. A.), many associate editors.
This is the chief journal devoted to the history of science and the most comprehensive. It includes new contributions, reviews, notes, abundant illustrations, and a very elaborate critical bibliography covering the whole field. That bibliography is arranged in the same order as SARTON's Introduction; it corrects and keeps up to date the volumes of the Introduction already published and accumulates materials in their proper sequence for the ulterior volumes.
See also Isis 2, 156.
See History of Science Society Publications.

1935- : **Istanbul Üniversite; Tip Tarihi enstitü.**
See Yayınlarından. (C. F. M.)

1928-1940: **Jahrbuch der Gesellschaft für die Geschichte und Bibliographie des Brauwesens.** Berlin.
Annual volumes on the history of the brewing industry. Vol. 8, 1935. The latest volume on record is vol. 12, for 1939-40, published in 1940. (C. F. M.)

1902- : **Jahrbuch der Gesellschaft für Geschichte und Literatur der Landwirtschaft.** Edited by MAX GÜNTZ and WILHELM SEEDORF. Published in Vippach-Edelhausen.
Annual volumes on the history of agriculture. Vols. 1-11 were published under the title: Landwirtschaftlich-historische Blätter. The latest issue on record is Heft 3, vol. 41, 1942. (C. F. M.)

1892- : **Jahresbericht der Deutschen Mathematiker Vereinigung.** Published by Teubner in Berlin and Leipzig.
Vol. 1 edited by G. CANTOR, W. DYCK, E. LAMPE appeared in 1892. Vol. 49 edited by E. SPERNER, in 1939/40. Vol. 10 (1901-4) was divided into two parts; the first part published in 1904 included a history of the German society of mathematicians and tables to vols. 1 to 12 (sic); that part was published at the time of the III. International Congress of Mathematicians in Heidelberg, August 1904. Publication was suspended from 1915 to 1929.
Ergänzungsbände (Supplementary volumes), vol. 1, 1906; vol. 6, 1930 (the last?)
It is a moot question whether this annual publication and its supplements should be included. They certainly contain a relatively large number of papers concerning the history of mathematics, biographies of mathematicians, retrospective bibliographies. Some of the supplements are important contributions to the history of mathematics; it will suffice to mention one item, GUSTAV ENESTRÖM: Verzeichnis der Schriften LEONHARD EULERS (Ergänzungsbände IV, 1-2, 388 p. Leipzig 1910-13), basis of the EULER edition. Latest vol. on record is vol. 53, 1943, containing three numbers.

1928-1930: Jahresbericht des Forschungsinstituts für Geschichte der Naturwissen-schaften. Edited by J. RUSKA; published in Berlin.
This annual report is the continuation of the next entry. Only three volumes were published. (C. F. M.)

1925-1927: Jahresbericht des Instituts für Geschichte der Naturwissenschaften. Ed-ited by J. RUSKA; published in Heidelberg.
Annual reports of the Heidelberg Institute comprise only three volumes. *Cf.* preceding entry. (C. F. M.)

1846-1848: Janus (I); Zeitschrift für Geschichte und Literatur der Medizin. Edited by A. W. E. TH. HENSCHEL (1790-1856). Three volumes published, Breslau, Eduard Trewendt.
Vol. 1, 884 p., 1846; 2, 830 p., 1847; 3, 842 p., 1848 (Isis 2, 143).
Photographic reprint published by the Alfred Lorentz Buchhandlung (3 vols. Leipzig 1929) with new preface by KARL SUDHOFF and dedication to WILLIAM HENRY WELCH apropos of the inauguration of the Welch Medical Library in Balti-more, Maryland.

N.B. At the same time, from 1847 to 1848, there has been issued another 'Janus' (Jahrbücher deutscher Gesinnung), a revolutionist biweekly, edited by V. A. HUBER and published in Halle & Berlin. (C. F. M.)

1851-1853: Janus (II); Central-Magazin für Geschichte und Literärgeschichte der Medizin, ärztliche Biographik, Epidemiographik, medicinische Geographie und Statistik. Edited by H. BRETSCHNEIDER of Gotha, A. W. E. TH. HENSCHEL of Breslau, C. FR. HEUSINGER of Marburg, J. C. THIERFELDER of Meissen. 2 vols. Gotha, J. G. Müller.
Vol. 1, 322 p., 1851; vol. 2, 664 p., 1853 (Isis 2, 143).
A separate note is devoted to Janus (II), because it began to appear three years after the demise of Janus (I) and also because its scope was much wider than that of its predecessor. It did not concern only the history and literature of medicine, but also epidemiology, medical geography and statistics. This confusion has been con-tinued in other medical books and journals, especially in Janus (III). The tradition of Janus (I) was continued in Janus (II) by one of the editors, HENSCHEL, who wrote the keynote essay introducing the new series.
Photographic reprint in one vol. issued by ALFRED LORENTZ, Leipzig, in 1929.

1896-1941: Janus (III). Archives internationales pour l'histoire de la médecine et la géographie médicale. Amsterdam, Leyden, Haarlem, De erven v. F. Bohn.
Founded and edited by H. F. A. PEYPERS (1853-1904). After his death, vols. 9 and 10 were edited by C. L. VAN DER BURG; vol. 11, 1906, was edited by A. W. NIEUWENHUIS and E. C. VAN LEERSUM.
Index to the years 1896-1905, published in 1907 (Isis 2, 146).
Last no. seen, no. 1/3. 45th year April to June 1941. No others published.

N.B. In 1950 a French monthly assumed the title 'Janus; la jeune poésie fran-çaise et américaine.' (C. F. M.)

1912-1932: Jenaer medizin-historische Beiträge. Edited by THEODOR MEYER-STEINEG; published by G. Fischer in Jena.
Monographic series, 24 cm by 16 cm. Complete in 15 volumes. Publication was suspended in 1921-1927. No. 1 (1912): Chirurgische Instrumente des Alter-tums (T. MEYER-STEINEG). No. 2 (1912): Darstellung normaler und krankhaft veränderter Körperteile an antiken Weihgaben (T. MEYER-STEINEG). No. 5 (1913): Zur Geschichte des Ammenwesens im klassischen Altertum (W. BRAAMS). No. 13 (1930): Pädiatrie in Hellas und Rom (S. GHINO-POULOS). No. 15 (1932): Sinnesempfindungen in Ilias und Odyssee (C. KÖRNER). (C. F. M.)

1940-   : Journal of the history of ideas. *See* p. 248.

1904-1920: The Journal of philosophy [psychology and scientific methods]. Vol. 1-16. Published in Lancaster and New York. (C. F. M.)

1946-   : Journal of the History of medicine and allied sciences. Published by
Henry Schuman, New York; London, Wm. Heinemann.
Vol. 1 appeared in 1946; vol. 3 in 1948.

1936-   : Journal of the Society for the Bibliography of Natural History. Published by the Society, British Museum (Natural History), Cromwell Road, London S. W. 7.
Vol. 1, 12 nos. appeared from 1936 to 1943. Vol. 2, began to appear in December 1943; Vol. 2, part 4 was published on 3 November 1948 (Isis 36, 54).

1889-   : Klassiker der exakten Naturwissenschaften. Founded by WILHELM
OSTWALD (1853-1932). and edited by ARTHUR VON OETTINGEN. Published by
Wilhelm Engelmann, Leipzig; later by Akademische Verlagsgesellschaft, Leipzig.
Vols. 238-39 appeared in 1934. Latest vol. (244) was published in 1938.
    Each volume contains the text of one of the classics of science in German trans-
lation, with notes. Sometimes a whole book is translated, sometimes only the pertinent parts. Some volumes contain many short texts concerning a single topic, e.g.,
the papers of LOTHAR MEYER and D. MENDELEEV on the Periodic Law (no. 68,
1913; Isis 1: 771).

1910-1942: Klassiker der Medizin, hrsg. von Dr. KARL SUDHOFF. Leipzig, Johann
Ambrosius Barth.
    See Isis 2, 150. Twenty volumes, each devoted to a medical classic had already
appeared in 1914. Latest volume seen by me (no. 27) deals with ALBRECHT VON
HALLER's memoirs of 1752 edited by KARL SUDHOFF (1922; Isis 5, 234). No. 29
(1923): The German translation of PARÉ's work on the treatment of gunshot wounds;
edited by H. E. SIGERIST.
    No. 30 is PASTEUR's work on the fowl cholera publ. in 1923. No. 32 appeared in
1927, while the last no. 33 was published in 1942. (C. F. M.)

1913-   : Klassiker der Naturwissenschaft und der Technik. Edited by Graf
KARL VON KLINCKOWSTROEM and FRANZ STRUNZ. Jena, Diederichs, 1913.
    The series started with FRANZ STRUNZ' work: Die Vergangenheit der Naturfor-
schung (1913). It was enlarged in 1915 by a reprint of LAMARCK, and in 1918 by
a reprint of KEPLER.
Isis 1, 246; 2, 155, 216-17. (C. F. M.)

1905: Klassiker der Naturwissenschaften, herausgegeben von LOTHAR BRIEGER-
WASSERVOGEL. Leipzig, F. Thomas.
    Six volumes published all in 1905, dealing with J. R. MAYER, DARWIN, K. E. v.
BAER, VARENIUS, PLATO and ARISTOTLE.

1935-   : Klassiki biologii i mediciny. Published by OGIZ, in Moskva & Leningrad, according to HENRY E. SIGERIST (History of Medicine, N. Y., 1951, vol. 1,
p. 519). (C. F. M.)

1920?-   : Klassiki prirodnykh nauk (Classics of natural sciences). Edited by
B. MENSHUTKIN.
    Of this Russian series of reprints of science classics there is but little informa-
tion available. The series includes works of MENDELEEV, of LOMONOSSOV, etc.
(C. F. M.)

1940-   : Klassisk dansk medicin. Edited by AXEL HANSEN; published by Løvens
Kemiske Fabrik. Printed by J. D. Qvist & Co., in København.
    We have seen the 3rd vol. of this monographic series which is the Danish re-
print of THOMAS BARTHOLIN's writings on the lymphatic system; it was edited by
G. TRYDE (282 p.). Any more? (C. F. M.)

1915-1937: Komisja do badania historii filozofii w Polsce (Commission on the history
of philosophy in Poland). Issued by the Akademja umiejetnosci in Kraków.
    There are 6 volumes in 8 parts in print. (C. F. M.)

1877-1886: **Kosmos;** Zeitschrift für einheitliche Weltanschauung auf Grund der Entwicklungslehre. Leipzig.
Typical serial for the darwinistic philosophy of science. 19 volumes complete the set. (C. F. M.)

1913-1926: **Kulturgeschichte der Zahnheilkunde in Einzeldarstellungen.** Edited by CURT PROSKAUER. Published by H. Meusser in Berlin.
Complete in 4 volumes. Monographs of 28.5 cm by 22 cm size. No. 1: Das Zahnsticher und seine Geschichte (H. SACHS). No. 4 (1926): Iconographia odontologica (C. PROSKAUER). (C. F. M.)
Cf. Isis 2: 151.

ca 1931: **Kulturgeschichtliche Beiträge;** aus dem Forschungsinstitut für Geschichte der Zahnheilkunde des Reichsverbandes der Zahnärzte Deutschlands, E. V. Edited by Dr. CURT PROSKAUER, in Breslau.
Issued as part of Zahnärztliche Mitteilungen (only evidence is No. 31, 1931 of this dental journal). No more? (C. F. M.)

1928-1932: **Kyklos;** Jahrbuch des Instituts für Geschichte der Medizin an der Universität Leipzig. Edited by HENRY E. SIGERIST, published by Georg Thieme, Leipzig. Vol. 1, 1928; vol. 2, 1929; vol. 3, 1930; vol. 4, 1932.
Vol. 2 dedicated to WM. H. WELCH, contains *a)* papers from the Institute, *b)* research in medical history and *c)* activities of the Institute. Typical papers: O. TEMKIN: Studien zum Sinn-Begriff in der Medizin: E. HIRSCHFELD: VIRCHOW; E. IRSAY: A physiological synthesis; C. F. MAYER: Die Personallehre in der Naturphilosophie von ALBERTUS MAGNUS; A. W. BOCK: Dietetische Wundbehandlung im Mittelalter, etc. (C. F. M.)

1902-1913: **Landwirtschaftlich-historische Blätter.** Organ der Gesellschaft für Geschichte und Literatur der Landwirtschaft. Edited by MAX GUNTZ, Weimar.
Small monthly publication. In 1913 it was changed into a quarterly with a new title Jahrbuch der Gesellschaft für Geschichte und Literatur der Landwirtschaft (*q.v.*).
Isis 2, 141.

1936- : **Lavori del Istituto di storia della medicina della Università di Roma.**
Series of annual volumes, the first one for 1936/37, published in 1938. Each volume has also a separate significant title; *e.g.*, vol. 1: Per il sacrario di ASCLEPIO. (C. F. M.)

1819-1826: **Leben und Lehrmeinungen berühmter Physiker** am Ende des XVI. und am Anfange des XVII. Jahrhunderten als Beiträge zur Geschichte der Physiologie in engerer und weiterer Bedeutung. Edited and written by THADDAEUS ANSELM RIXNER and THADDEUS SIBER. Published in Sulzbach.
There are 7 fascicles. Each fascicle contains a single biography: Heft 1: PARACELSUS (1819; 2. ed., 1829); H. 2: GIROLAMO CARDANO (1820); H. 3: BERNARDINUS TALESIUS (1820); H. 4: FRANCISCUS PATRICIUS (1823); H. 5: GIORDANO BRUNO (1824); H. 6: THOMAS CAMPANELLA (1826); H. 7: J. B. v. HELMONT (1826). (C. F. M.)

1927- : **Legacy series.** Published by the Clarendon Press, Oxford.
Publisher's series of unnumbered volumes issued at irregular intervals. The earliest volume is the one written by EDWYN BEVAN and CHARLES SINGER on Legacy of Israel. Other volumes are: Legacy of Islam (T. W. ARNOLD), Legacy of Rome (C. BAILY), Legacy of the Middle Ages (C. G. CRUMP), Legacy of India (G. T. GARRATT), Legacy of Egypt (S. R. K. GLANVILLE), Legacy of Greece (R. W. LIVINGSTONE). (C. F. M.)

(1920)1921: **Liber memorialis;** premier congrès de l'histoire de l'art de guérir (Anvers, 7-12 Aug. 1920).
This is the "comptes-rendus" of the first congress devoted exclusively to medical history. Many others followed. (C. F. M.)

1926-1927: **Library of medical history.** New York.
. *See* Historia medicinae. (C. F. M.)

1948-   : **The Life of Science library.** Collection of books on the history of
science published by Henry Schuman, New York.
Keynote volume The Life of Science, Essays in the history of civilization by
GEORGE SARTON (1948; Isis 40). Thus far, 14 volumes have appeared, each dealing
with a great man of science (BENJAMIN SILLIMAN, COPERNICUS, ARCHIMEDES,
CLAUDE BERNARD, etc.), the history of an idea or a technique (anaesthesia, the
ships, . . .) or the history of a scientific institution (the Royal Society, the Smithsonian Institution . . .). The latest volume (the 14th) is R. J. FORBES: Man the
Maker, a History of Technology and Engineering (1950).

1803-1805: **Lucine française;** ou, Recueil d'observations médicales, chirurgicales,
pharmaceutiques, historiques, critiques et littéraires, relatives à la science des
accouchemens. Edited, and chiefly written, by JEAN FRANÇOIS SACOMBE; published in Paris.
A very curious publication, being a mixture of truly synthetical history and
obstetrical practice, including a history of obstetrics, history of Cesarean section
(vol. 1), and a peculiar drama in three acts entitled: Henri et Jeanne de Seymour, première victime de l'opération Caesarienne. Three volumes make the set.
(C. F. M.)

1936-   : **Lychnos.** Lärdomshistoriska samfundets årsbok (Annual of the Swedish
history of learning society). Edited by JOHANN NORDSTRÖM, professor at the
University of Uppsala; published by Almquist and Wiksells, Uppsala and Stockholm. Published normally once a year, vol. 1 appeared in 1936 (560 p., ill.;
Isis 28, 177-80); the latest volume received was the one for 1950-51, published
in 1951.
The Society was founded in 1934; its first meeting was held in 1935.

1936-   : **Lychnos-bibliotek;** studier och källskrifter (studies and sources). Issued by the Lärdomshistoriska samfundet; published by Almqvist-Wiksells in
Uppsala.
Unnumbered series, each volume devoted to a special topic: reviewed in Isis as
it appeared. No. 1: N. v. E. NORDENMARK: ANDERS CELSIUS professor i Uppsala,
1701-44. (*See* Isis 26: 177-80). (C. F. M.)

1802-1806: **Magazin der berühmtesten und interessantesten See- und Landreisen,
Entdeckungen und Schiffbrüche von Columbus Zeiten.** Published by Sommer
in Leipzig.
Complete in 6 volumes (each of 4 numbers) and no. 1 & 2 of the 7th vol.
(C. F. M.)

1920-1925: **Les Maitres de la pensée scientifique;** collection de mémoires publiés
par les soins de MAURICE SOLOVINE. Paris, Gauthier-Villars.
Each 16° volume is devoted to a man of science: D'ALEMBERT, AMPÈRE, PIERRE
BOUGUER, LAZARE CARNOT, CLAIRAUT, RENÉ DUTROCHET, SPALLANZANI, EINSTEIN,
HUYGHENS, LAPLACE, LAVOISIER, MARIOTTE, MONGE, PAINLEVÉ (the great majority
are French).
Publisher's unnumbered, irregularly issued series of volumes containing basic
memoirs and works of contemporary or older investigators; under the general direction of Maurice Solovine who is also the translator of some volumes. Of general
interest to all branches, including methodology and philosophy of science. Latest
vol. on my record is from 1925: EINSTEIN, A., Sur l'électrodynamique des corps en
mouvement.

1892-1893: **Maitres de la science;** bibliothèque rétrospective. Published by Masson
in Paris.
Ten volumes of 12*mo* size edited by CHARLES RICHET. (C. F. M.)

1923-   : Makers of science. Edited by CHARLES SINGER; published by the Ox-
ford University Press in London.
    Unnumbered series of volumes 18 cm by 12 cm. The volumes have the word
"Makers" in their titles; they include mathematics, physics and astronomy (I. B.
HART, 1923), electricity and magnetism (D. M. TURNER, 1927), chemistry (E. J.
HOLMYARD, 1931), etc. (C. F. M.).

1927-   : Mathematisch-naturwissenschaftlich-technische Bücherei. Edited by E.
WASSERLOSS and GEORG WOLFF; published by Otto Salle in Berlin.
    Numbered series of volumes, 19 cm by 13.5 cm. Many of the numbers are on
history of a science.   Bd. 4 (1927): Galilei (A. WENZEL).   Bd. 7 (1927): OTTO VON
GUERICKE (E. HOPPE).   Bd. 20-21 (1928): Kulturgeschichte der Technik (F. M.
FELDHAUS).   Bd. 24 (1928): Mathematische Quellenbücher (H. WIELEITNER).
(C. F. M.)

1936-   : La Médecine à travers le temps et l'espace. Published in Paris.
    No. 1 published in 1936; no. 2, 1938.   Any more?   (C. F. M.)

1947-1948: Medical Bookman and Historian. Issued monthly, later bimonthly.
    Edited by F. CROXON-DELLER and W. R. BETT.   Publishers, Harvey and Blythe,
    Hanover Square, London W. 1
    The journal had two sections: a) historical section, edited by W. R. BETT, and
b) bookman section, edited by F. CROXON-DELLER.   The last issue is no. 10-11,
Oct.-Nov., 1948.   It is continued as Medicine Illustrated (q.v.), a monthly.
(C. F. M.)

1887-1889: Medical classics. Edited by FERDINAND SEEGER and JOHN MACMULLEN;
    published in New York.
    Vol. 1 appeared June 1887, and the last number was no. 4, vol. 3 December
1889; a bimonthly periodical which may be called a "medico-historical' journal inasmuch as it reprinted old texts, e.g., treatises of CULLEN on the Peruvian Bark (1789).
or a curious treatise on the tobacco written by T. VENNER in 1637, etc.; but the old
material was used as a bait for gaining respectability and a good sale of advertising-
space.   Quack medical history!   (C. F. M.)

1936-1941: Medical classics. Compiled by EMERSON C. KELLY; published in Balti-
    more.
    Five volumes complete the set of quarto numbers.   The last volume appeared in
1940-1941.   Many classical texts are included in the form of reprint (HOLMES, POTT,
PAGET, LISTER, SMITH, etc.).   (C. F. M.)

1937-1943: Medical leaves. Edited by ABRAHAM LEVINSON and others; published
    by a corporation in Chicago.
    As the subtitle reads this serial is a review of the Jewish medical world and
medical history.   Publication ceased on account of the war.   (C. F. M.)

1903-1907: Medical library and historical journal. Published by the Association of
    Medical Librarians.   Edited by ALBERT TRACY HUNTINGTON and John Smart
    BROWNE.   5 vols.   Brooklyn (Bedford Ave., 1313).
    Isis 2, 148.

1920-1938: Medical life. Edited by VICTOR ROBINSON; published by the Froben
    Press in New York.
    Monthly issues each of which is numbered.   There are 214 numbers, polygraphs
as well as monographs, on many medical men and on various medical topics, from
the point of view of a historian, but more often for entertainment and less frequently
for serious study.
    Some of the specially "named" issues are on PASTEUR, MECHNIKOV, intravenous
medication, GORGAS, goiter, acidosis, American surgery, primitive medicine, BER-
ZELIUS, Army Medical Library Centenary, etc.   (C. F. M.).

1915-1927: **Medical Pickwick;** a monthly literary magazine of wit and wisdom. Edited by SAMUEL M. BRICKNER, later by PHILIP FRANK; published at Saranac Lake, later at St. Louis.
There are 13 volumes in a complete set. It is a mixture of facetiae, anecdotes, witty poems, medical cartoons, fiction, also some history and biography, *e.g.*, history of uromancy (A. ALLEMANN), life of Surgeon-General GORGAS, etc. (C. F. M.).

1937- : **Medical sketches.** Published by Lobica Laboratories, Inc., in New York.
Monthly publication for the advertisement of a pharmaceutical laboratory. It contains light essays or notes of medico-historical interest, biographies of famous physicians, anecdotes, medicine in art, hobbies of physicians, and other paramedical affairs. (C. F. M.)

1940- : **Medicinalhistoriske dokumenter til belysning af laegevaesenets og pharmaciens udvikling i Danmark.** Published by H. Lundbeck & Co., in København.
Small, irregularly issued, numbered pamphlets, each one containing old Danish laws related to medicine, pharmacopoeias, medical notebooks, etc. Until 1944, there have been five issues. (C. F. M.)

1949- : **Medicine illustrated.** Published by Harvey & Blythe in London.
This is the new monthly that continues the Medical Bookman and Historian (*q.v.*). (C. F. M.)

1838-1846: **Medicinische Unterhaltungs-Bibliothek;** oder, Collectiv-Blätter von heiterem und ernstem Colorite für alte und junge Aerzte. Published by Wilhelm Engelmann in Nordhausen and Leipzig.
The journal has seven sections (as seen in vol. 9, 1842); among them there is one for biographies, another for such "sketches" as NAPOLEON's last sickness and death, then a section is devoted to medical geography and folklore; others are for poetry, miscellanea, aphorisms, and anecdotes. (C. F. M.)

1912-1917: **Medicinsk-historiske smaaskrifter.** Edited by VILHELM MAAR. Copenhagen, V. Tryde.
Isis 2, 151. VILHELM MAAR (1871-1940), obituary in Mitteilungen (39, 212-13). *See* also note in Mitt. (12, 319) announcing the collection, and naming the first two titles. The series is complete in three volumes.

1941: **Medico-historisches Jahrbuch.** Published by MENTZEN in Berlin. Complete in one octavo volume; 96 p. (C. F. M.)

1821-1833: **Medicorum Graecorum opera quae extant.** Edited by CARL GOTTLOB KÜHN; published in Leipzig.
Complete in 28 octavo volumes; vol. 1-20, GALEN; vol. 21-23, HIPPOCRATES; vol. 24, ARETAEUS; vol. 25-26, DIOSCORIDES. (C. F. M.)

1921-1925: **Meister der Heilkunde.** Edited by MAX NEUBURGER; published by the Rikola-Verlag in Wien and Berlin.
Seven volumes complete the set; 21 cm by 14 cm. No. 1 (1921): VIRCHOW (by C. POSNER); No. 2 (1922): EHRLICH (by A. LAZARUS). (C. F. M.)

1945- : **Mémoires de la Société française d'histoire de la médecine et de ses filiales.** Tome 1. Chez le Secrétaire général, 66 Boulevard Raspail, Paris 6. Vol. 3, 1947, same address.
Continuation of the Bulletin de la Société française d'histoire de la médecine. Separately paged, irregularly issued volumes. Tome 1, 1945, 86 p.; tome 2, 1946, 107 p., tome 3, 1947, 222 p. (C. F. M.)

1775: **Mémoires littéraires, critiques, philologiques, biographiques et bibliographiques,** pour servir à l'histoire ancienne et moderne de la médecine. Edited by GOULIN; printed by the Imprimerie de Grange for Pyre & Bastien, in Paris.

A truly medico-historical periodical. Issued every 1. and 15. of the month in
small fascicles of 4 leaves; each fascicle is marked at the bottom of its first page with
a distinct number. There are 52 numbers for "année 1775"; the first fascicle of the
year 1776 was also issued. The volume was dedicated to Monseigneur HUE DE
MIROMENIL, le Garde des Sceaux.

The volume of 1775 contains 14 major articles: on origin of medicine, on PIETRO
D'ABANO, history of anatomy, bibliographical notes and a letter to the editor of
the memoirs; there is a biography of J. F. BORRI, notes on the history of the SEBIZIUS
family, on history of inoculations, on life of ASCLEPIADES, THEMISON, TRYPHON,
CASSIUS and other ancient physicians; contemporary notes, bibliography also.
(C. F. M.)

1701-1774: **Mémoires pour l'histoire des sciences et des beaux arts.** Published at
various places, also in Trévoux.

It is also called Journal de Trévoux or Mémoires de Trévoux. Small-size serial
in 166 volumes. Table by CARLOS SUMMERVOGEL (3 vols., Paris 1864-65). Introd.
(3, 1871).

1919-1935: **Mémoires présentés à la Société Sultanieh de géographie.** Published
under the auspices of AHMED FOUAD, sultan of Egypt. Folio volumes published by the Imprimerie de l'Institut français d'archéologie orientale, Le Caire.

Each volume (or group of volumes) deals with a historical subject, or much importance is given to the history of the subject. E.g., volume 1 is devoted to the
Suez harbor, the history of which is given. The following volumes are more
definitely and completely historical in scope.

Later, the title was changed to Mémoires de la Société royale de géographie
d'Egypte (sous les auspices de sa Majesté FOUAD I-ER roi d'Egypte).

Last volumes published: 15-16, ALBERT KAMMERER: La Mer Rouge, l'Abyssinie
et l'Arabie depuis l'antiquité (2 heavy folios, Cairo 1929-35). (Introd. 3, 1891).

1943-   : **Memoria de sus trabajos de la Sociedad peruana de historia de la
medicina.** Published in Lima.

This seems to be the first volume, of 48 p. issued for the 1942-43 year. Any
more? (C. F. M.)

1922-   : **Memorie e documenti per la storia della Università di Padova.** Issued
by the Istituto per la storia della U. di Padova; published by La Garangola in
Padova.

Series of unnumbered (?) monographs and polygraphs related to the history of
science in Padova and at the University of Padova. In 1922: E. MORPURGO: Lo
studio di Padova, le epidemie, i contagi. (C. F. M.)

1947-   : **Měsíčník Ciba.** Published by the Czechoslovak branch of the Ciba
Company. Partly translation of earlier numbers of the Ciba Zeitschrift. Printed
in Praha.

First number was issued October 1947. No. 3, January 1948 is identical in
contents with the 1942 September issue of Ciba Zeitschrift. Last number on record:
No. 7, 1948. (C. F. M.)

1945-   : **Métaux et civilisations;** les métaux dans l'histoire, les techniques, les
arts. Edited by LOUIS DELVILLE. Editions Métaux, 32 rue du Maréchal-
Joffre, St. Germain-en-Laye, Seine-et-Oise.

Vol. 1, was published in 6 quarto parts, 132 p., ill.

1909-   : **Minerva medica.** Published in Torino.

Regular monthly journal of medicine which contains a section called "Varia."
This section often contains medico-historical curiosities and anecdotes; e.g., in vol.
32, 1941, it discussed miraculous waters, alcoholism in ancient Egypt, FRANCESCO
ALFORTI, historical notes on cancer, leprosy in the Middle Ages, etc. (C. F. M.)

1902-1942: **Mitteilungen zur Geschichte der Medizin und der Naturwissenschaften.** Published by the Deutsche Gesellschaft für Geschichte der Medizin und der Naturwissenschaften.

Vol. 1, 1902, edited by George W. A. KAHLBAUM, MAX NEUBURGER and KARL SUDHOFF. The last volume published was vol. 40, 1941-42, 372 p. (Isis 39, 70); this volume covers really the years 1941-43, the last years of the Germany which HITLER destroyed. The editor of vol. 40 was RUDOLPH ZAUNICK of Dresden. Vols. 1 to 40 published by Leopold Voss, Leipzig. Ceased publication.

This journal was almost exclusively bibliographical; practically all the German publications concerning the history of science and a good many foreign ones, for the period 1900-42, are recorded. For an account of the earlier vols., see Isis 2, 153.

1890-1936: **The Monist;** a quarterly magazine devoted to philosophy of science. Published by the Open Court Publishing Company in Chicago.

First vol. was published in 1890; the last issue was No. 2, vol. 46, July 1936. There is an index to the first 30 vols. (1890-1920). (C. F. M.)

1919- : **Monografie Vinciane;** pubblicazioni del Istituto Vinciano in Roma. Edited by MARIO CARMENATI; published by Zanichelli in Bologna.

Numbered series of Leonardo studies. No. 1(1919): La critica e l'arte di LEONARDO DA VINCI (L. VENTURI). No. 3 (1920): LEONARDO DA VINCI e la geologia (DE LORENZO). No. 5, 1922. Any more? (C. F. M.)

1897-1904: **Monographien aus der Geschichte der Chemie.** Edited by GEORG W. A. KAHLBAUM of Basel [1853-1905], 8 parts, Leipzig, J. A. Barth.

Each part deals with a special chemical subject such as LAVOISIER, DALTON, BERZELIUS, SCHÖNBEIN, LIEBIG, FRIEDRICH MOHR.

1923-1928: **Monumenta medica.** Edited by HENRY E. SIGERIST; published by Lier & Co., in Milano, and Firenze.

Numbered volumes, of various sizes, being the facsimile re-editions of book rarities or publications of manuscripts. The series includes works of JENNER, KETHAM, CANANO, HARVEY (1928), and the early prints on syphilis edited by K. SUDHOFF (1924-25). (C. F. M.)

1914-1915: **Monumenta pharmaceutica.** Published by D. B. Centen in Amsterdam.

The series includes five numbers; each number contains several articles related to the history of pharmacy. (C. F. M.)

1926-1930: **Münchener Beiträge zur Geschichte und Literatur der Naturwissenschaften und der Medizin.** Edited by ERNST DARMSTAEDTER. Verlag der Münchener Drucke, München.

Numbered series of monographs, biographies and reprints related to the history of the natural sciences; vols. of 23 cm by 15 cm size. Heft 1 (1926): GEORG AGRICOLA (E. DARMSTAEDTER). Heft 7-8 (1927): Die heilige HILDEGARD VON BINGEN (H. FISCHER). Heft 11-12 (1928): ALBERTUS MAGNUS als Zoologe (H. BALSS). Heft 19 is the last one published.

There is also a secondary series of extra volumes ("Sonderheft") consisting of 5 numbers issued in 1926-1928. Heft 1 (1926): Des WALAFRID VON DER REICHENAU Hortulus (K. Sudhoff). Heft 2 (1927): reprint of a work of ULRICH ELLENBOG (F. KOELSCH). (C. F. M.)

Cf. Isis 10: 252.

1893-1904: **Neudrucke von Schriften und Karten über Meteorologie und Erdmagnetismus.** Edited by GUSTAV HELLMANN (1854-   ). Berlin, Asher.

Fifteen parts, the last of which contains addenda and errata to the whole series. Isis 1, 706; 2, 139.

1930- : **New York Academy of Medicine Library.** *See* History of medicine series. (C. F. M.)

1938-   : **Notes and Records of the Royal Society.**   Vol. 1, no. 1 April 1938, published by the Royal Society of London, Burlington House, London W. 1.
See Isis 30, 383.   Last no. seen, vol. 8, no. 2, April 1951.
This is a continuation and expansion of the Occasional notes (1937).   The Notes and Records will include the "occasional notes" concerning F. R. S., but also matters of historical interest which could not be printed in either Philosophical Transactions or Proceedings.   The format is similar to that of the Proceedings.   The articles concern the history, chiefly but not exclusively, of the Royal Society.

1918-   : **Nouvelles annales des voyages.**
See Annales des voyages.   (C. F. M.)

1944-   : **Nova acta Paracelsica;** Jahrbuch der Schweizerischen Paracelsus-Gesellschaft.   Verlag Birkhäuser, Basel.
Vol. 1, 192 p., ill., 1944; vol. 2, 199 p., ill., 1945; vol. 3, 194 p., ill., 1946 (Isis 39, 82), vol. 4, 138 p., ill., 1947.
See Acta Paracelsica.

1823-1845: **Nuova raccolta ed opuscoli idraulici diversi.**   Published in Bologna.
Seven volumes.   *Cf.* Raccolta.   (C. F. M.)

1927-1930: **Ocherki po istorii znanii** (Studies in history of science), issued by the Leningrad Academy of Sciences.
Eight numbers complete the series which includes several biographies (NEWTON, KASTRÉN, BERTHELOT, etc.)   No. 4 (1928): Ocherk istorii russkoi geograficheskoi nauki (L. F. BERG).   (C. F. M.)

(1926?)-   : **Old Asmolean Reprints.**   Oxford.
Collection of facsimile reprints of old scientific books concerning the history of science in Oxford.   The collection was edited by R. T. GUNTHER.   No. 1, Museum Tradescentium, 2. ASHMOLE's diary, 3. L. DIGGES, 4. J. DIGGES, 5. MAYOW, 6. HOOKE, 7. BOYLE.

1915(?)-   : **The Open Court classics of science and philosophy.**   Published in Chicago and London by the Open Court Publishing Company.
Unnumbered series of a publisher, containing small booklets (19 cm by 13 cm) related chiefly to the history of exact sciences, especially mathematics and geometry. It also includes translations or reprints of early philosophers.   In 1915: Selections from the Scottish philosophy of common sense (G. A. JOHNSTON).   In 1919: A history of the conceptions of limits and fluxions in Great Britain (F. CAJORI).   Last issue (?): History of mathematical notations by F. CAJORI (2 vols. 1928-29). (C. F. M.)

1923-   : **Opuscoli Vinciani.**   Issued by the Istituto di studi Vinciani in Roma; published by Maglione & Stoini.
No. 1 (1923): Gli studi intorno a LEONARDO DA VINCI nell'ultimo cinquantennio (E. VERGA).   Any more?   (C. F. M.)

1907-1943: **Opuscula selecta Neerlandicorum de arte medica.**   Collection of medical works written by Dutch men of science, edited by the Dutch medical journal Nederlandsch Tijdschrift voor Geneeskunde, Amsterdam.   Vol. 1, 1907; vol. 17, 1943.   Published by De erven v. F. Bohn, Haarlem.   Irregularly issued.
See Isis 7, 595; 10, 304; 11, 267; 12, 152; 16, 567; 20, 600; 23, 606; 25, 600; 28, 294; 35, 357; 39, 130.
See Bijdragen tot de geschiedenis der geneeskunde.

1936-   : **Organon.**   International review, published by the Mianowski Institute for the promotion of science and letters.   Editor: STANISLAW MICHALSKI, Warsaw, Staszic Palace.
Organon is devoted to the 'science' of science, the explanation of general science and the history of Polish science.   Vol. 1, 312 p., 1936 (Isis 26, 562), vol. 2, 302 p., 1938 (Isis 30, 297-98).

1925-1929: **Orvostörténelmi jegyzetek** (Medico-historical notes). Edited and written by CLAUDIUS F. MAYER; published by the Orvosi Hetilap (Medical Weekly), Budapest.

A series of about 20 reprints of articles dealing with medico-historical topics, including the analysis of the Oribasius codex of the Hungarian National Museum, and other medieval manuscripts, the gynecological works of CLEOPATRA, history of the treatment of syphilis, etc. (C. F. M.)

1936-   : **Osiris**. Studies on the History and Philosophy of Science, and on the History of Learning and Culture. Edited by GEORGE SARTON with the help of ALEXANDER POGO. Vol. 1, 1936; vol. 9, 1950. Published by Saint Catherine Press in Bruges, Belgium.

This series is supplementary to Isis. It includes volumes devoted to a single subject or group of subjects (as vol. 1, devoted to the history of mathematics) and the longer and more technical papers; Isis is for the shorter ones, the reviews, notes, queries, and critical bibliography. Each volume of Osiris is dedicated to a historian of science and includes his biography, bibliography and portrait. Vols. 1 to 9 are thus dedicated to D. E. SMITH, Sir THOMAS HEATH, E. O. VON LIPPMANN, JULIUS RUSKA, JOSEPH BIDEZ, GINO LORIA, P. VER EECKE, and MAX MEYERHOF.

1889-   : **Ostwald's Klassiker der exakten Wissenschaften.** Leipzig, Engelmann. *See* Klassiker.

1925: **Pagine di scienza.** Published by Mondadori in Milano.

Numbered series of monographs, 21 cm by 14 cm, each volume being an anthology of the writings of a famous physicist, chemist, biologist, etc. No. 1 (1925): LEONARDO (by S. TIMPANARO). No. 2 (1925): GALILEO (S. TIMPANARO). Any more? (C. F. M.)

1946-   : **Pagine di storia della scienza.** *See* p. 248.

1940-   : **Pallas.** Edited by FRANS VERDOORN; published by the Chronica Botanica in Waltham, Mass.

Numbered reprints of rare historical reference works of botany. No. 1 (1948): K. F. W. JESSEN: Botanik der Gegenwart und Vorzeit in culturhistorischer Entwickelung (Isis 40, 82). No. 2 (1952): C. DARWIN: Journal of Researches, ed. 1 (1839). (C. F. M.).

1918-1920: **Papers of the Agricultural Historical Society**, Washington.

These are volumes of reprints from the annual reports of the American Historical Society. Only 3 vols. were published. For continuation *see* Agricultural History. (C. F. M.)

1886-   : **Periodico di matematiche, storia, didattica, filosofia.** Edited by F. ENRIQUES and G. LAZZERI; published by various publishers in Roma, Bologna and Livorno. Issued for the Associazione Mathesis.

Current in its fourth series now. Ser. 1, v. 1-13, 1886-1898; ser. 2, vol. 1-5, 1899-1903; ser. 3, v. 1-15, 1903-1918; ser. 4, v. 1, 1921: vol. 10, 1930. There is also a set of supplements, vol. 1-20, 1898-1917. (C. F. M.)

1924-1932: **Per la storia e la filosofia delle matematiche.** Edited by F. ENRIQUES; published by Stock in Roma, and later by Zanichelli in Bologna. Issued for the Istituto nazionale per la storia delle scienze fisiche e matematiche.

Numbered series of volumes, 20 cm by 14 1/2 cm. No. 3: NEWTON, I. Principi di filosofia naturale (ed. F. ENRIQUES). No. 7 (1929): BOMBELLI, R. Algebra (Isis 14, 425). No. 9 (1931): GALILEO. Last one is No. 11, 1932(?) (C. F. M.)

1937-   : **Petrus Nonius:** publicação do grupo Portuges da historia das ciencias. Review of the Portuguese group of the history of sciences, edited by ARLINDO CAMILO MONTEIRO.

The first volume was published in Lisbon 1937-38, the first part of vol. 7 reached me in July 1949. The address of the editor is now Caixa Postal 2581, Rio de Janeiro, Brazil.

Isis 29, 255.

1926-1930: **Philosophes et savants français du XX**^{e} **siècle.** Extraits et notices. Published by Alcan, in Paris.
Publisher's irregular, numbered series in 16*mo*. No. 1 (1926): Philosophie de la science, by R. POIRIER. Last issue seen, No. 5 (1930). (C. F. M.)

1934-   : **Philosophie et histoire de la pensée scientifique:** exposés edited by FEDERIGO ENRIQUES; published by Hermann & Cie in Paris.
Booklets of 17 cm by 15 cm size. No. 1: F. ENRIQUES: Signification de l'histoire de la pensée scientifique. (C. F. M.)

1934-   : **Philosophy of science.** Published quarterly for the Philosophy of Science Association by the Williams & Wilkins Co., Baltimore, Maryland. Founded by WILLIAM MARIAS MALLISOFF (1895-1947). Edited by C. W. CHURCHMAN. Latest current volume is vol. 16, 1949.

1942-   : **Physis.** Beiträge zur naturwissenschaftlichen Synthese. Edited by ADOLF MEYER-ABICH.
Seen only vol. 2-3 (206 p., ill. Hippokrates-Verlag, Stuttgart, 1949; Isis 41, 393). The editor was formerly known under the name ADOLF MEYER.

1919-   : **Pioneers of progress; man of science.** Published by the Society for Promoting Christian Knowledge, in London.
Booklets of 16*mo* size; publisher's unnumbered series of biographies of famous men of science. In 1919: JOSEPH PRIESTLEY (by H. PEACOCK). Other volumes describe GALILEO, FARADAY, HERSCHEL, etc. The society was still active in 1940. (C. F. M.)

1902-   : **Proceedings of the Charaka Club** (New York). Published by the Williams & Wilkins Company in Baltimore.
Very irregularly published; limited to ca. 500 copies for the club members. It discusses the literary, artistic and historical aspects of medicine. Vol. 1, 1902; vol. 2, 1906; vol. 3, 1910; vol. 4, 1916; vol. 5, 1919; vol. 7, 1931; vol. 10, 1941 (the last). Vol. 10 includes the story of BARBARA FRITCHIE, Figleaves for SHAKESPEARE and MONTAIGNE, GALEN on malingering, the mystery of ROBERT SEYMOUR, etc. (C. F. M.)

1913-   : **Proceedings of the Royal Society of Medicine, Section of the History of Medicine.** London W., Royal Society of Medicine, Longmans, Green and Co. Isis 2, 151. The Section of the History of Medicine was inaugurated on Nov. 20, 1912, Sir WILLIAM OSLER, Bt., President of the Section, in the chair. The reports of that section began to appear in vol. 6 of the Proceedings of the Royal Society of Medicine; Reports of the first year 1912-13, in that vol. 6 cover 246 p. Vol. 38 contains the reports of the historical section for 1944-45, p. 1-18, 409-12, 485-94, 697-706.

(1916)-   : **Profili.** Published by Formiggini in Roma.
A series of small booklets, 17 cm by 10 1/2 cm, numbered. Single volumes deal with biographies of scientists. No. 42 (1916): LAVOISIER (A. MIELI; 2nd ed., 1926). No. 46 (1918): CRISTOFORO COLOMBO (R. ALMAGIA; 2nd ed. 1927). No. 62 (1922): GIAMBATTISTA MORGAGNI (G. BILANCIONI). No. 91 (1927): VOLTA (A. MIELI). Any more? (C. F. M.)

1919-1928: **Profili bibliografici de "L'Italia che scrive."**
See Guide Ics. (C. F. M.)

1828-   : **Proteus;** Zeitschrift für Geschichte der gesammten Naturlehre. Edited by KARL WILHELM KASTNER; published in Erlangen.
One volume, two numbers only. Its historical nature remains to be seen. (C. F. M.)

1931-1937: **Proteus.** Verhandlungsberichte der Rheinischen Gesellschaft für Geschichte der Naturwissenschaft, Medizin und Technik. Edited by PAUL DIERGART, 2 vols. Published Bonn 1931-37.

Pubblicazioni del Istituto di storia della medicina della R. Università di Roma. Edited by ADALBERTO PAZZINI. Published by V. Ferri in Roma.
Includes several series. The 'C' Collection is: Studi e ricerche storico-mediche. It is an unnumbered series. It includes C. GRASSI: Storia dei tumori nella antichità Greco-Romana (1941). (C. F. M.)

1919-1926: Pubblicazioni del Istituto Vinciano in Roma. Edited by M. CERMENATI.
It includes two different series, or two different titles. Ser. 1, Studi e testi Vinciani, vol. 1-7, 1919-1926. Ser. 2, Testi Vinciani, vol. 1, 1923 (the only volume). All volumes deal with an aspect of the genius of LEONARDO. (C. F. M.)

1938- : Publicaciones; Cátedra de historia de la medicina; Facultad de ciencias médicas. Edited by JUAN RAMÓN BELTRÁN; published in Buenos Aires.
Vol. 6 was published in 1943; latest vol. seen, vol. 7, 1944. (C. F. M.)

1913-1914: Publications de la Société française d'histoire de la médecine. Paris, chez le secrétaire général, 16, rue Bonaparte, 1913.
Monographs concerning the history of medicine. I know only two volumes. Vol. 1, PAUL DORVEAUX (1913; Isis 1, 517-18); vol. 2, LOUIS DUBREUIL-CHAMBARDEL (1914; Isis 2, 438).
Cf. Bulletin; Mémoires.

1848- : Publications of the Hakluyt Society.
See Hakluyt Society. (C. F. M.)

1934- : Publications of the Institute of the History of Medicine. Johns Hopkins University, Baltimore. Edited by HENRY E. SIGERIST and successors.
There are four different series included under the general title of this periodical publication.
Series 1, Monographs; *e.g.*, No. 1: Ornithologists of the U. S. Army Medical Corps (E. E. HUME).
Series 2, Texts and documents; *e.g.*, No. 1: Four treatises of THEOPHRASTUS VON HOHENHEIM.
Series 3, The H. Noguchi Lectures, *e.g.*, No. 1 (1934): The renaissance of medicine in Italy (A. CASTIGLIONI).
Series 4, Bibliotheca medica Americana; *e.g.*, No. 1 (1937): A brief rule to guide the common people of New England (reprint of the 1671 work of T. THACHER). This series includes reprints of works of MORGAN, W. H. WELCH, BEAUMONT, B. WATERHOUSE, etc. (C. F. M.)

1844- : Publications of the Ray Society.
See Ray Society.

(1941-): Quaderni dell'Impero, scienza e tecnica ai tempi di Roma Imperiale. Published by the Istituto di Studi Romani, Roma; printed in Spoleto, by Panetto & Petrelli.
Octavo volumes in a numbered but irregularly issued series; related to history of sciences and technic. No. 16 (1941): DE VECCHIS, B., La odontoiatria e la protesi dentaria ai tempi dell'Impero Romano, 20 p. (C. F. M.)

1925-1927: Quaderni di storia della scienza. Published by the Casa Editrice Leonardo da Vinci in Roma.
Numbered series of monographs on history of science; each volume 26 cm by 17 cm. No. 3 (1926): Medicazioni strane (&c.) (D. GIORDANO). No. 6 (1926): Punti interrogativi nella storia delle matematiche (G. LORIA). No. 7 (1927): Il sistema aristotelico della generazione degli animali (G. MONTALENTI). (C. F. M.)

Quellenbücher, *see* Voigtländers Quellenbücher.

1921-1922: Quellen und Beiträge zur Geschichte der Zahnheilkunde. Edited by CURT PROSKAUER; published by H. Meusser in Berlin.

234 Journals and Serials

Only two numbers were published. No. 1 is a reprint of A. Tylkowski's Disquisitio physica (1624). No. 2 is a 1530 dental booklet: Zene Arznei. (C. F. M.)

1901-1918: Quellen und Forschungen zur alten Geschichte und Geographie. Edited by W. Sieglin; published in Leipzig by E. Avenarius, later in Berlin by Weidmann.
Thirty volumes make a complete set, but vol. 16 and vol. 20 were not published. Bd 8(1904): Die Entdeckung des germanischen Nordens im Altertum (Detlefsen). No. 9 (1904): Plinius: Die geographischen Bücher der naturalis historia (Detlefsen). (C. F. M.)

1909-1934: Quellen und Forschungen zur Erd- und Kulturkunde. Edited by R. Stübe and C. F. Andreas. Leipzig, Otto Wigand, later W. Heims.
Eight volumes published by 1914 (Isis 2, 141). Vol. 13 (Leipzig, Heims, 1934). This is the last volume published. Publication was suspended during 1922-1929.
Paul Schwarz: Iran im Mittelalter nach den arabischen Geographen (9 vols., Leipzig, Harrassowitz 1896-36). Vol. 1 published as Habilitationschrift, Leipzig 1896; vols. 2 to 4 form vols. 3, 6, 9 of the series Quellen und Forschungen zur Erd- und Kulturkunde 1910, 1912, 1921 (Isis 5, 275); vols. 5-7 are vols. 1-3 in the series Quellen und Forschungen zur Kultur- und Religionsgeschichte 1925, 1926, 1929. Index to vols. 1-7 (Leipzig 1929). Vols. 8-9, mimeographed handwriting, Zwickau in Sachsen, F. Ullmann 1932-36. Single pagination through the nine volumes, 1600 p., except the index to vols. 1-7, paginated separately 94 p. This example has been described to illustrate the bibliographic difficulties caused by erratic editorship of series.

1938-   : Quellen und Forschungen zur Geschichte der Geographie und Völkerkunde. Edited by Albert Herrmann; Leipzig, K. F. Koehler.
Numbered series of monographs. No. 1 (1938): Das Land der Seide und Tibet im Lichte der Antike (A. Herrmann). No. 7 (1941): Am Hofe des persischen Grosskönigs, 1684-85 (E. Kämpfer).

1930-1938: Quellen und Studien zur Geschichte der Mathematik, Astronomie und Physik. Herausgegeben von O. Neugebauer, J. Stenzel, und O. Toeplitz. Published by Springer in Berlin (Isis 13, 541).
Section A, Quellen, began to appear in 1930, the last part seen by me is called 4. Band (80 p. 1936; Isis 27, 120). Vol. 3 containing Neugebauer's studies on mathematical texts in cuneiform writing (Isis 28, 490-91) is divided into three parts (1935, 1935, 1937), the last two of which are of very large size (34 cm high) and hence bound separately. Section B, Studien, began to appear in 1931. Vol. 4 (in 4 parts) was published in 1938.

1931-1942: Quellen und Studien zur Geschichte der Naturwissenschaften und der Medizin. Edited by Paul Diepgen and Julius Ruska. Continuation of the Archiv für die Geschichte der Naturwissenschaften und der Technik (1909-30, see above). Vol. 1 appeared in 1931. Last part received vol. 8, Heft 3/4, 1942. Berlin, Julius Springer.

1765-1845: Raccolta d'autori italiani che trattano del moto dell'acque. Bologna.
Reprint of historical texts on hydrodynamics and hydrology. There is an older series of nine volumes published 1765 to 1774. Several of the volumes were often reprinted. The newer series has the title: Nuova raccolta ed opuscoli idraulici diversi; it is composed of seven volumes published from 1823 to 1845.
It seems however that the old series still continued after 1823. A vol. 10 is on record from 1826; it is the reprint of Leonardo da Vinci's Del moto e misura dell'acqua, edited by Cardinali. (C. F. M.)

1905-1934: Raccolta Vinciana. Founded by Luca Beltrami; edited by Ettore Verga (1867-   ); published by the Archivo storico e civico in the Castello Sforzesco of Milano.
Numbered fascicles devoted to the study of Leonardo da Vinci; irregularly

published. Each fascicle contains several articles and elaborate bibliography. Fasc. 1, 1905; fasc. 8 (1912) 1913; fasc. 14, 1930-1934; fasc. 15-16, 1935-39.

1929-   : Rassegna per la storia dell'Università di Modena. Published by the University. Fasc. 1, 1929. (C. F. M.)

1844-   : The Ray Society Publications.
The Society was founded in London in 1844 for the publication of works on natural society. It is named after the English naturalist, JOHN RAY (1627-1705). Some of the works published by the Society concern the history of natural history, e.g., LOUIS AGASSIZ: Bibliographia zoologiae et geologiae (4 vols. 1848-54). Memorials of JOHN RAY (1846). The correspondence of JOHN RAY (1848). Miscellaneous botanical works of ROBERT BROWN (1886-68). Classical works of J. J. S. STEENSTRUP, WILHELM HOFMEISTER. No. 111: K. VON GOEBEL: Life of WILHELM HOFMEISTER (1926). No. 114: Further correspondence of JOHN RAY, edited by ROBERT W. T. GUNTHER (1928). No. 132: THOMAS PENNANT: Tour on the continent 1765 (1948). The books can be obtained from Messrs. Bernard Quaritch, Grafton St., London W. 1.

1882-1923: Recueil de voyages et de documents pour servir à l'histoire de la géographie depuis le XIIIe jusqu'à la fin du XVIe siècle. Edited by CHARLES SCHEFER and HENRI CORDIER. Paris, Ernest Leroux.
In 1914, 22 octavo volumes had appeared, plus 3 atlases of maps (Série cartographique), in folio (Isis 2, 140, 169).
Vol. 1 (HENRY HARRISSE 1882); last vol. 24 (ANTONIO PIGAFETTA 1923).
Section cartographique (GABRIEL MILLET 1896).

1929-   : Report of the Science Museum, London.
Numbered series which includes also handbooks and monographs for the historian of science. No. 1 is the report for 1927-1928. No. 3 (1930): Handbook of the collections illustrating aeronautics (M. J. B. DAVY). (C. F. M.)

1922-   : Research series of the American Geographical Society. Published in New York.
Numbered series of 19 cm by 12 cm volumes related to the history of geography. No. 1 (1922) and N. 2: BERING's voyages. No. 3 (1922): Legendary islands of the Atlantic; a study in medieval geography (W. H. BABCOCK; Isis 5, 167-70). No. 15 (1925): The geographical lore of the time of the Crusades (J. K. WRIGHT; Isis 7, 495-98). (C. F. M.).

1922-1925: Research studies in medical history.
See Wellcome Historical Medical Museum.

1942-   : Revista argentina de historia de la medicina; publicación cuatrimestral; organo oficial del Ateneo de historia de la medicina. Edited by JUAN RAMÓN BELTRÁN. Echeverria 1606, Buenos Aires.
First year in 3 parts, with separate pagination, 1942. Second year in 3 parts, 1943. Año 5, 1946.

1949-   : Revista brasileira de historia de medicina. Published in Rio de Janeiro, Rua México 164. Vol. 1, 1949. (C. F. M.)

1945-   : Revista de la Sociedad venezolana de historia de la medicina. Caracas. No. 1, vol. 1, published in 1945. (C. F. M.)

(1936?)-   : Revue Ciba. Published by the Ciba Pharmaceutical Company. Basel.
Is this the French companion of Ciba Zeitschrift? No. 56 is cited from 1947. (C. F. M.)

1931-   : Revue de synthèse; organe de la Fondation "Pour la Science"; Centre international de synthèse. Edited by HENRI BERR, published by La Renaissance du Livre, Paris.

This is a continuation of the Revue de synthèse historique; vol. 1 of the Revue de synthèse is called vol. 51 of the Revue de synthèse historique. The change of title indicates a broadening of purpose: not historical synthesis only, but general synthesis of knowledge.

Vol. 21 (62 of the general series), second half of 1947, is divided into two parts entitled respectively "Sciences de la nature et synthèse générale," "Synthèse historique." Last part seen vol. 22, 1 (63[98] of the general series), 1948, first half, is entitled Synthèse générale and is largely devoted to Descartes. During proofreading received vol. 26 (or 67), 240 p., Paris, Janvier-juin 1950 which was published to celebrate three anniversaries, the 50*th* of the Revue de Synthèse, the 25*th* of the Centre de Synthèse, and the 15*th* of the Semaine de Synthèse. It includes the history of these three dovetailed undertakings, all of which were created by the same man, HENRI BERR (Isis 42, 381; Osiris 10).

1900-30: Revue de synthèse historique (50 vols. in 38). Edited by HENRI BERR. Published in Paris, by Cerf 1900-22, then by La Renaissance du Livre 1923-30. Table for the years 1900-10 (1912).

As the title indicates, this was a general review of history but the editor attached from the beginning much importance to the history of science and enlisted for that purpose such collaborators as PAUL TANNERY, ANDRÉ LALANDE, LUCIEN POINCARÉ, ABEL REY, MAURICE CAULLERY. TANNERY's inaugural lesson, never delivered, appeared in vol. 8 (Isis 38, 31-51, 1947). I am especially grateful to BERR's Revue because it provided a part of my initiation.

The 50 vols. make two series: series 1, vol. 1-26, 1900-1913; ser. 2, vol. 1-24, 1913-1930. Continued by the preceding title, Revue de synthèse.

1948-   : Revue d'histoire de la médecine hébraïque. Edited by I. SIMON, Paris 9ᵉ, 55, rue de Clichy; published by the Société d'histoire de la médecine hébraïque in Paris.

Irregularly published. No. 1 was issued in June 1948; No. 2 is the latest on record (Sept.-Dec., 1948). The Society was founded by I. SIMON and others in 1936; it was inactive during the war (1939-1947); activities resumed in June 1947. The society also wants to establish a library for the history of Hebrew medicine and science. (C. F. M.)

1913-   : Revue d'histoire de la pharmacie. Issued by the Société d'histoire de la pharmacie which was founded February 1913. Edited by E. H. GUITARD, Paris, VI, 4 Ave. de l'Observatoire.

Vol. 1-17, 1913-1930, published as Bulletin (*q.v.*). Issued quarterly; single numbers are marked by continued notation of volume, whole-numbering and special numbering of Revue issues; *e.g.*, vol. 22, No. 100 is also No. 34 of the revue, issued December 1937. No. 110 was published June 1940. Thereafter, during the turbulent period of the war, it was temporarily replaced by an annual publication called Séances et travaux de la Société d'histoire de la pharmacie. With No. 117, the title of Revue was again assumed and the frequency made quarterly. No. 117, March 1947, année 35; No. 121 (part of année 36) is the issue for June-September 1948. For its literature review *see* Dionysos. (C. F. M.)

    Cf. Bulletin . . . ; Séances et travaux . . .

1926-1939: Revue d'histoire de la philosophie (et d'histoire générale de la civilisation). Published by the Librairie universitaire in Paris.

Quarterly. Series 1 is of five vols. 1926-1931. A new series was published in seven volumes from 1933 to 1939. (C. F. M.)

---

[98] I first thought that 62 and 63 were misprints for 72 and 73, but Mlle. SUZANNE DELORME kindly informed me (Paris 29 Jan. 1949): "Les volumes 21-22 de la nouvelle collection s'appellent 62 et 63 de l'ancienne revue (et non 72-73). C'est qu'il s'agit des volumes de synthèse historique, alors que la nouvelle collection comprend en outre dix volumes de synthèse générale des sciences de la nature qui ne comptent pas dans l'ancienne tomaison. La série complète ne comprend que la synthèse historique."

1947-   : **Revue d'histoire des sciences et leurs applications;** organe de la Section d'histoire des sciences. Edited by PIERRE BRUNET (Centre international de synthèse, Fondateur-directeur: HENRI BERR). Presses Universitaires de France.
Each volume contains 4 parts.   Seen vol. 1, no. 1, Sept. 1947 to no. 3 March 1948; vol. 2, 1948-49 (the latest on record).
In the first editorial (vol. 1, 5-8) HENRI BERR recalls that this Revue is to some extent a continuation of the Revue de synthèse historique founded by him in 1900, which included a number of articles on the history of science.   The collection of books founded by him a little later L'évolution de l'humanité (1912) contains also many books on the history of ancient science by ABEL REY (1873-1940).   REY died before he could begin his synthesis of medieval science.

1904-05: **Revue historique et médicale.**   Edited by PAUL TRIAIRE, Paris.
Monthly journal which began to appear in Nov. 1904; died at the age of three months.   Isis 2, 148.

1910-   : **Rivista di storia (critica) delle scienze mediche e naturali.**   Official organ of the Italian Society for the History of Science that was founded in 1907.
The first preface was signed by D. BARDUZZI and V. PENSUTI.   The putting in order of that publication is made difficult by two serial numbers relative to years and volumes.   Thus vol. 1 covers the years 1910 to 1912.   The numbers published in 1950 represent the year 50 (8th series).   Address of the editor: Museo di storia delle scienze, Piazza dei Giudici, Firenze.   Publisher: Leo S. Olschki, Firenze.   The earliest volumes were published from Faenza and Sienna.
For a previous publication of the same Italian society see Atti . . . 1907 sq. For the earlier volumes of the Rivista see Isis 2, 155.

(1942): **Schriften der Arbeitsgemeinschaft für Technikgeschichte** des Vereins deutscher Ingenieure im NSBDT.   Published by the Verein deutscher Ingenieure-Verlag in Berlin.
A numbered series of history of technology.   The date of the first volume remains to be seen.   No. 18 was issued in 1942; it is K. HRADECKY's Geschichte und Schrifttum der Edelmetallstrichprobe.   Any more?
NB.   The NSBDT is a symbol of the Nazionalsozialistischer Bund deutscher Techniker.
See also Schriftenreihe der Fachgruppe (etc.).

1921-   : **Schriften zur Karitaswissenschaft.**   Issued by the Deutscher Caritasverband; edited by HEINRICH AUER and others; published in Freiburg i. B.
Bd 1 (1921): Caritas und Volksepidemien (F. MEFFERT).   Bd. 4: Mittelalterliche Caritas (F. ZOEPFL).   Latest vol. on record is Bd 5.   (C. F. M.)

(1933)-   : **Schriftenreihe der Fachgruppe für Geschichte der Technik** beim Verein deutscher Ingenieure.   Published by the German Society of Engineers in Berlin.
Unnumbered monographs related to the history of engineering.   In 1933: e.g., LOUIS DE GEER, 1587-1652 (O. JOHANNSEN).
See also Schriften der Arbeitsgemeinschaft (etc.).   (C. F. M.)

1946(?)-   : **Science in Britain.**   Published by Longmans-Green & Co. in London.
Unnumbered series of the publisher.   Date of first issue not known.   Each volume is of 22 cm size.   In 1946 the following titles were issued: A. H. GIBSON: OSBORNE REYNOLDS and his work; L. BRAGG: History of X-ray analysis; W. L. RANDELL: DE FERRANTI and his influence upon electrical development (2nd ed.); F. H. A. MARSHALL: The science of animal breeding in Britain; a short history.   In 1947: G. LEE: OLIVER HEAVISIDE.   (C. F. M.)

Science Museum, London.
See Report.

1898-1901: **Scientific memoirs.** Edited by JOSEPH SWEETMAN AMES (1864-1943). 15 vols. New York, American Book Co. Vols. 1-7, title reads Harper's Scientific Memoirs.

Each volume contains various papers dealing with one physical or chemical subject: free expansion of gases, prismatic and diffraction spectra, X-rays, law of radiation and absorption, stereo-chemistry, etc.

1921-1923: **Gli scienziati italiani dall'inizio del medio evo ai nostri giorni.** Repertorio bio-bibliografico dei filosofi, matematici (etc.). Edited by ALDO MIELI and published by A. NARDECCHIA in Roma.

One volume published in two parts (474 p., ill.) including 58 biographies (Isis 4, 112-14). (C. F. M.)

1932-   : **Scripta mathematica;** a quarterly journal devoted to the philosophy, history and expository treatment of mathematics. Edited by JEKUTHIEL GINSBURG; published by Yeshiva College, Amsterdam Avenue and 186th St., New York. Volume 1 appeared in 1932-33; vol. 14, in 1948.

The first no. of vol. 1 (92 p.) appeared in September 1932 (Isis 19, 589).

The journal has two numbered sets of monographs. One is the Scripta Mathematica Library the vol. 1 of which appeared in 1934; it is D. E. SMITH's The poetry of mathematics and other essays. The other set is complete in one number published in 1936; its title is Scripta Mathematica Studies.

1941-1946: **Séances et Travaux de la Société d'histoire de la pharmacie.** Published at Paris, 4 Avenue de l'Observatoire; also at Toulouse, 14 rue Peyras.

Annual publication containing the writings of members; it temporarily replaced the Revue d'histoire de la pharmacie which was last published in June 1940. Numbering is, however, unchanged. Hence, No. 111 is the first annual issue, containing the papers read during 1941; it was published in 1942. No. 112, for 1942, appeared in 1943. No. 113, for 1943, the year of German occupation, was printed in 1945. Latest number seen is No. 116, 1946, année 34. With No. 117 (March 1947) the publication resumed its original form as Revue d'histoire de la pharmacie (*q.v.*). (C. F. M.)

1869-   : **Sitzungsberichte der Physikalisch-medizinischen Sozietät zu Erlangen.**

It is out of the question to list the academic serials, but an exception may perhaps be made in favor of the Erlangen society because it includes a long series of papers on Arabic science by EILHARD WIEDEMANN (1852-1928; Isis 14, 168-86) and some of his disciples. These articles appeared under the general title Beiträge zur Geschichte der Naturwissenschaften (no. 1, 1902 to no. 79, 1929). There is a complete set of these Beiträge, two bound volumes, in the Sarton Library. The same society also published ERNST ZINNER: Entstehung und Ausbreitung der Coppernicanischen Lehre (1943; Isis 35, 61; 36, 261-66).

1929-   : **Source books in the history of the sciences.** Edited by GREGORY D. WALCOTT. New York, McGraw-Hill.

HARLOW SHAPLEY: Astronomy (1929; Isis 13, 130-34); DAVID EUGENE SMITH: Mathematics (1929; Isis 14, 268-70); W. F. MAGIE; Physics (1935; Isis 26, 176); KIRTLEY F. MATHER: Geology (1939; Isis 31, 578); MORRIS R. COHEN and I. E. DRABKIN: Greek science (1948; Isis 40, 277).

1914-1930: **Stoicheia.** Studien zur Geschichte der antiken Weltbildes und der griechischen Wissenschaft (Leipzig, Teubner). 9 thin vols.

Vol. 1 to 7, (1914-25) were edited by FRANZ BOLL (1867-1924); vols. 8-9 published in 1927 and 1930, still bear his name as founder of the collection, no other editor being named.

1911-1933: **Storia delle scienze.** Società tipografico-editrice nazionale (Sten), Torino.

Complete in eight volumes.

1) Sir EDOARDO THORPE: Chimica (1911; Isis 1, 565).   *2*) RINALDO PITONI:

Fisica (1913; Isis 1, 742-44). 3) OTTAVIO ZANOTTI-BIANCO (1852-   ): Astronomia (1913). 6-8) GINO LORIA: Storia delle matematiche (3 vols. 1929, 1931, 1933; Isis 13, 228; 19, 231; 22, 598).

This collection was probably suggested by the English series 'A history of the sciences,' witness the title, date, and choice of first volume.

1919-1926: Studi i testi Vinciani.
See Pubblicazioni del Istituto Vinciano. (C. F. M.)

1947-   : Studi di storia della medicina. Edited by NICOLA LATRONICO. Published by U. Hoepli, Milano.

Publisher's numbered, irregularly issued series in octavo. No. 8 (1947): BELLINI, A., GEROLAMO CARDANO, 327 p. No. 9 (1947): BOTTERO, A., CARLO FORLANINI, inventore del pneumotorace artificiale, 131 p. (C. F. M.)

1920: Studi di storia della scienza. Edited and published by Nardecchia in Roma.

Numbered series. No. 1 (1920): L'orecchio e il naso nel sistema antropometrico di LEONARDO DA VINCI (G. BILIANCIONI). Any more? (C. F. M.)

1922-1926: Studi di storia del pensiero scientifico. Collection edited by ALDO MIELI and published by the Casa Editrice "Leonardo da Vinci" Roma.

1)A. MIELI: Pagine di storia delle chimica (277 p., ill., 1922; Isis 5, 173-74). 2) GUGLIELMO BILIANCIONI: Veteris vestigia flammae (560 p., ill. 1922; Isis 5, 475-77), etc.

Five volumes were announced in 1932. MIELI's programs were often modified. For example vol. 1 of his I prearistotelici (Firenze 1916; Isis 4, 347) appeared as first volume of a Storia del pensiero scientifico dalle origini a tutto il secolo XVIII; vol. 2 of I prearistotelici was announced as vol. 5 of the Studi di storia del pensiero. It did not appear in either series. In 1925, the series was stabilized as follows.

Vol. 1 and 2 as above.

Vol. 3. QUIRINO CELLI: La medicina greca nella tradizione mitologica ed omerica (260 p., ill., 1923; Isis 6, 196).

Vol. 4. A. MIELI: I Prearistotelici I. (522 p., 1916; Isis 4, 347).

Vol. 5. A. MIELI: Manuale di storia della scienza. Antichità (610 p., ill., 1925; Isis 8, 578).

Vol. 6. ALFRED SCHMIDT: Droghe e commercio delle droghe nell'antichità.—Did this book actually appear? It did appear in German, Drogen und Drogenhandel im Altertum (144 p., Leipzig 1924; Isis 7, 252; 8, 192).

1942-   : Studi e Ricerche storico-mediche. Published by the Istituto di storia della medicina dell'Università di Roma.

Small 16mo series of medico-historical monographs; unnumbered(?). BAFFONI, A., Storia delle pleuriti, 177 p. (1947). (C. F. M.)

1907-1937: Studien zur Geschichte der Medizin. Published by the Puschmann Foundation at the University of Leipzig. Edited by KARL SUDHOFF, later by H. E. SIGERIST, et al. Leipzig, Johann Ambrosius Barth.

Collection meant to include the memoirs too bulky for the Archiv für die Geschichte der Medizin. See Isis 2, 149.

Last no. published Heft 23, 1937 (Isis 35, 249 under ARTELT, WALTER). Complete in 23 numbers.

List of parts 1 to 14 (1907-25) on the back cover of part 15; list of parts 15 to 23 (1926-37) on the back cover of part 23. Parts 1 to 6 and 8 to 12 (1907-18) were written by SUDHOFF himself.

1917-1921: Studies in the history and method of science. Edited by CHARLES SINGER. Only 2 vols. published, quarto, richly illustrated. Clarendon Press, Oxford.

Vol. 1 includes articles on ST. HILDEGARD, vitalism, MANFREDI, cramp rings, J. WEYER, a treatise of MAIMONIDES, etc. Vol. 2 has articles on the history of biology, astronomy, ROGER BACON, LEONARDO, ASCLEPIADES, GALILEO, paleobotany, etc.

1907-1938: Studi i memorie per la storia dell' Università di Bologna.
Complete in 14 volumes. It forms series 1 of Pubblicazioni of the Historical
Commission of the Bologna University. (C. F. M.)

1925-1943: Sudhoffs Archiv, see Archiv für die Geschichte der Medizin.

1844-1857: Sydenham Society. Publications. The society was instituted in London in 1843.
Published early medical texts in English translation and other books dealing with
the history of medicine. Forty vols. and one atlas appeared between 1844 and
1857. They include works of HIPPOCRATES, ARETAEOS, PAULOS AEGINETA, AL-RAZI,
HARVEY, SYDENHAM, W. HUNTER, DUPUYTREN, THEODOR SCHWANN, J. F. K. HECKER
(Epidemics of the Middle Ages), collections of papers on puerperal fever, aneurism,
etc.
The activities of the society were continued by the New Sydenham Society which
published 194 volumes from 1859 to 1906.

1936: Symposium on prehistoric agriculture; held April 1936 at Flagstaff, Arizona.
The report of this meeting forms No. 296 of the University of Mexico Bulletin.
(C. F. M.)

1921-1926: Tage der Technik; illustrierter technisch-historischer Abreiss-Kalender.
Edited by F. M. FELDHAUS; published by R. Oldenbourg in München.
Six years were published, from 1921 (for 1922) to 1926 (for 1927). (C. F. M.)

1932-   : Technik-Geschichte. Berlin.
See Beiträge zur Geschichte der Technik.

1923: Testi Vinciani. Edited by MARIO CERMENATI; issued for the Istituto Vinciano in Roma; published by Zanichelli in Bologna.
The only volume of this series was Del moto e misura dell'acqua of LEONARDO,
edited by L. M. ARCONATI.
Cf. Pubblicazioni. (C. F. M.)

(1929)-   : Textes et traductions pour servir à l'histoire de la pensée moderne.
Edited by ABEL REY; published by Alcan in Paris.
Unnumbered octavo volumes, being the reprints or translations of historical texts
from science, philosophy, etc. In 1929: CESALPINO: Questions péripatéticiennes.
In 1930: NICOLAS DE CUSA: De la docte ignorance; also GIORDANO BRUNO: Cause,
principe et unité. Any more? (C. F. M.)

1940-   : Texte und Untersuchungen zur Geschichte der Naturwissenschaften.
Edited by JULIUS SCHUSTER; published by Triltsch in Würzburg.
No. 1 (1940): HERMANNUS DE SANCTO PORTU: Der Herbarius communis (edited
by H. EBEL). This number is the latest on record. (C. F. M.)

1934-1940: Thalès. Recueil annuel des travaux de l'Institut d'histoire des sciences
et des techniques de l'Université de Paris. 5 vols. published, Paris 1934-48.
Presses universitaires de France. Edited by ABEL REY (1873-1940), PIERRE
DUCASSÉ, LUCIEN BRUNET (Isis 25, 272).

1933-   : Trabajos de la Cátedra de historia crítica de la medicina. Edited by
EDUARDO GARCÍA DEL REAL. Published in Madrid.
Vol. 1 for 1932/33 was published in 1933. It contains history of obstetric for-
ceps, treatment of toothache, ARNALDUS OF VILLANOVA, history of Caesarean section,
of podalic version, JUAN DE AVIÑÓN, GIMBERNAT, G. CASAL, history of vitamines, of
angina pectoris, etc. (I have not seen later issues). (C. F. M.)

1922-   : Transactions of the Newcomen Society for the study of the history of
engineering and technology. Vol. 1, 1920-21, Printed for the Society by Courier
Press, Leamington Spa, 1922.
See Isis 4, 496-98; 5, 312.

The Newcomen Society, founded in 1919, also issues Extra Publications, that is, separate volumes, different from the Transactions, devoted to special subjects. These volumes are analyzed or listed in Isis under their authors' names (*e.g.*, 12, 372; 15, 349-50).

General index to vols. 1 to 10, 1920-30. General index to vols. 11 to 20 and extra publ. nos. 1 to 4.

The American branch of the Newcomen Society has issued a relatively large number of publications of a showy kind, many of them worthless, and badly integrated.

1945-   : **Tratados fundamentales.** Colección dirigida por GREGORIO WEINBERG (y MANUEL SADOSKY). Lautaro, Buenos-Aires.

Series of translations of books concerning philosophy and science. *See* list by ALDO MIELI in Archives internationales (Oct. 1948, p. 212-14).

1941-   : **Trattato enciclopedico di storia della medicina.** Under the direction of ADALBERTO PAZZINI. Roma & Milano.

Though apparently an encyclopedia of medical history, this work is an irregularly published monographic series. No. 1 (1941): PAZZINI, A., La medicina primitiva, 366p. Further volumes are planned and announced to be published as follows: No. 2: TERGOLINA, U., Fonti antiche per lo studio dell'Arte Sanitaria. No. 3 (listed as No. 8; 1943): CASARINI, A., Storia della medicina militare. Any more? (C. F. M.)

1933-   : **Trudy Instituta istorii nauki i tekhniki** (Transactions of the Institute for the history of science and technology). Published by the Akademiya Nauk SSSR (Academy of sciences of the Soviet Union) in three series all printed by the Soviet Academy Press, Moscow and Leningrad.

The Institute for the History of Science being an intrinsic part of the USSR Academy, its publications are publications of the Academy.

1933: First Series: Arkhiv istorii nauki i tekhniki (Archives for the history of science and technology). Edited by Academician N. I. BUKHARIN with various colleagues of his.

Vol. 1 appeared in 1933; last vol. seen, vol. 9, 1936. These nine volumes were analyzed in Isis.

1935: Second series with the general title Trudy instituta istorii nauki i tekhniki. There is no special title for the series. Each volume deals with a separate subject and has its own title. *E.g.*, I. SMORGONSKY: Foreign shipbuilding terms in the Russian language (195 p., 1936; Isis 25, 592).

Vol. 1 (1935) LEONARD EULER (Isis 25, 219). Vol. 4 (1935) S. G. STRUMILIN: Siderurgy in USSR. Technical progress in 300 years (Isis 25, 285).

Vol. 7 (1936) P. P. ZABARINSKIY: The first fire engines at the port of Cronstadt (Isis 26, 524).

Vol. 9 (1936) E. A. ZEITLIN: The technical revolution in flax-spinning (Isis 27, 180).

(All these publications are in Russian).

1934: Third series with the same general title Trudy etc. No special title for the series. Each volume deals with a special subject and has its own title.

Vol. 1 (1934). History of the dynamo; vol. 2 (1936) History of the electric motor. Both volumes compiled by D. V. EFREMOV and M. I. RADOVSKIJ, edited by V. TH. MITKEVITCH (Isis 24, 518; 25, 590).

Other books on the history of science were published by the Soviet Academy of Sciences, but without serial numbers and without mention on the title pages of the Institute for the history of science.

M. N. MLADENTSEV and V. E. TISHCHENKO: DMITRI IVANOVICH MENDELEEV. Vol. 1, parts 1-2 (1938).

S. I. VAVILOV: Symposium on NEWTON (1943; Isis 35, 232).

The Academy has published elaborate bibliographical studies which may interest historians of science.

Geological literature. Vol. 1. Geology in the publications of the Academy, edited by J. S. EDELSTEIN (vol. 1, 1938).

Bibliography of IGNATII JULIANOVICH KRACHKOVSKI (1936; Isis 28, 572). Bibliography of ALEXANDR PETROVICH KARPINSKI (1938; Isis 33, 117).

The works of MIKHAILO VASILIEVICH LOMONOSOV were edited for the Academy by BORIS NIKOLAEVICH MENSHUTKIN (1936; Isis 28, 106-09) and the same author wrote a biography of LOMONOSOV (1711-65) included in the "popular science series" of the Academy (1937; Isis 29, 226).

This bibliography is incomplete but such as it is it is sufficient to show the variety and greatness of the efforts already made by the Soviet Academy to promote the study of the history of science. See also Isis 37, 77.

See also, above, Akademiia nauk SSSR. Institut istorii estestvoznaniia, 1947 *ff.*

1927-1931: **Trudy; Komissia po istorii znanii** (Proceedings of the Commission on history of science). Published by the Leningrad Academy of Sciences.

Numbered series of monographs complete in 11 volumes (?). No. 1 (1927): V. VERNADSKY's work on the actual importance of the history of sciences. No. 2 (1927): The BAER jubilee volume. No. 3 (1927): B. TURAEV's bibliography of Russian scientific works on the classical Orient. No. 11 (1931): OBRUCHEV's History of geological researches in Siberia.

Continued as preceding entry (Trudy Instituta istorii nauki, etc.). (C. F. M.)

1935-   : **Türk tıp tarihi arkivi** (Archives of history of Turkish medicine). Edited by A. SÜHEYL ÜNVER and F. NAFIZ UZLIK. Published by Kader in Istanbul.

Numbered but irregularly issued series. Numbering is continuous, but it is grouped by arbitrary volume numbering. Vol. 1, no. 1 was issued March 1935. No. 5 to no. 9 make vol. 2, 1937-1938 (partly edited by METINE BELGER). No. 10 (1938) and no. 11 & 12 (1939) complete vol. 3. Vol. 4 includes nos. 13 to 16, 1939-1940. Vol. 5 includes nos. 17, 18 and 19/20, published in 1940 to 1942. Latest volume on record is the 6th, with no. 21/22 published in 1943. (C. F. M.).

1922: **Unanúe.** Founded and edited by HERMILIO VALDIZÁN. Published in Lima.

Only no. 1, vol. 1 (March) and no. 2, vol. 1 (June) were published. The periodical is dedicated to the medical history of Peru. No more. JOSÉ HIPÓLITO UNANÚE (13 Aug. 1775-15 July 1833) is called "padre de la medicina Americana." His chief work was the 'Observaciones sobre el clima de Lima' (2nd ed., Madrid, 1815). Cf. Isis, 1941-42, 33:636-8. (C. F. M.)

1923-1928: **Universitas scriptorum.** Published by the Casa Editrice Leonardo da Vinci in Roma.

Numbered series of small reprints of historical classics of science; volume size 15 1/2 cm by 13 cm. Certain numbers form the subseries Classici della scienza. No. 2/3 (1924): Viaggi di Russia (F. ALGAROTTI). No. 12/13 (1926): Gli Aforismi (HIPPOCRATES), this number forms no. 3/4 of the mentioned subseries. No. 14/15 (1928): ALESSANDRO VOLTA; forms no. 5/6 of subseries. Latest known issue is no. 16/17 (1928): Prodromo . . . sui corpi solidi (N. STENO); forms no. 7/8 of subseries. (C. F. M.)

(1935)-   : **Untersuchungen zur Astronomie der Maya.** Published in Berlin.

Numbered series, partly composed by HANS LUDENDORFF. This is a series of reprints on Maya astronomy taken from the Sitzungsberichte of the physico-mathematical class of the Preussische Akademie der Wissenschaften. No. 9, 1935; No. 10, 1936. (C. F. M.)

1907: **Urkunden zur Geschichte der Mathematik im Altertume.** Published by B. G. Teubner, in Leipzig.

Only the first no. was published: Der Bericht des Simplicius über die Quadraturen des Antiphon; by F. RUDIO. (C. F. M.)

1922-   : **Veröffentlichungen der Schweizerischen Gesellschaft für Geschichte der Medizin und der Naturwissenschaften.** Publications de la Société suisse d'histoire de la médecine et des sciences naturelles. Aarau, H. R. Sauerländer.

The following volumes have appeared. Only the authors and dates are given which suffices for identification.

1. CONRAD BRUNNER (Isis 5, 450-51), 1922
2. G. A. WEHRLI (Isis 7, 209), 1923
3. O. BERNHARD, 1924
4. ARTHUR TROENDLE (Isis 8, 806), 1925
5. O. BERNHARD (Isis 7, 250), 1926
6. BERNHARD PEYER, H. R. REMUND, 1928
7. ANDRÉ GUISAN, 1930
8. GUSTAV SENN (Isis 27, 68-69), 1933
9. A. MORITZI (1806-50), 1934
10. FABRICIUS HILDANUS, 1936
11. PAUL AEBISCHER, EUGÈNE OLIVIER (Isis 29, 487), 1938
12. EDUARD FUETER (Isis 34, 32), 1941
13. HANS FISCHER, BERNARD and HEINRICH PEYER. (Lychnos 417, 1943)
14. P. NIGGLI. Kristallologia of HOTTINGER, 1946
15. HEINRICH BUESS (Isis 38, 111-14) 1946
16. HENRY NIGST, 1946
17. HANS BUSCHER, 1947
18. GWER REICHEN, 1949

The society also publishes (since 1944) the periodical Gesnerus (q.v.).

1921-1938: Veterinärhistorische Mitteilungen. Issued by the Gesellschaft für Geschichte und Literatur der Veterinärmedizin (founded 1920). Edited by WILHELM RIECK; published by M. & H. Schaper in Hannover.
Irregularly published, numbered Beilage to Deutsche tierärztliche Wochenschrift. Twelve numbers to a volume.
Vol. 18 (for 1938/39) published in 1938 becomes vol. 1 of Beiträge zur Geschichte der Veterinärmedizin (q.v.). (C. F. M.)

1925-1935: Veterinärhistorisches Jahrbuch. Issued by the Gesellschaft für Geschichte und Literature der Veterinärmedizin; edited by W. RIECK, and R. FRÖHNER. Published in Leipzig-Mölkau.
Vol. 1-7, 1925-1935. With vol. 8, 1936 the title of this annual changed to Cheiron (q.v.). Each volume contains shorter and longer articles such as Zur Mulomedicina Chironis (K. HOPPE), Die älteste Myologie des Hundes (RIECK), Die Tierheilkunde des ABU BEKR IBN BEDR (FRÖHNER), Die Entwicklung der veterinärhistorischen Forschung (W. RIECK), etc. (C. F. M.)
Cf. Cheiron.

1928-1932: Viaggi e scoperte degli navigatori ed esploratori italiani. Published by the Edizioni Alpes in Milano.
Unnumbered series of monographs related to the history of geography; 20 1/2 cm by 15 1/2 cm. Complete in 18 volumes. The first book of the set is Viaggio a Tartari by Fra GIOVANNI DA PIAN DEL CARPINO (1928). (C. F. M.)

1923-1925: Vinciani d'Italia; biografie e scritti. Issued by the Istituto di studi Vinciani in Roma (founded 1919); published by Maglione & Strini in Roma.
This is a short set of volumes on Italians who studied and admired LEONARDO DA VINCI. Numbered series of monographs, 17 cm by 24 cm. No. 1 (1923): GILBERTO GOVI, 1826-1889 (A. FAVARO). No. 2 (1924): GIAMBATTISTA VENTURI (G. B. DE TORRI). Latest issue is vol. 3, 1925. (C. F. M.)

1914-1915: Vite dei medici e naturalisti celebri. Published by the Instituto di micrographia italiana in Firenze.
Short series of 16° booklets. No. 2 (1914): FRANCESCO REDI (M. CARDINI). No. 3 (1915): UGOLINO DA MONTECATINI (D. BARDUZZI). No further trace of this serial. (C. F. M.)

1912-1915: Voigtländers Quellenbücher. Collection of little books illustrated, many of them dealing with the history of science. R. Voigtländers Verlag, Leipzig.
A number of titles are quoted in Isis 1, 476-77. Vol. 88, 1915 (Isis 4, 440). This is the last vol. on record.

The main purpose of the collection was to invite the reader to return to the sources; this was done well and the volumes were sold at a low price. A very fine effort for the sound popularization of knowledge and of the history of science.

1931-1936: **Vorträge der Hauptversammlung der Gesellschaft für Geschichte der Pharmazie.** Published by Nemayer in Mittenwald.
This is the set of papers of the annual conventions of the Society for History of Pharmacy. The latest volume on record is for the year 1936. (C. F. M.)

1928-1932: **Vorträge des Instituts für Geschichte der Medizin an der Universität** Leipzig. Edited by HENRY E. SIGERIST; published by G. Thieme in Leipzig.
Numbered volumes of essays related to history, philosophy or sociology of medicine. Bd. 1: Grundlagen und Ziele der Medizin der Gegenwart, contains articles on the anatomical idea, the functional idea, the clinic, the medical practice and the neurologist. Bd. 2 discusses the problems and relations of physician and state (Der Arzt und der Staat). Last volume is Bd. 4. (C. F. M.)

1907-1923: **Vorträge und Berichte; Deutsches Museum von Meisterwerken der Naturwissenschaften und Technik.** Published in München.
Complete in 20 volumes.
Cf. Abhandlungen und Berichte (etc.). (C. F. M.)

1922-   : **Wellcome Historical Medical Museum.** Present address: 28 Portman Square, London W. 1.
Three volumes were published in 1922-25 under the general title Research studies in medical history.
   1. JOHN ARDERNE: De arte phisicali (60 p., 1922).
   2. PIETRO CAPPARONI: Magistri Salernitani nondum cogniti (68 p., 1923).
   3. M. H. SPIELMANN: The iconography of VESALIUS (243 p., 1925).
Without serial number: J. D. COMRIE: History of Scottish medicine (304 p., 1927; *2nd* ed. 2 vols., 1932). SPANISH influence on the progress of medical science (121 p., 1935), also in French, Italian and Spanish translations.
Guide to the WHMM (100 p., 1926?); plus various other guides. We list only the following:
Lister Centenary Exhibition Handbook (1927, 216 p.).
Lister Centenary Celebration. American College of Surgeons, Detroit (1927, 140 p.).
Cinchona Tercentenary Exhibition (1930, 115 p.).
Hickman Centenary Exhibition (1930, 86 p.).
New series:
   1. CHARLES SINGER and C. RABIN: A prelude to modern science; the Tabulae anatomicae sex of VESALIUS (144 p., 59 figs., 1946; Isis 38, 109-11).
   2. BARBARA M. DUNCUM: Development of inhalation anesthesia (656 p., 161 figs., 1947; Isis 38, 131-33).

1947-   : **Wiener Beiträge zur Geschichte der Medizin,** edited by EMMANUEL BERGHOFF. Published by Wilhelm Maudrich, Wien.
Vol. 1. E. BERGMANN: Entwicklungsgeschichte des Krankheitsbegriffes (1947); vol. 2, Festschrift MAX NEUBURGER (1948); vol. 3. E. BERGHOFF: MAX NEUBURGER. *See* also Beiträge zur Geschichte der Medizin. (C. F. M.)

1935-1937: **Wiener medizingeschichtliche Beiträge.** Published by the Ars Medici Verlag. IX. Spitalgasse 1 a, Wien.
Numbered series of monographs; 22 1/2 cm by 15 1/2 cm. Complete in 3 vols.
No. 1 (1935): Wiens Mediziner und die Freiheitsbewegung des Jahres 1848 (I. FISCHER). No. 2 (1935): Laboratoriumpestfälle in Wien (I. SCHILDER). No. 3 (1937): Beitrag zur Geschichte der Pockenschutzimpfung in Wien (E. STRANSKY). (C. F. M.)

1880-1884: The **Willughby Society** for the reprinting of scarce ornithological works. The Society was founded in London in 1879 by ALFRED NEWTON and WILLIAM BERNHARD TEGETMEIER, editors of The Ibis. Twelve volumes were published. The Society was called after the early English zoologist, FRANCIS WILLUGHBY (1635-72).

1935- : Yayınlarından; **Istanbul üniversite Tıp tarihi enstitü** (Publications; Istanbul University; Medico-historical Institute). Edited by SÜHEYL ÜNVER, the director of the Institute; published in Istanbul.
Numbered series published irregularly. Each number ("aded" or "sayi") is either a collection of offprints from other journals or a monograph, with occasional summaries in western languages. No. 2, 1935; no. 4, 1936; no. 6, 1937; no. 11, 1938; no. 15, 1939; no. 16, 1939; no. 19, 1940 have been analyzed in Isis. No. 12 (1939): Kitabül Cerrahname, 870-1465 (S. SABUNCUOĞLU). No. 25 (1943): Tıp tarihi (Medical history; 308 p.) (S. ÜNVER). Latest issue on record is no. 29, 1945.
Cf. Türk, etc. (C .F .M.)

1924: **Yperman.** Issued by the Société belge d'histoire de la médecine. Edited by TRICOT-ROYER.
It is reported that one volume of the Belgian medico-historical journal has been published in 1924. I have no record of the journal. Is there any more? (C. F. M.)

1935-1940: **Zeitschrift für die gesamte Naturwissenschaft** einschliesslich Naturphilosophie und Geschichte der Naturwissenschaften. Edited by A. BENNINGHOFF, K. BEURLEN, K. HILDEBRANDT and K. WOLF. Published in Braunschweig, later in Berlin.
The first number was issued in April 1935. It was a monthly publication. Yet vol. 2 appeared in two years. Vol. 5, 1939, has only nine nos. Ceased publication with vol. 6, 1940. (C. F. M.)

1856-1917: **Zeitschrift für Mathematik und Physik.** Published in Leipzig.
Complete in 64 volumes. Vol. 1-45, 1856-1900, with a special section for the history and bibliography of mathematics and physics; the section was called "Literaturzeitung" in the first 19 volumes; in later volumes it was "Historisch-literärische Abteilung."
The Abhandlungen (*q.v.*) zur Geschichte der mathematischen Wissenschaften is the supplement of this serial. (C. F. M.)

1904-1919: **Zoologische Annalen;** Zeitschrift für Geschichte der Zoologie. Edited by MAX BRAUN, published by A. Stuber's Verlag (C. Kabitzsch) in Würzburg. Seven volumes 1904 to 1916 (the seventh and last volume appeared in 4 parts dated 1915, 1916, 1916 and 1919; the table of contents of the whole does not contain references to a fourth part).
Isis 2: 142.
See Archiv für die Geschichte der Medizin, vol. 27, 1934 *ff.*

1924- : **Zürcher medizingeschichtliche Abhandlungen.** Published by Orell Füssli, later by Leemann in Zürich.
Numbered monographs; 23 1/2 cm. Irregularly published. No. 1 (1924): THEODOR BILLROTH in Zürich (HUBERT). No. 2 (1924): Der medizinische Inhalt der schweizerischen Volkskalender (LOMBARD). No. 6 (1926): Gesundheitspflege im mittelalterlichen Basel (BAAS). No. 7 (1926): Pestprophylaxe im alten Zürich (TREICHLER). No. 12 (1927): Missgeburten und Wundergestalten in Einblattdrucken und Handzeichnungen des 16. Jahrhunderts (SONDEREGGER). No. 19 (1943): Beitrag zur Geschichte der Wohnungshygiene der Stadt Basel (O. MAUDERLI).
The latest issue known to me is no. 20 (1943): Über die Cholera asiatica in Kanton Aargau anno 1854 (W. WITZ). (C. F. M.)

1910-1914: **Zur historischen Biologie der Krankheitserreger.** Materialien, Studien und Abhandlungen, gemeinsam mit V. FOSSEL, TIBERIUS GYŐRY, W. HIS, hrsg. von KARL SUDHOFF und GEORG STICKER. Giessen, Alfred Töpelmann. Isis 2, 150. Seven thin parts appeared between 1910 and 1914. The main authors were the two editors SUDHOFF and STICKER. Short memoirs were contributed also by GRAFTON ELLIOT SMITH and MARC ARMAND RUFFER, GYŐRY and ARNOLD KLEBS.

MISLEADING TITLES
APPENDIX TO CHAPTER 20
by CLAUDIUS F. MAYER

A glance into the Index-Catalogue under any subject of medico-historical research reveals many references in journals not primarily of medico-historical nature. It often happens that, with the change of editorship, a periodical publication assumes a new character, opens perhaps a new historical section, or closes it.

There are many serials whose title is misleading. Without the examination of a publication nothing should be said about its true nature. In the late 18th and early 19th centuries, the meaning of the terms "philosophy" and "history" was also different, and the occurrence of these terms in the title or the subtitle of a publication may lead the 20th century man to wrong assumptions. "Philosophy" often means "theoretical discussion," while "history" can be either "natural history" or the record of any current event.

Another way of being misled is by believing that a generic name commonly associated with a serial polygraphic publication is always the label of a journal or periodical. In the literature of science the words "Beiträge," "Abhandlungen," or "Vorträge," or "Transactions" do not mean necessarily that we are dealing with a journal.

In order to avoid the pitfalls of terminology and to save time for those who should like to enlarge this list of true historico-scientific serials the following roll of journals is published as a warning!

Acta medica et philosophica Hafniensia. Copenhagen, v. 1-5 (1671) 1673-(1679) 1680.
It has nothing to do with medical philosophy.
Annali di Ippocrate. Milano, v. 1-7, 1906-1912.
A journal of clinical medicine; not historical.
Annals of medicine; exhibiting a concise view of the latest and most important discoveries in medicine and medical *philosophy.* Edinburgh, ser. 1, v. 1-5, 1796-1800; ser. 2, v. 1-3, 1801-1804.
Neither medical history nor philosophy of medicine.
Ars médica. Barcelona, v. 1-12, 1925-1936.
Clinical medicine.
Ars medici. Wien, v. 1, 1911-
Clinical medicine.
Asclepios. La Habana, v. 1-14, 1915-1928.
Clinical medicine.
Aus dem Archiv F. A. Brockhaus; Zeugnisse zur Geschichte geistigen Schaffens; ed. by Hermann Michel. Leipzig, v. 1-4, 1926-1929.
Not history of science.
Beiträge zur bayerischen Kulturgeschichte. München, v. 1, 1927.
Not history of science.
Beiträge zur Geschichte der Chemie. Braunschweig, v. 1, 1869, etc.
Not a serial but a collection of various writings of the single author (Dr. Kopp) on a single topic.
Beiträge zur Geschichte der Erfindungen (or, Erfindungskunst). Leipzig, Bd 1-5, 1780-1805.
Not a true serial but the work of a single author (J. BECKMANN).

Beiträge zur Geschichte der Meteorologie. Berlin, no. 1-5, 1914.
The single work of a single author, G. HELLMANN; forms no. 273 of Veröffentlichungen des K. Preussischen meteorologischen Instituts.
Beiträge zur Kulturgeschichte des Mittelalters und der Renaissance. Leipzig, Heft 1-55, 1908-1939.
It contains little of importance to the historian of science.
Bibliothèque des philosophes (chimiques) (ou Recueil des oeuvres des auteurs des plus approuvez qui ont écrit de la pierre philosophale). Paris, 1741-54.
Not a true serial; it is a collection of alchemic works compiled by WILLIAM SALMON, M.D.; originally published in 1672.
Le Censeur médical; journal de littérature, de philosophie et de bibliographie médicales, françaises et étrangères. Paris, vol. 1, 1834.
Does not contain anything medico-historical or philosophical; discusses current events only.
Chiron; eine der theoretischen, praktischen, literarischen und historischen Bearbeitung der Chirurgie gewidmete Zeitschrift. Edited by JOHANN BARTHEL VON SIEBOLD. Nürnberg & Sulzbach, v. 1-3, 1805-1812/13.
Though one of the five sections of the journal is supposedly historical, the section discusses only current events, biographies and anecdotes; medico-historical matters are found only as introductions of clinical articles or occasional historical additions of the editor. Vol. 1 was published in 1805-1806; vol. 2, 1806; vol. 3, 1812-13.
Deutsche Studien zur Geistesgeschichte. Würzburg, Triltsch, vol. 1, 1936-
This and similar serial titles have no relationship to the history of science as defined for the purposes of this guide.
Dioscorides. Bruxelles, v. 1, 1937-
A historical name for a military medical journal.
Erläutertes Preussen. Königsberg, v. 1-5, 1724-42.
Devoted to contemporary science ("Gelehrten-Historie").
Historisches Taschenbuch für Aerzte, Chemiker und Pharmazeutiker. Erfurt, vol. 1-3, 1803-1805.
This is but an almanac without any historical article in it; compiled by JOH. BARTH. TROMMSDORFF.
History of Learning; giving a succinct account and narrative of the choicest new books (etc.) London, no. 1, 1694.
Just a record of contemporary printing.
Hygie (Gazette de santé) . . . mélanges critiques, historiques et philosophiques; revue générale des journaux de médecine (etc.) Bruxelles & Paris, 1823-1843.
Of no medico-historical value; contains contemporary affairs.
Journal complémentaire du Dictionnaire des sciences médicales. Paris. v. 1-44, 1818-1832.
Not on history of medicine.
Journal de l'Institut historique. Paris, v. 1-12, 1934-40.
Not important for the history of science.
Journal der Erfindungen, Theorien und Widersprüche in der Natur- und Arzneiwissenschaft. Gotha, v. 1-11, 1792-1809.
Neither history nor philosophy of science.
Journal of Ayurveda; or, the Hindu system of medicine. Calcutta, v. 1, 1924-
Discusses current affairs and practice of the Ayurvedist physicians of India.
Journal of the Pierre Fauchard Academy. Minneapolis, vol. 1, 1943-
A regular dental journal of a practical dental society; not for dental history.
Maimonides bulletin. Detroit, v. 1-7, 1925-1931.
A journal for medical practice; not historical.
Medical commentaries . . . exhibiting a concise view of the latest and most important discoveries in medicine and medical philosophy. London & Edinburgh, 1783-1795.
Not on philosophy of medicine.
Medical world; biographical sketches. New York, Bentley Pub. Co., 1915.
Not a serial.

Medicina misontologica; opera periodica, Milano, 1840.
    Work of F. G. GEROMINI issued in parts; not a true serial.
Medicinische Denkwürdigkeiten aus der Vergangenheit und Gegenwart. Berlin,
    Aug. Hirschwald, 1834.
    Numbered abstracts only, taken from old and current journals as well as from old
    books (*e.g.*, from the 1595 edition of HIPPOCRATES).
Medicinisches Journal.   Edited by E. G. BALDINGER.   Göttingen, 1784-1796.
    Not medical history.
Medycyna i kronika lekarska.   Warszawa, vol. 1-49, 1873-1914.
    Not historical.
Memorabilien der Heilkunde, Staatsarzneiwissenschaft und Thierheilkunst. Edited
    by J. J. KAUSCH.   Züllichau, v. 1-3, 1813-1819.
    Current veterinary medicine.
Miscellanea physico-medico-mathematica.   Erfurt, 1727-1732.
    Nothing on medical history.
Monatsblatt für Menschenkunde . . . und Geschichte.   Zwickau, 1829.
    Not on history of medicine.
New York medical and philosophical journal and review.   New York, v. 1-3, 1809-
    11.
    Nothing philosophical about it.   But, it contains abstracts from the Philosophical
Transactions.
Ospedale maggiore; rivista mensile illustrata di storia.   Milano, ser, 2, vol. 1-4, 1913-
    16.
    Not medico-historical.
Der Philosophische Arzt.   Frankfurt, Hanau & Leipzig, vol. 1-4, 1775-1777; n. ser.,
    vol. 1-3, 1798-99.
    An early neurological journal, not philosophy of medicine.
Producteur; journal philosophique de l'industrie, des sciences et des beaux-arts.
    Paris.   vol. 1, 1826.
    Not philosophy of science.
Raccolta d'opuscoli scientifici.   Venezia, 51 vol., 1728-1757.
    Contemporary science only.
Revue médicale historique et philosophique.   Paris, 6 vols., 1820-21.
    Current material only; nothing historical, or philosophical.
Sammlung von Natur- und Medicin-, wie auch hierzu gehörigen Kunst- und Litera-
    tur-Geschichten, etc. Leipzig, 19 vols., 1717-26.
    Contemporary science only.
La Scienza italiana.   Bologna, vol. 1, 1876.
    Not history of science.
Studi sassaresi.   Sassari, vol. 1, 1901.
    Clinical medicine, not history of medicine.

*Addenda to the Journals and
Serials concerning the History of Science*

1940-   : **Journal of the History of Ideas.**   A quarterly devoted to intellectual his-
    tory founded by ARTHUR O. LOVEJOY (Isis 32, 483).   Editor: JOHN HERMAN
    RANDALL, jr.
    Published by the College of the City of New York.   Vol. 12, no. 2 appeared in
April 1951.

1946-   : **Pagine di storia della scienza e delle tecnica.**   Published by the Centro
    di storia della scienza, della tecnica e del lavoro, under the auspices of the
    Ministerio della Marina, Roma.
    Issued as supplement to Annali di medicina navale e coloniale.   Only 1946
issues seen.

D. ORGANIZATION OF THE STUDY AND TEACH-ING OF THE HISTORY OF SCIENCE

21. NATIONAL SOCIETIES DEVOTED TO THE HISTORY OF SCIENCE

There is generally but one society concerning the history of science in each country, though in the larger countries it may be necessary to establish local sections or branches in various districts. In addition to the society devoted to the history of science, there may be others devoted to the history of medicine, the history of chemistry, etc. We shall not attempt to enumerate those other societies but restrict ourselves to the main societies defined by our title.

The term "national" in that title should not be understood in the sense of "official" (approved and supported by the government); the societies enumerated by us are not official, or they are official only in an indirect way.

The earliest of these societies is an English one founded in London in 1841, but it soon ceased to exist. It is mentioned here *pro memoria*.

1841: Historical Society of Science.—Founded by JAMES ORCHARD HALLIWELL (- PHILLIPPS) in London 1841, it lasted only a year or two. For its publication (2 vols.) see list of serials under the Society's name. The Society was duly constituted under the presidency of the Duke of Sussex assisted by an imposing council; HALLIWELL was the secretary. At the end of its vol. 1 (out of 2) one may find its by-laws and a list of members.

H. W. DICKINSON: J. O. HALLIWELL and the Historical Society of Science, London 1841 (Isis 18, 126-32, 1932).

The first society which survived was the German one, born in 1901. We may thus say that the existing societies devoted to the history of science are all creations of the twentieth century.

1901: Deutsche Gesellschaft für Geschichte der Medizin und der Naturwissenschaften.—Founded at Hamburg, Sept. 25, 1901, by KARL SUDHOFF and others. Publishes the Mitteilungen (*q.v.*).

The German Society met each year with the Versammlung Deutscher Naturforscher und Aerzte. Reports of its proceedings were issued by a German medical journal (name not indicated on the offprints) and also by Janus. I have reports of the 9th to 12th annual meetings, 1910-14, which were parts of the 82nd to 85th meetings of the Deutsche Naturforscher. I also have reports of the meetings which took place from 1920 to 1922, from 1926 to 1932.

The German Society became in 1932 a group of the Académie.

The Deutsche Gesellschaft has been recently reorganized under the slightly different name Deutsche Vereinigung der Medizin, Naturwissenschaft und Technik. Its first meeting was held on 24 September 1949. The president is PAUL DIEPGEN, director of the Medizinhistorisches Institut der Johannes Gutenberg Universität in Mainz, and the secretary, Dr. JOHANNES STENDEL, (22c) Bonn, Reuterstr. 2 B.

1907: Società Italiana di Storia Critica delle Scienze Mediche e Naturali.—Founded at Perugia, October 9, 1907 by DOMENICO BARDUZZI (1847-1929) and others.

See our notes on the 1907 Atti della Società and on the 1910 Rivista di storia critica delle scienze . . .

LUIGI CASTALDI and UMBERTO TERGOLINA: Trent' anni di vita della Società . . . (Ott. 1907-Ott. 1937). Cenni illustrativi e indice delle publicazioni sociali. A cura dell' Ufficio stampa medica italiana (122 p., Siena 1938).

Address care of Museo di storia delle scienze, Piazza dei Giudici, 1, Firenze.

1913: Genootschap voor Geschiedenis der Geneeskunde, Wiskunde en Natuurwetenschappen (Society for the History of Medicine, Mathematics and Natural Sciences).—The Dutch society was founded in June 1913, in Leiden, at the initiative of E. C. VAN LEERSUM and J. A. VOLLGRAFF. A history of its activities during the first thirty-five years (1913-48) was prepared by the secretary D. BURGER: Gedenkboekje (44 p., many portraits, Amsterdam 1948).
The annual reports of the Society are published in the Dutch journal of medicine (Nederlandsch Tijdschrift voor Geneeskunde).
The address of the Society is c/o the University of Leiden, The Netherlands. The address of the Secretary, D. BURGER, is Statensingel 183a, Rotterdam, Netherlands.

1922: Schweizerische Gesellschaft für Geschichte der Medizin und der Naturwissenschaften (Société Suisse d'Histoire de la Médecine et des Sciences Naturelles). —The Society publishes Veröffentlichungen (q.v.) and Gesnerus (q.v.). The secretary (Jan. 1949) is Prof. HANS FISCHER, Pharmakologisches Institut der Universität, Gloriastr., Zürich 6.

1924: History of Science Society.—This society was founded in Boston on Jan. 12, 1924 and the international journal, Isis, became its organ from vol. 6 on (1924). The history of the foundation of the HSS is told at the beginning of that volume.
It should be noted that the Society is international, though on account of its location and of the preponderant use of English, the great majority of its members are Americans.
In addition to Isis, it has published a number of books (thus far 9, listed in Isis 34, 411). The publication of other books has been encouraged by the Society.
The present secretary of the HSS is Mr. FRED KILGOUR (Yale Medical Library, New Haven, Conn.).
The dues are now $6 a year. Members receive Isis free of charge.
Original statutes of the HSS (Isis 6, 521-22, 1924). Revisions, 1931 (Isis 16, 125), 1942 (Isis 33, 731-32), 1943 (Isis 35, 51-52); reprinted 1949 (Isis 40, 195-97). The annual meetings of the HSS take place generally either with the American Association for the Advancement of Science or the American Historical Association; in Dec. 1948, the HSS met with the Modern Language Association of America; in 1951 it will meet separately in Brown University, Providence, Rhode Island.

1931: Groupe Français d'Histoire des Sciences.—That group has been constituted informally on 13 May 1931, at the address which has remained the same until at present 12 rue Colbert, Paris 2.
Its officers have first been appointed in 1935. Proceedings have appeared in the Revue de synthèse, in Thalès, and now in the group's organ, Revue d'histoire des sciences.
The present secretary is RENÉ TATON, 12 rue Colbert, Paris 2 (Isis 39, 66).

1933 Comité Belge d'Histoire des Sciences (Constituted on 10 June 1933).—Reports of their proceedings have sometimes appeared in Isis (29, 410; 32, 129-30; 38, 245, etc.).
The secretary is JEAN PELSENEER, 51 Avenue Winston Churchill, Uccle-Bruxelles.

1934: Lärdomshistoriska Samfundet (Swedish Society for the History of Learning). —Founded at Uppsala on 12 May 1934. Publishes an annual volume Lychnos (1936) and a collection of books Lychnos-Bibliotek (1936) each of which deals with a separate subject.
Founder and secretary JOHAN NORDSTRÖM. For an account of the foundation, statutes, charter members etc., see Lychnos (vol. 1, 483-543, 1936).
Address: Kyrkogårdsgatan 25, Uppsala, Sweden.
This society was and still is the most successful of all the societies devoted to the history of science; its membership was already well over 2,000 in 1936, in spite of the fact that the main language of its publications, Swedish, is little understood outside of Scandinavia (Isis 26, 177-80).

Note that the Swedish Society is devoted to the history of learning, but that is made to include science (like the German word die Wissenschaft). The Swedish society is a group of the Académie since 1936.

1937: **Grupo Português da História das Ciências** (Portuguese Group of the History of Science, founded in 1937).—It publishes the review Petrus Nonius (*q.v.*). The national grupo or society has sections in Lisbon, Pôrto and Coimbra. Secretary, Dr. CARLOS TEIXEIRA, Faculdade de Ciências, Lisboa.

1941: **Japanese Society for the History of Science.**—Founded on 22 April 1941 (Isis 33, 338). The title and address are not known to me.
The society published Studies in the history of science, in Japanese (Isis 40, 160; 41, 197).

1947: **British Society for the History of Science.**—Constituted in London, 12 Feb. 1947.
Secretary: F. H. C. BUTLER, 10 Exhibition Road, South Kensington, London S. W. 7 (Isis 37, 182; 38, 102).
The Society publishes a Bulletin, vol. 1, no. 1, January 1949, Vol. 1, no. 4, October 1950.

SUMMARY—THE ELEVEN EARLIEST NATIONAL SOCIETIES (or groups) *:

7.	° BELGIUM 1933		3.	THE NETHERLANDS 1913
6.	° FRANCE 1931		9.	° PORTUGAL 1937
1.	GERMANY 1901		8.	SWEDEN 1934
11.	GREAT BRITAIN 1947		4.	SWITZERLAND 1922
2.	ITALY 1907		5.	UNITED STATES 1924
10.	JAPAN 1941			

After the establishment of the Académie internationale d'histoire des sciences in 1928, various national groups were constituted in order to satisfy the academy's regulations and make possible the nomination of members belonging to their nation. The French, Belgian and Portuguese groups mentioned above were constituted, respectively in 1931, 1933, 1937 for that very purpose. It is not necessary to speak now of other national groups for the majority of those groups have only a derivative academic function and their proceedings are practically unknown to the rest of the world. The Academy will be described in the following chapter, and the national groups related to it will then be enumerated.

Some national societies (whether founded before 1928 or after) are identified with national groups of the Academy, others are not.

Some national societies are identified with a section of the national scientific societies, others are not; their mutual connections vary from case to case. The connection is closest in the German case; it is loose in the case of the History of Science Society. There is no need of worrying our readers with such details which concern the administrative history of each society (or each group) and have no influence on the progress of learning.

Alphabetical list of a few other national societies:—

1927: **American Association of the History of Medicine.**—22nd annual meeting, Lexington, Kentucky, May 1949. See Bull. of the History of Medicine, vol. 22, 837, 1949. Previous meetings have been reviewed in the same journal.

1937: **Chinese Medical History Society.**—The Society was organized in Shanghai during a conference of the Chinese Medical Association in April 1937 (Isis 34, 28). President (in 1948), Dr. K. CHIMIN WONG.
Publishes the Chinese Journal of medical history (*q.v.*). See Archives (30, 843-46, 1951).
Address (Jan. 1949): 41 Tzeki Road, Shanghai 9.

1926: **Gesellschaft für Geschichte der Pharmazie.**—Founded in Innsbruck (Austria) on 18 August 1926 to serve as an international center for the history of pharmacy; established in Berlin.
The organization is described in Mitteilungen (25, 342, 1926). The society has

sponsored the publication of some 40 books and pamphlets dealing with the history of pharmacy and chemistry.

Examples of its publications:—

FRITZ LÜDY, jr.: Alchemistische und Chemische Zeichen (1928; Isis 13, 232).

Facsimile of the Dispensatorium of VALERIUS CORDUS 1546, this being the earliest printed pharmacopoeia. (Mittenwald 1934; Isis 24, 215).

OTTO ZEKERT: CARL WILHELM SCHEELE (in 7 parts, Mittenwald 1931-35; Isis 24, 226).

FRITZ FERL; A SÜSSENGUTH: Kurzgeschichte der Chemie mit 200 Abb. (Mittenwald 1936; Isis 28, 262), English translation entitled Pictorial history of chemistry (London 1939; Isis 37, 257).

Dispensatorium pro pharmacopoeis Viennensibus 1570 (Berlin 1938; Isis 31, 163).

The Gesellschaft also published Mitteilungen, a few small nos. a year describing its activities, and Vorträge including the lectures and proceedings of the general assemblies. I have before me two volumes of Vorträge published in 1934 and 1936. The editor before the war was Dr. F. FERCHL, Mittenwald, and the publisher, Verlag Arthur Nemayer, Mittenwald, Bayern.

An international meeting of the Society took place in Basel 1934. The first post-war meeting was held in Hamburg 1949; the second in Rothenburg ob der Tauber, Bavaria, 1950.

1921: **Münchener Vereinigung für Geschichte der Naturwissenschaften und der Medizin.**—Founded in Munich, 5 Nov. 1921 by SIEGMUND GÜNTHER, ERNST DARMSTAEDTER and others.
Mitteilungen 25, 343, 1926.

1920: **Newcomen Society for the Study of the History of Engineering and Technology.**—Founded in London 1920. Publishes Transactions (q.v.). See Isis (4, 496-98; 5, 312).
Address: The Science Museum, South Kensington, London, S. W. 7.

1947: **Palestine Society for Medical History.**—Founded in Jerusalem, April 1947.
Address: Baltinester House, Street of the Prophets, Jerusalem (Isis 37, 182).

Russian Society.—The need of a Russian society and of a Russian institute for the history of science was explained by Prof. P. P. LASAREV, member of the Russian Academy on 2 Dec. 1926 (Mitteilungen 26, 227-31, 281-82, 1927). These needs are now satisfied by a department of the Soviet Academy of Sciences. See chapter 22.

Scottish Society of the History of Medicine.—Its third meeting was held in the hall of the Royal Faculty of Physicians and Surgeons, Glasgow, Dr. DOUGLAS GUTHRIE in the chair. An account of that undated meeting is given in the Journal of the History of Medicine (4, 112, 1949).

1902: **Société française d'Histoire de la Médecine.**—Published from 1902 to 1942 a Bulletin de la Société (q.v.), and since 1945 Mémoires (q.v.). Vol. 3 1947. Secrétaire général, 66 Boulevard Raspail, Paris 6. The meetings take place at the Faculté de Médecine of Paris.

1913: **Société d'Histoire de la Pharmacie.**—See Isis 1, 250; 2, 152. Publishes the Revue d'histoire de la pharmacie (q.v.). Secrétaire perpétuel, EUGÈNE GUITARD (Isis 1, 529-30). See Archives (28, 1262-66, 1949).
Address: Faculté de Pharmacie, 4 Avenue de l'Observatoire, Paris 6.

The names of more societies could be deducted from the list of journals and serials in the preceding chapter. A society is less tangible than a journal and it is often far easier to remember the latter's name. For example, it is easier to remember the name Gesnerus than the longish name of the Swiss society publishing that review; in that particular case, the difficulty is increased by the circumstance that the Swiss society has four names (one in each of the four national languages); the Swiss society has four long names, but its journal has but one short name, Gesnerus.

22. INTERNATIONAL ORGANIZATION
OF THE STUDY OF THE HISTORY OF SCIENCE

The first international organization for the study of the history of science was the History of Science Society founded in Boston, Massachusetts, on 12 January 1924 at the initiative of DAVID EUGENE SMITH (1860-1944), about whose life and work *see* Osiris 1, 1936. The society was established primarily in order to promote the journal Isis, which had been founded by GEORGE SARTON in 1913 and was then in jeopardy. Isis was always an international journal published in the six international languages (EFGILS), but during the first years of its existence, when its editor lived in Belgium, the French language was naturally predominant; later, when the editor settled in the United States and the responsibility of publication was partly taken over by the History of Science Society, English became the main language. Nevertheless, Isis has always preserved its international character; its subtitle reads "an international review devoted to the history of science and civilization." It is an international journal published mainly in English, which is the language of greatest international currency.

It is a mistake to confuse internationalism with polyglottism. Consider the query: Which journal is likely to be the most international, the one (A) written almost exclusively in English, or the other (B) written in six languages (EFGILS): Will more readers of more nations read (B) than (A)? By reading, we mean of course reading the whole of it, or at least most of it. Obviously, there are far more people all over the world capable of reading English, than there are people capable of reading English, plus French, German, Italian, Latin and Spanish. Yet, some men are not satisfied with those six languages; they would want the addition of other languages, particularly of their own; they are like those idiots who would want the international express to stop in their own bailiwick. If all those wishes were granted, the famous express would become an omnibus train. If too many languages are used, nobody is properly served.

The History of Science Society, however, is less international than its own organ Isis. Indeed, that organ can circulate equally well everywhere, and it can find readers and collaborators in many nations; the nationality of an author has never been considered by the editor, that would be irrelevant to his purpose. On the other hand, the majority of members and officers of the History of Science Society dwell in the United States. Its annual meetings have always taken place in the United States, and it cannot help being more sensitive to American than to foreign opinions. As far as location is concerned, one must bear in mind that every international society is obliged to have a central office within the territory of a definite nation, and it is submitted because of that to more influences emanating from that nation than from any other.

Perhaps the fairest summary of the matter would be to say that the History of Science Society, in spite of its being born in a foreign cradle, is a national society. It is a national society with genuine international concerns, and its foreign membership is relatively large.[99]

We may now consider another organization, primarily and deliberately international, the **Académie Internationale d'Histoire des Sciences**, the existence of which we owe to the foresight and devotion of ALDO MIELI.[100] The latte had organized in 1927 a committee which arranged for the discussion of the subject at the International Historical Congress of Oslo in 1928. The section of the history of science

---

[99] The number of articles in Isis devoted to "American science" is remarkably small. The editor is always pleased to include such articles but makes no effort to increase their number. His point of view is international.

[100] For ALDO MIELI (1879-1950), *see* Isis 41, 57, with portrait, and the biography by his successor PIERRE SERGESCU in the Archives internationales d'histoire des sciences (29, 519-35, 1950), with portrait.

of that congress intrusted the creation of the Academy to a committee of seven members: ALDO MIELI, ABEL REY, GEORGE SARTON, HENRY E. SIGERIST, CHARLES SINGER, KARL SUDHOFF, and LYNN THORNDIKE. The Academy was constituted in August 1928 and the seven men just named were its first members. The first meeting of the executive committee took place in Paris in May 1929; the first annual meeting in Paris in May 1930. The seat of the Academy is 12 rue Colbert, Paris 2 (close to the Bibliothèque Nationale). ALDO MIELI was from the beginning its permanent secretary; he was succeeded in 1950 by PIERRE SERGESCU.

For more information on the Academy see its official organ, Archeion,[101] now called Archives internationales, and also the Annuaire de l'Académie (3rd ed. 1936).

The purpose of the Academy was to organize the study and teaching of the history of science on an international basis. In order to implement that purpose it was necessary to organize national committees in as many countries as possible. There are at present some 27 national groups.[102] Their names are given below in alphabetical order, together with the dates of constitution and of their affiliation to the Academy as far as known to me. These dates are not always unambiguously known because the definition and constitution of a group is not always clear or may be challenged by another group in the same country, etc. The dates given below are tentative.[103] It is possible that some of those national groups either do not function at present, or do not communicate regularly with the Academy. To the usual difficulties caused by the creation of a new society relative to a new discipline must be added the chaos resulting from wars and revolutions.

National groups affiliated to the International Academy:—

Argentina	1933	1948	Luxemburg		1948
Belgium	1933	1947	Morocco (French)	1932	
Brazil		1947	Netherlands		1948
Czechoslovakia	1930	1947	Palestine	1935	1947 [104]
Denmark		1949	Poland	1933	
Egypt		1950	Portugal	1932	1947
France	1931	1947	Romania	1932	1947
Germany	1932		Spain	1931 1936	
Great Britain		1947	Sweden	1948	1950
Greece	1935		Switzerland	1935	1947
Hungary		1948	Turkey		1950
India		1950	United States		1949
Israel		1950	Uruguay	1935	1948
Italy	1931	1948			

Reports from each national group appear periodically in the Archives. In addition, information is given concerning groups in process of organization.

For example, consider India. A national committee for the study of the history of science in India was convened on 2nd Jan. 1949 at Muir Central College, by Professor A. C. BANNERJI, president of the National Academy of Sciences. This will probably lead to the constitution of a National Group or Society for the History of Science. Details of the proceedings may be read in the Archives internationales (28, 812-14, 1949).

The Academy was reorganized in December 1948 in order to harmonize its activities with those of two overall international organizations UNESCO and ICSU (the first is the United Nations Educational Scientific and Cultural Organization, the second the International Council of Scientific Unions).

---

[101] The existence of Archeion (under the name Archivio) preceded that of the Académie (1919, 1928) even as the existence of Isis preceded that of the History of Science Society (1913, 1924).

[102] Strictly speaking the number of national groups officially recognized by the International Union in October 1950 was 19. The figure given by me is larger, because it includes groups which have vanished, say, Palestine replaced by Israel, or whose official link is in abeyance because of the late war. For example, the German group was affiliated in 1932, the affiliation is temporarily broken, but it will soon be renewed.

[103] When many dates are given they refer to different steps in organization, the last date is that of formal reorganization.

[104] The ambiguity Palestine-Israel is caused by the fact that the group was first affiliated during the British mandate; if I remember right the first (Palestinian) group included Arabic and Jewish members.

For a general account of UNESCO, *see* JULIAN HUXLEY (its first director, from 1946 to 1948 incl.): UNESCO, its purpose and its philosophy (62 p. American Council on Public Affairs, 1947). For the UNESCO concern with history of science, *see* ARMANDO CORTESÃO: L'UNESCO, sa tâche et son but concernant les sciences et leur développement historique (Archives 1, 211-21, 1947-48, reprinted in Actes du Ve Congrès, p. 25-35, 1948).

The latest list of members of the Academy may be found in Archives (1, 188-204, Oct. 1947). That list contains unfortunately many errors caused by lack of communications in war time and post-war chaos.

Latest constitution of the Académie (Archives 1, 142-45, Oct. 1947).

At first, the members of the Académie were elected exclusively on the basis of work done in the history of science, but it was soon recognized that on that basis the great majority of the members would belong to a few leading countries where studies in that field have been encouraged. Some restrictions were then introduced in the rules in order to facilitate the election of members belonging to other countries, yet that was not enough to insure the representation of every (UNESCO) country. It is clear that if elections were arranged in such a way that every country were represented, the intellectual level of the Academy would be degraded, and the Academy would cease to be an Academy in the ordinary sense of the term (a limited group of men selected on the basis of individual merit). In order to solve that dilemma a new international organization was created. **L'Union Internationale d'histoire des Sciences** was established in Paris in 1947, and its constitution may be read in Archives (1, 145-46, 1947).

The first article of the Academy's new constitution (1947) reads "The international organization of the study of the history of science includes two institutions closely bound together, the International Academy and the International Union."

According to other articles (2) the Academy is located in Paris, (3) it counts 50 effective and 100 corresponding members. A minimum number of places is reserved for historians of science of countries which could not be represented otherwise.

According to the Union's constitution (1947), article 1, "The Union's purpose is to coöperate directly with UNESCO and ICSU, in the field of the history of science," article 2. "The Union recognizes the Academy as the directive organ of its scientific activity."

The Academy organizes international congresses, the meetings of which have taken place as follows. For each meeting we indicate the corresponding publication, and name the President. In each case, the President of the Academy was *ipso facto* the president of the congress.

I.1929: Paris, 20-25 May. President: GINO LORIA of Genoa. Accounts in Archeion, vol. II, p. i-cix, 1929.

II.1931: London, 30 June-4 July. President: CHARLES SINGER of London. Accounts in Archeion, vols. 13-14. An English translation of the Russian papers was published in book form, Science at the Cross Roads (London, Kniga, 1931; Isis 20, 591, 535).

III.1934: Porto and Coimbra, 30 Sept.-6 Oct. President: Karl Sudhoff of Leipzig, who was not able to come. The acting president was GEORGE SARTON of Cambridge, Massachusetts. Accounts in Archeion 16, 335-72, 1934. Congrès du Portugal. Actes, conférences et communications (xlix+462 p., pl., maps, Lisboa 1936; Isis 28, 135-38).

IV.1937: Praha (Prague). 22-27 Sept. President: QUIDO VETTER of Prague. Accounts in Archeion (vol. 19, 390-96).

V.1947: Lausanne. 30 Sept.-6 Oct. President: ARNOLD REYMOND of Lausanne. Actes du Ve Congrès, in Collection de travaux de l'Académie (no. 2, 288 p., Académie, also Hermann, Paris 1948). The papers reprinted in the Actes were first printed in the Archives.

VI.1950: Amsterdam. August 1950. President: P. SERGESCU of Paris. The Proceedings will be published in 1951.

At the VI. International Congress of the History of Science (Amsterdam, August

1950) the following presidents were appointed, for the Academy, Dr. J. A. VOLL-GRAFF of Leiden, for the Union, GEORGE SARTON of Cambridge, Mass.

The Perpetual Secretary is Prof. PIERRE SERGESCU. The offices of the Academy and of the Union are located 12 Colbert, Paris 2 (near the Bibliothèque Nationale).

There may be other international organizations devoted to the history of science in general, or the history of particular sciences. The line between a national organization and an international one is not always easy to draw as we exemplified in the case of the History of Science Society. In the first place, national societies may recruit members in other nations, and if their publications are made in one of the international languages (EFGILS) and are sufficiently useful, the number of foreign members may exceed that of the domestic ones. On the other hand, every international organization is of necessity established and domiciliated in a definite country and cannot help being more or less nationalized, because its contacts with that country are more frequent and more intense than with any other.[105]

1921: Société Internationale d'Histoire de la Médecine.—Founded in Paris on 8 October 1921 by JOSEPH TRICOT-ROYER of Antwerp, and others, at the meeting of the permanent committee of the International Congress of the history of medicine. Its official organ was first the Bulletin de la Société française d'histoire de la médecine (*see* 1921, 15: 312-13). When Aesculape resumed its publication in 1923 with vol. 13 it became the organ of the society and remained so until 1940 when it ceased to appear. The Société also published Archives (?), no. 4 of which is said to have appeared in 1938. Not seen.

The permanent committee of the Société meets at the Faculty of Medicine of Paris. President, Prof. LAIGNEL-LAVASTINE, general secretary, JULES GUIART (Archives intern. d'hist. des sciences 28, 733-35; 29, 154-56; etc.).

1948: International Plant Science Relations and Phytohistorical Commission of the International Union of Biological Sciences.—Founded by, and under the chairmanship of, FRANS VERDOORN, Chronica Botanica House, Waltham, Mass. Chiefly concerned with the preparation of (1) the World List of Plant Science Institutions and Societies (ed. 21, 1952), (2) BIOLOGIA, an international year-book (vol. 3, in press, includes the VERDOORNS' eleventh report on International Coöperation in the Pure and Applied Plant and Animal Sciences and emphasizes work on the borderland between the natural sciences and the humanities), (3) the INDEX BOTANICORUM, a biographical dictionary of plant scientists of all times. The Commission also maintains a card index of current research projects concerned with the history of any branch of the pure and applied plant sciences.

See Leaflet 2 (May 1950), Botanical Section, Int. Union of Biological Sciences.

Further information on the INDEX BOTANICORUM will be found in Chronica Botanica 8, 425-448, 1944. A four-page progress report, with a list of collaborators, was issued in 1948. The commission is at present preparing a three-volume Concise Dictionary of Botanical Biography (a prodromus to the Index Botanicorum.).

---

[105] This would be the case even if the small territory occupied by the international organization was internationalized. The Popes of Avignon were influenced by the French environment even as the Popes of Rome by an Italian one.

23. THE TEACHING OF THE HISTORY OF SCIENCE

Institutes for the history of science will be dealt with in the next section; institutes are often integral parts of universities and in such cases whatever teaching is organized is done in those institutes or with their coöperation. The next section dealing with institutes should thus be consulted with reference to teaching.

What kind of teaching is given in various universities? And where does that teaching lead? To which degrees or positions? At its executive meeting held in Paris in May 1948 the International Academy charged one of its members, Dr. E. J. DIJKSTERHUIS of Oisterwijk (Netherlands) to make investigations concerning the teaching of the history of science all over the world, and his report was published under the title, La place de l'histoire des sciences dans l'instruction supérieure (Archives internationales d'histoire des sciences 29, 39-76, 1950). This is only a first approximation, however, for it is not very helpful to know that Prof. JOHN DOE gives a course on the history of science in the University of Podunk. One would like to know what kind of a course he is giving and what are his own qualifications. Is JOHN DOE really a historian of science, or simply a schoolteacher or a charlatan? The total number of courses does hardly matter, but one would like to know how many courses are offered by competent scholars who have a technical knowledge of science, of history, of historical methods, and of the history of science.

The teaching of the history of science has been used for nationalistic purposes, as a means of stimulating the national pride of students. That was done in Italy during the fascist regime. See ALFRED PERNA: Les cours d'histoire des sciences en Italie (IIIe Congrès international d'histoire des sciences, 1934, p. 113-20, Lisbôa 1936). It is of course natural that teachers should pay special attention to the great men of science of their own country; that is legitimate if done with moderation and frankly. It is to be hoped, however, that the teaching of the history of science will be as international, or supernational as possible, for it is only then that it acquires its full value from the point of view of humanistic education. The history of science must be a means of uniting men, rather than of increasing their self-conceit and their separation from other men. In that respect, students of the New World are privileged, for it is relatively easy for their teachers to be internationally-minded in their account of the progress of science before modern times.

Notes concerning the teaching of the history of science in various countries or universities are frequently published in Isis. See, e.g., for Switzerland, Isis 38, 244; for the Netherlands, Isis 38, 98; 39, 67.

It is now possible to obtain a doctor's degree in the history of science in various universities, e.g., in London, Harvard, Cornell, Columbia, Univ. of Wisc. The field of the history of science is so immense and so complex that in order to guide doctoral work it is necessary to establish a committee ad hoc establishing a special program for each candidate. See Regulations for the degree of Ph.D. in the history of science and learning (Official register of Harvard University, vol. 32, no. 30, 8 p., June 22, 1935). Such a committee should be made up in the following way: one half of the members to be professors or teachers of science, medicine, engineering, the other half to be professors of the humanities; a professor of the history of science to be the chairman. It should be noted that while such a committee is needed to organize examinations in the history of science, it is superfluous for the history of learning. The regular scientific departments are not qualified to conduct examinations in the history of science, because their members have generally no technical knowledge of history, and what is worse, have no idea of historical methods; they are hardly aware of the existence of such methods. On the contrary, every department of learning is ipso facto a historical department; every historian or philologist is acquainted with historical methods. Should a student wish to study the history of Thucydidean scholarship he would find all the help he might need in the classical department and nowhere else.

Teaching the history of science in a university should be a full-time position. It is foolish to expect a professor of science to teach the history of science as a secondary job, for he will have to neglect his scientific research and teaching, or else his teaching of the history of science will remain mediocre and sterile. This will be realized more keenly when we consider the qualifications of a teacher of the history of science. These qualifications may be summarized under five heads:

1) Deep knowledge and long experience (including laboratory experience) in one field of science.

2) More superficial knowledge of various other branches of science.

3) Knowledge of history in general and familiarity with historical methods. Historical spirit.

4) Knowledge of philosophy, and especially of the philosophy of science. Philosophical spirit.

5) Good knowledge of many European languages, including Latin (and if possible, Greek or Arabic).

The prospective teacher must have proved his ability by a "masterpiece" (in the mediaeval sense), that is, by the publication of a genuine piece of research in a particular field of the history of science. A botanist can hardly hope to obtain a good teaching position without having proved that he has an overall knowledge of botany, experience in one special branch of it, ability to promote botanical knowledge and to train other students; even so, a historian of science must have proved his familiarity with the whole field, his deeper experience of one part of it, his power to increase knowledge and to transmit it to others.

The training of a historian of science is so complex that it requires a long time. On the other hand, teaching positions are thus far very few. Fortunately, such training is excellent not only for this purpose but for many others. It affords perhaps the best kind of preparation for many para-scientific professions, all the literary, historical, philosophical or even administrative activities connected with scientific investigations, or with scientific teaching, scientific libraries and museums, the editing of scientific periodicals or the writing of scientific books. Such activities are already numerous and their number is steadily increasing.

The teacher should be ready to teach the whole history of science, or at least the essential parts of it, from prehistoric days down to our own. If he secures an appointment in a larger university where his work is shared with other men he may be permitted to focus his attention on a part of the field, but even then a preliminary knowledge of the whole field will be of great advantage to him.

Some teachers may qualify for the teaching not of the history of science in general, but rather of the teaching the history of one particular science (or group of sciences) such as mathematics, physics, biology or geology. Even in such cases familiarity with the history of science in general would enable them to accomplish their own task better.

When the size and resources of a university make it possible to divide the work between many teachers, the division of labor might be accomplished in many ways, according to the general program and to the several qualifications of the teachers. Let us assume, e.g., that four teachers are employed, A, B, C, D. A might teach the history of ancient science, and also the history of mathematics; B might explain mediaeval science, and also the history of geography and anthropology; C, the history of biology, and also the history of science during the fifteenth to the seventeenth centuries; D the history of physics (or of chemistry), and also the history of modern science.

Most universities and colleges will have to be satisfied with one teacher and that teacher must be able to teach the whole history of science. It is much to be hoped that one university at least will have enough courage and vision to establish a kind of normal school for the history of science, with from four to ten teachers of various standing—from instructor to full professor. This would become the cradle of good teachers for the whole nation and even for other nations. It is easier to raise the standards of research in a place where many men are working together and where there develops naturally a keen emulation between them.

For more details, *see* GEORGE SARTON: Qualifications of teachers of the history of science (Isis 37, 5-7, 1947; 40, 311-13, 1949).

HENDRIK BODE, FREDERICK MOSTELLER, JOHN TUKEY, CHARLES WINSOR: The education of a scientific generalist (Science 109, 553-58, 1949). This article is mentioned as a witness of the need for men of science having a general training in science rather than a special one, but in its tentative program of a curriculum of 40 semester courses, the humanities are represented only by two courses in English, and by seven or eight courses which are left undefined under the general label "distribution." As far as the purely scientific instruction is concerned that curriculum would be a very good one for a future historian of science.

HENRY GUERLAC: Development and present prospects of the history of science (Report submitted to the 9th International Historical Congress, Paris 1950).

24. INSTITUTES, MUSEUMS, LIBRARIES

This section contains an enumeration of all the places where research (as distinguished from plain teaching) is carried on. The words museums and libraries need no definition, except to say that the only museums and libraries dealt with are those relative to the history of science or technology. The term institute is vaguer and it has often been abused. In European universities, an institute for this or that, often means no more than that a room or two have been set apart in one of the academic buildings for Dr. So-and-So, who studies or/and teaches the history of science. Those rooms may contain a small library and are eventually used for lectures, conferences or seminars. The rooms which I occupy in Widener (185-189) house what is perhaps the richest collection of pamphlets and archives on the subject; they have often been used for discussions, conferences, seminars; they are the publication center of Isis, yet it has never occurred to me to call them "Institute." A good many so-called institutes are far less important, but we do not wish to go into that.

Ambiguities of the same kind concern the libraries and museums. A list of special libraries of whichever kind might include all the largest general libraries as well, say, all the libraries of over a million volumes. Those immense libraries often contain more items on any special subject than the libraries exclusively devoted to that subject; these items, however, are not assembled but are scattered and may be very difficult to consult and to collate. There is no need of enumerating the largest general libraries, each scholar knows those which are available to him.

In a similar way, every large museum of antiquities contains a number of scientific objects: celestial and terrestrial globes, quadrants, astrolabes, weights and measures, scales, instruments conceived for various kinds of observation or measurement, or for teaching and demonstration; physical, astronomical, mathematical, chemical and surgical instruments, pharmaceutical pots and vases, all kinds of tools.[106] Every large museum has more than enough of such items to devote (if it chose to do so) one or two halls to the history of science, either local, regional or international.

Similar remarks might be made apropos of the War Museums, established in many cities. These Museums always contain a number of exhibits illustrating scientific or technical aspects of warfare. These exhibits might be included in a museum on the history of science and technology, but it is perhaps better to leave them where they are.

Museums of natural history also contain a number of objects of historical interest, objects illustrating investigations or explorations of the past, or objects which were wrongly labelled in the light of ancient knowledge and have become as it were witnesses of that knowledge. We cannot enumerate the "potential" collections included and "lost" in the larger collections, nor can we hope to enumerate all the collections, small or large, devoted to our studies. Our enumeration, however, will be sufficient to show what has been done and what is already available to students, and also to suggest what might be done in many places where all that is needed is a modicum of initiative, intelligence, and perseverance; the objects are there, waiting to be gathered and to be put in order.

Every scientific museum or library of sufficient size is potentially an institute for the history of science, even if it has not yet been exploited for that purpose, and if the curators are obliged to devote all of their time and energy to the proper registration, classification, and exhibition of the items intrusted to their care. Sooner or later, those museums and libraries will be fully used, and if they be kept in good order, they can be used profitably at any time by any competent person.

---

[106] Scientific objects of various kinds are particularly abundant in cities where universities or other colleges, academies and scientific societies are (or were) located.

Universities, academies and other scientific societies,[107] observatories and laboratories, botanic gardens, etc. own objects of historical interest, for example, objects which illustrate their creation and early days, portraits of their presidents and famous members, etc. but these objects, scattered in the public and private rooms, do not constitute museums and are not generally accessible to the public.

The situation with regard to museums is the same as for periodicals and serials and for the same reason: the history of science is not yet a well-known and recognized discipline; few periodicals, or museums are exclusively devoted to it, but almost every learned periodical, and almost every serious museum, may contain items of interest to us. Museums may be divided into the following categories: museums of art, museums of archaeology or history (national, provincial, regional, local), museums of natural history, museums of anthropology and ethnology, museums of science and industry. The last-named deal generally with modern, contemporary, conditions, but they often include historical exhibits. The other museums may also contain items (and sometimes very important ones) concerning the history of science. For example, some of the best portraits of men of science and other iconographical monuments are to be found in the museums of art.

It is to be hoped that for each country or region catalogues of the main documents and monuments available will eventually be compiled, and that their unavoidable dispersion will thus be compensated. Such catalogues would be easier to compile for special objects, such as surgical instruments, astrolabes, clocks. A great many Roman surgical instruments are scattered in museums devoted to classical archaeology. Astrolabes and clocks have often been collected for their beauty and found their place in art museums. For example the Wallace Collection of London boasts a fine series of eighteenth century French clocks.

The function of institutes for research has been examined in all its aspects in the work edited by Ludolph Brauer, Albert Mendelssohn Bartholdy and Adolf Meyer: Forschungsinstitute, ihre Geschichte, Organisation und Ziele (2 vols., ills., Hamburg 1930). These two splendid volumes are a memorial of the great Germany destroyed by Hitler. The problems concerning the history of science were discussed by Henry E. Sigerist (vol. 1, 391-405).

When a professorship in the history of science or medicine is established, the foundation should include enough funds for the creation of an institute ad hoc. This has been done in some countries (Germany, Poland) with regard to the history of medicine. A professor of the history of science without a special library (with archives and other collections) is very much like a professor of science without a laboratory, without staff and budget; his activities are doomed to second-handedness and mediocrity.

Without an institute where all the necessary information is steadily collected there can be no continuity in the work done, no creative tradition.

George Sarton: An institute for the history of science. Three articles (I. Science 45, 284-88, 1917; II. Science 46, 399-402, 1917; III. Isis 28, 7-17, 1938). The third article was partly reprinted in Sarton: The life of science (p. 169-74, New York 1949).

The following notes are arranged in alphabetical order of countries (English names) and for each country in alphabetical order of cities:

ARGENTINA

— Buenos Aires —

Ateneo de historia de la medicina:
Institute founded and directed by Prof. Dr. Juan Ramon Beltran for the study of the history of medicine. It issues Publicaciones de la catedra de historia de la medicina (vol. 1, 1938; vol. 4, 1940) and Revista argentina de historia de la medicina (1942 ff.).
Address: Edison 548-80, Martinez.

---

[107] Consider the objects decorating the rooms of the Royal Society, the Académie des Sciences, or the Lincei.

Institución Cultural Española (Calle Bernardo Irigoyen 672):

This institute deserves to be listed in spite of the fact that it is not primarily concerned with the history of science, because when the government arbitrarily closed MIELI's institute in Sante Fe in 1943, the Institución Cultural Española had the generosity and wisdom of offering asylum to him and his library. Moreover, it enabled him in 1945 to realize his first "coloquio" (colloquy, symposium) on the history and philosophy of science, and promoted his publications (except Archeion which was forbidden).

JOSE BABINI: Historia de la ciencia argentina (p. 184-87, Mexico 1949; Isis 41, 84).

— SANTA FE —

1938-1943: Instituto de historia y filosofia de la ciencia:

Institute established as a part of the Universidad Nacional del Litoral in 1938 at the instance of ALDO MIELI, who was brought from Paris to Santa Fe in order to take charge of it. At the same time MIELI transferred the editorial office of Archeion (Archivio di storia della scienza, q.v.) from Paris to Santa Fe. Unfortunately, MIELI's Instituto was one of the first victims of the political intolerance and stupidity which dominated the Argentine nation; the government closed it in 1943 and stopped the publication of Archeion.

Asylum was given to MIELI by the Institución cultural española in Buenos Aires.

ALDO MIELI: La historia y la filosofia de la ciencia (Suppl. to the Bulletin of the history of medicine, no. 3, CASTIGLIONI Festschrift, p. 205-16, Baltimore 1944). In the Italian appendix to this Spanish paper MIELI describes the persecution of which he was the victim. CORTES PLA: ALDO MIELI en la Argentina (Archives 29, 907-12, 1950).

AUSTRIA

— VIENNA (WIEN) —

1907: Institut für Geschichte der Medizin:

This institute for the history of medicine was created at the instance of ROBERT VON TOEPLI (1856-   ) and MAX NEUBURGER in 1906; it was opened modestly in 1907. In 1918, it was moved to the Josephinum, where it was close to a rich library. Six rooms were added to it in 1935-38. The Institute including a museum and library is very largely the creation of MAX NEUBURGER, who was professor of the history of medicine in the University of Venna.

EMANUEL BERGHOFF: MAX NEUBURGER. Werden und Wirken eines Oesterreichischen Gelehrten (Wien 1948; Isis 41, 97), description of the museum on pp. 66-95, many objects being reproduced.

BELGIUM

— ANTWERPEN —

Musée Plantin-Moretus:

This museum concerning the history of early typography and graphic arts in Antwerpen is established in the very buildings which were occupied for three centuries (1576-1876) by the illustrious printer, CHRISTOPHER PLANTIN (1520-89), his son-in-law, JOHN MOERENTORF or MORETUS (1543-1610), and their descendants.

Many editions of the Catalogue have appeared in French, Dutch and English. I have used the second English edition of the Catalogue by MAX ROOSES (Antwerpen 1909).

The Museum has published many books and prints concerning its own collections or the lives and activities of the PLANTIN and MORETUS printers. Many other books on the same subject have appeared elsewhere. A full PLANTIN-MORETUS bibliography would require much space. Good general account by MAURICE SABBE: L'oeuvre de CHRISTOPHE PLANTIN et de ses successeurs (210 p., Bruxelles, 1937).

There are in other European cities many museums or collections concerning the history of typography, but no attempt has been made to list them here. The Musée

Plantin must stand as an example of a relatively large class of collections, which important as they be, do not concern the historian of science as much as the historian of arts and crafts.

— Bruxelles —

Institut international des sciences théoriques:
This Institute was created about 1948 to organize research work in the field of the philosophy (not history) of science, yet its publications may interest historians of science.

The Archives de l'Institut international des sciences théoriques are published in separate parts of the Actualités scientifiques et industrielles (Paris, Hermann). One of the series (A) has the subtitle Bulletin de l'Académie internationale de philosophie des sciences.

Director: I. Dockx; address of the secretary, 221 Avenue de Tervueren (Isis 40, 119).

The House of Erasmus (1466?-1536) in Anderlecht:
Catalogue de la Maison d'Erasme (600 items, 38 p., Isis 27, 416).

Daniel Van Damme: Ephéméride illustrée de la vie d'Erasme (64 p. quarto ill., Anderlecht 1936; Isis 26, 463-64; 27, 416-29, 4 ill., 1937).

Musée Stas:
Collection of objects, MSS, etc. concerning the chemist, Jean Stas (1813-91), in a special room of the main building of the University of Brussels (Avenue des Nations). Catalogue by Jean Pelseneer (Bull. Société chimique de Belgique t. 48, 1937, 10 p.; Isis 28, 95).

Collection Michel:
A collection of astrolabes and other astronomical instruments has been made by the engineer, Henri Michel in Brussels. Partial catalogue by himself, Introduction à l'étude d'une collection d'instruments anciens (quarto 112 p., 15 pl., Anvers 1939), see also his Traité de l'astrolabe (quarto, 210 p., 24 pl., Paris 1947; Isis 39, 194).

— Gent —

Museum of the history of science in the old Byloke Abbey:
This museum which I was privileged to visit on 4 May 1948 before its opening has been organized by Professor A. J. J. Van de Velde.

The Byloke abbey is devoted to the exhibition of objects illustrating the history, archaeology and folklore of Gent and East Flanders; a part of it has been set aside for the history of science. That part contains a number of instruments and memorials concerning the scientific professions in Flanders and scientific teaching and research in the University of Gent. It was formally inaugurated on Sunday 28 November 1948. The opening speech by Prof. Van de Velde (7 p. in Dutch) was published in the Jaarboek 1948 van de Kon. Vlaamse Academie voor Wetenschappen van Belgie. No catalogue is yet available.

Since the writing of this note the Museum has been moved to the Museum of Fine Arts. It was reinaugurated in its new location on Dec. 10, 1950.

— Liége —

Collection Max Elskamp:
Collection of mathematical and astronomical instruments made by the Belgian-French poet, Max Elskamp. It is now preserved in the Musée de la vie wallonne, a museum devoted to every aspect of Liégeois and Walloon history and folklore.

— Saint Nicholas —

Saint Nicholas is a small town in the Land of Waes, eastern Flanders. Its local museum includes a room dedicated to the Flemish geographer, Gerhardus Mercator (1512-94).

CHINA

— SHANGHAI —

Medical History Museum:
Organized by the Chinese Medical History Society; opened in 1938.   K. C. WONG
(Arch. internat. hist. of science 1949, 2, 545-51; 1951, 4, 845).

CZECHOSLOVAKIA

— PRAGUE —

Technical Museum:
This museum includes historical exhibits, notably the reconstruction of an alchemical laboratory of the sixteenth century and many objects illustrating the history of geography, geodesy, mining, technology, arts and crafts.   The alchemical laboratory was briefly described and illustrated in Svetozor (čislo 14, ročnik XIV, Praha 1914?).

Professor Q. VETTER wrote to me (Praha, 26 Oct. 1949) that there are museums in almost every city of Czechoslovakia, and that almost every one of those museums includes objects which may interest historians of science.   He kindly wrote again (Praha, 6 January 1950), after having obtained the help of the Svaz českých musei (union of Czech museums) which circulated my queries among its members.   This enabled him to send me a list of some sixty regional museums, which contain exhibits which would interest historians of science.   It is not possible to print the list here, because it would take too much space and because I could not do for Czechoslovakia what I did not do for other countries (similar lists for the United States would fill a good sized volume, *see* the publications by L. V. COLEMAN quoted below).

Dr. VETTER's list includes collections concerning the history of mining (Bánská Štiavnice, Slova; Kutná Hora, Boh.; Ostraya, Mor.; Stříbro, Boh.), the history of pharmacy and medicine (Benešov u Prahy; Bojkovice, Mor.; Klatovy, Boh.; Polná, Boh.; Praha, Národní museum; Prostějov, Boh.; Znojmo, Mor.); the history of astronomy, physics and mathematics (Duchcov, Boh.; Plzeň, Boh.; Praha, Observatory; Praha, Library of the Strahov monastery; Teplá, Boh.; Vyšší Brod, Boh.), the history of cartography (Praha, University Library).   There are also in Czechoslovakia many exhibits or museums illustrating regional arts, crafts, and industries; some are the equivalent of the American "company museums" and were probably such at the beginning even if they have now become national or municipal responsibilities.

In addition to his letter, Dr. VETTER also sent me a few printed catalogues.

Institute of the History of Medicine:
Including library and collection of portraits.

Medical Museum:
Collects documents and objects concerning the history of medicine in Czechoslovakia, and a medico-numismatic collection.

Museum of Pharmacology:
Collection of old apothecary shops attached to the Purkině Institute.

DENMARK

— COPENHAGEN —

Medico-historical Museum:
This museum was founded in 1907 as a private institution; it became a university institute in 1918.   It collects everything concerning medical history.   The main collections are (1) surgery, (2) X-ray, (3) pharmacy, (4) dentistry, (5) library. There is no printed catalogue.

The museum is established in the old Royal Academy of Surgery, founded in 1785 and abolished in 1942.

IDA RICH in Sudhoff's Archiv (31, 61, 1938).

This information was given to me by Dr. EDV. GOTFREDSEN, historian of medicine, in his kind letter dated Copenhagen, 20 Feb. 1949.

Open-air Museums.—*See* the letter of Dr. JEAN ANKER, printed below under "Norway."

Maison natale de Pasteur:
The house where LOUIS PASTEUR was born on 27 Dec. 1822 is now a national museum.

Illustrations of it may be found in PASTEUR VALLERY-RADOT: PASTEUR. Images de sa vie (Paris 1947; Isis 39, 99).

Bibliothèque et musée d'histoire de la médecine:
Organized by Prof. JULES GUIART at the University of Lyon.

JULES GUIART: L'Ecole médicale lyonnaise. Catalogue commenté de la section régionale du musée historique de la Faculté mixte de médecine et de pharmacie de Lyon[107a] (Annales de l'Université de Lyon, 3. series, médecine, fasc. 2, 272 p., 16 pl., Paris 1941).

1925: Centre international de synthése, "Pour la science."
Created by HENRI BERR, who 25 years earlier had founded the Revue de Synthèse historique. For a history of both undertakings *see* vol. 26 (67) of that Revue published in Paris 1950. The Centre is located 12 rue Colbert, Paris 2 (close to the Bibliothèque Nationale).

1928: Académie internationale d'histoire des sciences, for which *see* chapter 22.
The Académie is located 12 rue Colbert, Paris 2.

The Académie and Centre have close connections; reports of both were published in Archeion (vol. 9, 497-512, 1928; vol. 11, 22 p., 1929, vol. 12, 368-89, 1930, etc.). At present reports of the Centre appear regularly in the Revue de synthèse, those of the Académie in the Archives internationales d'histoire des sciences.

Institut d'histoire des sciences et des techniques (13 rue du Four, Paris 6):
Established as a part of the University of Paris. The first director was ABEL REY; the second GASTON BACHELARD.

It publishes Thales (5 vols. 1934-48).

1794: Conservatoire des Arts et Métiers (rue Réaumur):
Museum created by the Convention nationale on 19 vendémiaire an III (10 Oct. 1794), the earliest collection of its kind and size in the world. It should be noted, however, that the purpose was less historical than educational. It realized DESCARTES' views that students of science and artisans should be able to see instruments and mechanical objects (This was even more necessary in the seventeenth and eighteenth centuries than it is today, because graphic illustrations were less abundant and less cheap than they are now). The confusion of purposes is perhaps unavoidable and exists to this day in every museum of science and industry: these museums are often historical "par la force des choses" but the main purpose of the organizers is generally to popularize science, to familiarize the public with its tools and methods, and to fire the enthusiasm of potential inventors and future men of science. At any rate, every scientific collection, whichever be its purpose, obtains more and more historical value as time passes.

On 26 floréal an VI (15 May 1798) the Conseil des Cinq-Cents set aside a large part of the priory of Saint-Martin-des-Champs for the Conservatoire.

The early organizers of the Conservatoire were JACQUES DE VAUCANSON (1709-82), CHARLES AUGUSTE VANDERMONDE (1735-96), NICOLAS JACQUES CONTÉ (1755-1805), JOSEPH MICHEL MONTGOLFIER (1740-1810), FRANÇOIS EMMANUEL MOLARD (1774-1829). The first Catalogue des Collections du Conservatoire was published

---

[107a] What a title!

in 1817.   Third edition by A. Morin (327 p., Neuilly 1859).   Eighth edition in 6 parts: I. Mécanique 1905; II. Physique 1905; III. Géométrie, géodésie, cosmographie, astronomie, science nautique, chronométrie, instruments de calcul, poids et mesures, 1906; IV. Arts chimiques, matières colorantes et teinture, céramique et verrerie 1908; V. Arts graphiques, photographie, filature et tissage, mines, métallurgie et travail des métaux 1908; VI. Art des constructions et génie civil, art appliqué aux métiers, économie domestique, hygiène, statistique, agriculture et génie rural 1910.

The Conservatoire is not simply a museum; it is also a technical school including laboratories, workshops, a library.

Aimé Laussedat: Le Conservatoire des Arts et Métiers (folio, 24 p., ill., France Artistique et Monumentale Paris s. a., c. 1894).

Anatole de Monzie: Le conservatoire du peuple (154 p., Paris 1948).

1937: Palais de la Découverte:

This museum was created as a part of the Exposition internationale des Arts et Métiers in 1937.   Since that time it has been attached to the University of Paris. It realizes the general conception of Jean Perrin (1870-1942).

Like the Conservatoire des Arts et Métiers which it supersedes, its main purpose is not historical but educational in the broadest sense.   History comes in unavoidably; historical outlines are not only interesting (even to non-historians) but educative.   Its purpose is to show not only what has been done, but also what is being done today and what might be done tomorrow.   It is meant to be a living bridge between the public and the laboratories.   It is divided into eight sections: mathematics, astronomy, physics, chemistry, biology, medicine, surgery, microbiology. Special exhibitions are organized from time to time, some of them historical (Lavoisier, Davy and Faraday, discoveries of Hertzian waves, of radium, etc.)   Lectures and demonstrations are given frequently.   Everything is done to attract the public, interest it and teach it as much as possible.

The Palais de la découverte is already immense (50 rooms or halls in 1948) but it is planned to increase it considerably.

A few rooms have been recently opened (Isis 40: 353) which are devoted more specifically to the history of science.

The director is A. Leveillé, who wrote a short description of it in Experientia (vol. 1, 345-46, Basel 1945).

Musée et bibliothèque d'histoire de la médecine (Faculté de médecine, rue de l'Ecole de médecine, Boulevard St. Germain):

The Musée Orfila includes old surgical instruments and other historical objects, but it is mainly a collection of pathological anatomy founded in 1835 by the physician and toxicologist Mathieu Orfila of Minorca (1787-1853).

Institut Pasteur (rue Dutot, Paris 15):

The Institut was inaugurated on 4 Nov. 1888; Pasteur died in 1895.   The crypt of the Institut contains his tomb and that of his wife, Marie.

From the point of view of the historian of science, this is one of the most impressive shrines in the whole world.   Would that more people visited it than there are who visit the tomb of Napoleon in the Hôtel des Invalides.

Musée de Cluny:

This very rich museum has relatively few objects concerning the historian of science proper, rather than the historian of arts and crafts.   It has clocks, astrolabes, and the large wire-drawing bench made in 1565 for the Elector Augustus of Saxony (see note on Dresden below).   The bench is described in the Catalogue général. Bois sculptés et meubles by Edmond Haraucourt and Montrémy (no. 638, Paris 1925).

Musée d'histoire de la pharmacie (4 Avenue de l'Observatoire): See Arch. intern. hist. sci. 1949, 2, 810.

— ROUEN —

Musée Flaubert et d'histoire de la médecine:
Located in the Hôtel-Dieu (51 rue de Lecat). Catalogue published by R. M. MARTIN (Rouen 1947). Arch. internat. hist. sci. 1949, 2, 807.

GERMANY

— BERLIN —

1928: Forschungsinstitut für Geschichte der Naturwissenschaften:
This institute founded in 1928 is an expansion of the Heidelberg institute organized by RUSKA. The first director of the Berlin institute was also JULIUS RUSKA.

The first annual report was published in Berlin, 1928, the second and third in 1929 and 1930. I have no other (official) report. As the name "Forschungsinstitut" indicates, the institute was conceived as a "research institute" (with emphasis on "research"; of course, every decent institute is a research institute. What else could it be? commercial?); it was also conceived as a kind of German super-institute on a grand scale, and it was equipped in the best manner.

In 1929, this Institute was merged with a medical institute under the common title Institut für Geschichte der Medizin und der Naturwissenschaften (note that the word Forschungsinstitut has been replaced by Institut). PAUL DIEPGEN, who was professor of the history of medicine in Freiburg i. Br. was called on 2 Oct. 1929 to direct the new institute.

According to a statement by WALTER ARTELT (Mitt. 36, 281-84, 1937), the Institute located in Universitätstrasse 3b (close to the Preussische Staatsbibliothek and to the Universitätsbibliothek), extended to 21 rooms, and the staff consisted of a Director (DIEPGEN), 3 divisional chiefs, 2 assistants, 2 sub-assistants, 1 librarian, 2 secretaries and 1 helper; it had a library of c. 30,000 volumes. The three divisions were (1) history of medicine, (2) history of inorganic sciences, (3) history of organic sciences. Prof. RUSKA is not named, but it is assumed that he was the head of the second division.

The Institute is sufficiently near to the Kaiserin Friedrich Haus to use the latter's auditorium and its medico-historical collection.

Considering the encyclopaedic plan of the Institute partly due to the initiative of Kultusminister CARL HEINRICH BECKER[108] (Isis 6, 559-61), it is strange that the history of science was subordinated to the history of medicine. This is typical however of German efforts in our field and may be ascribed to the domineering influence of KARL SUDHOFF, and also no doubt to the importance of the medical profession, and to the fact that more physicians were interested in the history of science than other scientists.

Staatliche Mediko-historische Sammlung:
Located in the Kaiserin-Friedrich-Haus für das ärztliche Fortbildungswesen.

— CASSEL (KASSEL) —

1779: Kgl. Museum Fridericianum, Hessisches Landesmuseum zu Cassel:
This Museum of fine and applied arts, archaeology and history was founded in 1779 by the Landgraf of Hesse-Cassel FRIEDRICH II (ruling 1760-85). It includes a rich collection of clocks, mathematical, physical and astronomical instruments which illustrates the scientific interests of the rulers of Hessen from the sixteenth to the eighteenth century.

The scientific instruments were first exhibited in five rooms of the old Kunsthaus; they were brought to the new museum when the latter was built in 1911-13. Some of the instruments go back to the sixteenth century and were actually used by the Landgraf WILHELM IV (ruling 1567-92) and by the men of science who worked under his patronage.

A. CÖSTER and ERNST GERLAND: Beschreibung der Sammlung astronomischer,

---

[108] Preussischer Minister für Wissenschaft, Kunst und Volksbildung.

geodätischer und physikalischer Apparate im Königlichen Museum (Festgabe für die 51. Naturforscher-Versammlung, Cassel 1878). Briefer description in the Führer durch die historischen und Kunstsammlungen (p. 7-17, Marburg 1913?). The name Cassel is now spelled Kassel.

— DRESDEN —

Mathematisch-physikalischer Salon:
Collection kept in the NW angle of the Zwinger. Its nucleus was a part of the Kunstkammer of AUGUSTUS I, elector of Saxony (1553-86); it was gradually increased by his successors. It includes mathematical, surveying, astronomical, physical, meteorological, surgical, instruments, geographical and astronomical globes; tools used by AUGUSTUS I. It is especially valuable because of the relatively large number of early instruments.
Some of the early objects have been alienated, *e.g.*, the giant wire-drawing bench made in 1565 for the elector AUGUSTUS is now in the Cluny Museum, Paris (F. M. FELDHAUS: Die Technik, 203, 1914).
ADOLF DRECHSLER: Katalog der Sammlung des Königl. mathematisch-physikalischen Salons (68 p., Dresden 1874).
There was another collection in Dresden, the Modell-Kammer created in 1691 by GEORG IV, elector of Saxony, to include models of all kinds of machines, bridges, etc. A ms. inventory of it dating from 1827 exists in the Mathem-phys. Salon. Parts of the collection were auctioned off and dispersed in 1829, and following years.
W. G. LOHRMANN: Die Sammlung der Instrumente auf der Modelkammer in Dresden (Dresden 1835).

Deutsches Hygiene-Museum:
Its medico-historical and pharmaco-historical collection was started at the initiative of KARL SUDHOFF, who compiled the first catalogue.

— DÜSSELDORF —

1931: Institut für Geschichte der Medizin an der Medizinischen Akademie:
Opened in April 1931 to celebrate the 60th anniversary of its first director, WILHELM HABERLING. It is located in two rooms of the Institute for social hygiene.
W. HABERLING (Mitteilungen 36, 145-47, 1937).

— EISENACH —

Thüringer Museum:
This provincial museum includes a "Pharmaziegeschichtliche Sammlung." W. FIEK's booklet in the Veröffentlichungen d. Ges. f. Gesch. der Pharmazie describes it (*n.d.*).

— FRANKFURT AM MAIN —

1943: Institut für Geschichte der Naturwissenschaften (Institut des physikalischen Vereins Frankfurt a. M. Director: Prof. Dr. WILLY HARTNER):
The address at the time of writing (June 1949) is Feldbergstr. 47, but the Institute will probably be moved to the third floor of the reconstructed Senckenberg Library, adjoining the main building of the University this year (1949).
The Institut was founded in 1943 by the City of Frankfurt, independently of the university. It was located on Robert Mayerstr. 2-4, but was destroyed by air raid in May 18-22, 1944. The major part of the library was saved, and later the library and archives of the late PAUL DIERGART of Bonn were acquired; it is hoped to obtain the chemical library of the late GÜNTHER BUGGE (Isis 15, 298).
The purpose of the Institute is teaching and research.
Librarian: Dr. HERTHA VON DEEHEND; secretary, RUTH MARTIN.

Institut für Geschichte der Medizin:
Director, Prof. WALTER ARTELT. The institute will probably be located before the end of 1949 on the third floor of the reconstructed Senckenberg Library.
The Deutsche Gesellschaft für Geschichte der Naturwissenschaften, der Medizin und der Technik, recently refounded, will probably have an office on the same floor.

— HEIDELBERG —

1922-27: Institut für Geschichte der Naturwissenschaften:
This institute was created on 22 Nov. 1922 by the J. und E. v. Portheim-Stiftung. Its first and last director was JULIUS RUSKA. The first annual report appeared in 1925 (4 p., Carl Winter's Universitätsbuchhandlung); the second in 1926, the third and last in 1927. The Heidelberg institute was then merged with the Berlin one.

The publications of the institute listed in those three reports appeared in the Heidelberger Akten der von Portheim-Stiftung and in other series or journals.

— JENA —

Institut für Geschichte der Medizin:
Includes a collection rich in Graeco-Roman classical antiquities established by THEODOR MEYER-STEINEG (1873-1936).

— LEIPZIG —

1905: Institut für Geschichte der Medizin an der Universität Leipzig:
The Leipzig institute was founded in 1905, the widow of THEODOR PUSCHMANN having bequeathed to the University of Leipzig a fund (Puschmann-Stiftung) "to promote scientific research in the history of medicine." A chair for the history of medicine was created at the University at the same time; the first incumbent of it and first director of the institute was KARL SUDHOFF.

The institute includes a large library, archives, films, portraits, medals, etc. During the years 1905-25, under SUDHOFF's direction, its activities were astounding, witness the master's own publications, some 200 theses by students and many serials which are described in another chapter (Mitteilungen, Archiv für Geschichte der Medizin, Studien zur Geschichte der Medizin).

In 1925, the direction and professorship were given to HENRY E. SIGERIST and the activities were considerably modified, because of the new ideas which were now dominating medicine, medical teaching, medical duties to the people and medical history. The main organ of the Leipzig institute was now Kyklos (q.v.).

See SIGERIST's account in Forschungsinstitute (vol. 1, 391-402, 1930).

SIGERIST resigned in 1932 in order to assume the direction of the Baltimore Institute for the history of medicine. After an interregnum of 2 1/2 years, the direction of the Leipzig Institute was intrusted to Dr. WALTER VON BRUNN, and the Institute moved to a new address, in the Zoological Institute, Talstr. 33, second floor. Description of the new institute by WALTER VON BRUNN in Mitteilungen (36, 1-4, 1937).

The library of the Leipzig Institute houses the only copy of a card catalogue of all the notes published in Mitteilungen, that is, a catalogue of publications on the history of science since 1900-02, practically all the German ones and a very large number of non-German ones.

— MAINZ —

Medizinhistorisches Institut der Johannes Gutenberg Universität:
Director: PAUL DIEPGEN (formerly director of the Berlin institute).

— MUNICH —

1903: Deutsches Museum von Meisterwerken der Naturwissenschaft und Technik (often called, for short, Deutsches Museum):
This museum was founded in 1903, the ceremony of inauguration taking place on 28 June in the aula of the Royal Bavarian Academy. In 1906 a part of the collections was opened to the public and the construction of a special, enormous, building begun. The building should have been ready by 1916 but was delayed by the first war. It was finally inaugurated on 7 May 1925. The main founder and organizer of the Museum was OSKAR VON MILLER (1855-1934), electrical engineer.

It is the largest museum of science and technology in Germany and one of the largest (if not the very largest?) in the world. It owns a very large library and rich archives and has sponsored a great many publications.

Elaborate description in Das Deutsche Museum, Geschichte, Aufgaben, Ziele
(2. ed., VDI, Berlin 1929). Chronik des Deutschen Museums, 1903-25.
Guides: Rundgang durch das Deutsche Museum, Amtliche Ausgabe (94 p., ill.,
1931). Rundgang durch die Sammlungen (small album), available also in English.
Verwaltungsberichte. Administrative annual reports.
Special publications. WALTHER VON DYCK: GEORG VON REICHENBACH (1912;
Isis 1, 275-76). G. AGRICOLA: De re metallica in German translation (1928; Isis 13,
113-16). Technische Kulturdenkmale (München 1932).
1926: Abhandlungen und Berichte. *See* list of serials.
Criticism by FELDHAUS (Archeion 11, 353, 1929).

1937: Deutsches Apotheker Museum:

Created by FRITZ FERCHL, then President of the Bayerische Apotheker-Kammer,
and by ARMIN SÜSSENGUTH. Partly destroyed by enemy action in 1945. The remainder has been rearranged by Dr. FERCHL in six rooms of the "Hofküche der
neuen Residenz" in Bamberg.
There exists another collection illustrating the history of pharmacy in Waldenbuch
(near Stuttgart), brought together and owned by WALTHER DÖRR (GEORGE URDANG:
American Journal of pharmaceutical education 14, 577, 1950).

— WÜRZBURG—

1921: Institut für Geschichte der Medizin an der Universität Würzburg:

Founded in 1921 by Dr. GEORG STICKER, then ordinary professor of the history
of medicine, and established in a small room of the Pathological Institute, Bau 21
des Luitpoldkrankenhauses.
GEORG STICKER (Mit. 36, 5, 1937).

Another institute for the history of medicine was established in the University of
Jena (Prof. THEODOR MEYER-STEINEG) and seminars for the history of medicine in
the Universities of Frankfurt am Main (Prof. RICHARD KOCH) and Freiburg im
Breisgau (Prof. PAUL DIEPGEN).
SIGERIST: Forschungsinstitute (vol. 1, 402, 1930).

GREAT BRITAIN
— CAMBRIDGE —

Museum of the history of science:

This museum is not yet formally established but the elements of it have been
gathered and shown to the public. "An exhibition of historic scientific instruments
and books in the East Room of the Old Schools, 4-11 Nov. 1944" (20 p., Cambridge
1944).
The exhibition was arranged by the History of Science Lectures Committee.
The exhibits were drawn from the collection which R. S. WHIPPLE is presenting to
the University. As soon as the collection is permanently housed, it will be much
increased (as happened in Oxford) by donations from various sources, chiefly the
old Cambridge colleges.

— GLASGOW —

There are in Glasglow two important collections of books concerning the history
of chemistry.
The first was built by JAMES YOUNG (1811-83) and was the basis of an elaborate
bibliography by JOHN FERGUSON (1837-1916), about whom *see* Isis (39, 60-61,
1948, portrait), Bibliotheca Chemica (2 vols. Glasgow 1906). The Young collection
is now preserved in the Royal Technical College.
The second was built by FERGUSON himself and is preserved in the Library of the
University. Catalogue (2 vols. Glasgow 1943; Isis 35, 263). This collection includes many unpublished papers of JOHN FERGUSON (Isis 39, 61).

— GREENWICH —

1934: National Maritime Museum:

Established in the Queen's House with its wing buildings, the collections including those of the old Royal Naval Museum and those made and given by Sir JAMES CAIRD. The Queen's House was restored to the condition in which CHARLES I had finished it for HENRIETTA MARIA in 1635. The Museum was formally inaugurated on 27 April 1937.

Much in the Museum concerns naval history, yet there is also every kind of object illustrating maritime life in all its aspects. There are many instruments and tools needed for navigation, astrolabes, quadrants, sextants, etc. and also chronometers, from the earliest ones made by JOHN HARRISON (1693-1776).

Greenwich Palace. A history of what is now the Royal Naval College and the National Maritime Museum from earliest times to 1939 (quarto 50 p., 10 pl.)

RUPERT THOMAS GOULD: The marine chronometer (303 p., 39 pl., 85 fig. London 1923; Isis 6, 122-29); JOHN HARRISON and his timekeepers (Mariner's mirror 21, 1935; 24 pl., 9 pl.).

National Maritime Museum. Catalogue (260 p., ill., 1937).

Wren Society (vol. 6, 1930; Isis 15, 239). The Wren Society was founded in England to reproduce architectural drawings and other documents concerning Sir CHRISTOPHER WREN (1632-1723); its first volume appeared in 1924 (Isis 8, 553). Vol. 6 deals with the Royal Hospital for Seamen at Greenwich 1674-1728.

— LONDON —

Science Museum (South Kensington):

The Museum was founded in 1853 but remained until 1909 a department of the Victoria and Albert Museum. It is the "national museum of science and its applications to industry." It is one of the largest museums of its kind in the world.

Its publications are very numerous and there is no complete list of them. The mimeographed lists (themselves very long) mention only the items which are still available.

The exhibits have been described in a series of handbooks and descriptive catalogues, such as Chemistry (1937, reprinted 1947), Mechanical road vehicles (1936), Pumping machinery (1932-33), Railway locomotives and rolling stock (1931, reprinted 1947), Sailing ships (1932), Time measurement, etc.

In addition, there are many special publications such as H. T. PLEDGE: Science since 1500 (1939; reprinted 1946; Isis 33, 74), and the Annual reports, photographic prints, postcards, photographs and lantern slides.

Director since 1950, F. SHERWOOD TAYLOR.

1800: Royal College of Surgeons:

The present building on the S. side of Lincoln's Inn Fields was erected in 1835. The collections are mainly anatomical, anthropological, and pathological but some concern more directly the historian of science. These are gathered mainly in the Historical Room, the Instrument Room and the Library.

CHARLES JOHN SAMUEL THOMPSON (1862-1943): Guide to the surgical instruments and objects in the historical series (92 p., London 1930; Isis 16, 570).

The Wellcome Historical Medical Museum:

At the turn of the century Sir HENRY WELLCOME (1854-1936) began to collect books and objects of every kind illustrating any and every aspect of medical history. At the time of the International Congress of medicine which took place in London in 1913 and included a section devoted to the history of medicine he was persuaded to exhibit a part of his immense treasures. The exhibition was remarkably successful, and Sir HENRY was later induced to put up the material in the form of a small permanent introductory collection. He obtained premises for this purpose at Wigmore Street, and this remained the headquarters of the Museum until 1932 when the collection was removed to new premises in Euston Road. This fine building was built essentially for the accomodation of a few of Sir HENRY WELLCOME's scientific interests. It was hoped that the permanent collection would be exhibited on three floors, comprising ten large galleries. Before the war and after it ceased, work proceeded on the setting up of these galleries but rather slowly as a great deal of research was entailed.

The collection is vast, and the Euston Road premises were capable of housing only those sections of the Museum material which ought to be available for study purposes. Material which was likely to be used less frequently was put in store elsewhere.

As a result of great accommodation difficulties which have arisen directly as a result of the war, major changes of policy and procedure have had to be adopted. The headquarters of the Wellcome Historical Museum have been removed to 28, Portman Square, London, W.1. which is now its final address. It is impracticable in these premises to devote more than a small room for permanent exhibition purposes, but it is hoped to permit of certain small sections of the Museum material being seen by the public from time to time at contemporary exhibitions on subjects which may be of interest at that particular time. For example, in October, 1946, a special exhibition on the History of Anaesthesia was opened to commemorate the centenary of MORTON's operation. This exhibition covered the whole field and continued until 1st January, 1947. At the request of the Officials of the International Congress of Surgery which met in London from September 15th-20th the Wellcome Museum put up an exhibition illustrating the History of Surgery. This exhibition is in a gallery of the Science Museum at South Kensington which has been lent by the Director of that museum for this purpose. The History of Surgery Exhibition will remain open until February 1st.

The Library of the Museum is very rich especially in the earlier periods. It contains approximately 200,000 printed books. There are between 600 and 700 incunabula, and most of the great works of the early periods are represented.

For publications, see chapter 20, under Wellcome.

Director: E. ASHWORTH UNDERWOOD.

The Horniman Museum and Library (Forest Hill, London S.E.):

Founded in 1890 by FREDERICK J. HORNIMAN (1835-1906), tea merchant, and presented by him to the London County Council in 1901. It is devoted mainly to ethnology, archaeology, and zoology. Some of the ethnological collections are oriented towards the study of early technology.

Handbooks: From stone to steel; War and the Chase (2nd ed. 1929); Stages in the evolution of domestic arts (2 parts, 2nd ed. 1924-25); Simple means of travel and transport by land and water (1925), etc.

This suggests that other ethnological museums might be consulted for the same purposes.

The Horniman Museum has also very interesting (but unpublished) collections illustrating the superstitions of many peoples and many times (including our own).

1905: The Warburg Institute, University of London (Imperial Institute Buildings, South Kensington, London S.W.7):

Library and research institute founded in Hamburg by ABY WARBURG (1866-1929), for the study of the survival and revival of classic antiquity during the Middle Ages, the Renaissance and later. The date of foundation is difficult to determine, because what was originally WARBURG's private library developed gradually into a public institute. The date of foundation generally given by the Institute itself is 1905, when WARBURG's collecting became more systematic than it had been. In 1921 the librarian, FRITZ SAXL, began a card index, as well as a series of lectures and publications. The Institute was then called the Bibliothek Warburg. It remained in possession of the Warburg family until 1933, when the fear of Nazi persecution and confiscation caused its moving to Thames House, London. It was moved to the Imperial Institute in 1937 and was incorporated in London University in 1944.

FRITZ SAXL (1890-1948) was librarian since 1913; at the time of WARBURG's death (1929), SAXL became director. After SAXL's death, Dr. GERTRUD BING was acting director; HENRI FRANKFORT of Chicago became director in May 1949.

For an account of the early years in Hamburg see FRITZ SAXL in Forschungsinstitute (2, 355-62, 1930). When the Deutsche Gesellschaft für Geschichte der Medizin usw. met in Hamburg in 1928 it visited the Bibliothek Warburg.

The library is very rich; though its section on the history of science is a subordinate one, it is very useful, and for many investigations the Warburg Institute is one of the best working places in London.

Publications: Vorträge, edited by FRITZ SAXL, 1921-31 (9 vols. Leipzig 1923-32; Isis 6, 236; 10, 301).

Studien der Bibliothek Warburg, edited by FRITZ SAXL (24 vols., Leipzig 1922-32). Followed by Studies of the Warburg Institute edited by FRITZ SAXL, published in London since 1936 (16 vols. had appeared by the beginning of 1949).

Kulturwissenschaftliche Bibliographie zum Nachleben der Antike (vol. 1, for the year 1931, Leipzig-London 1934). Vol 2 was published in English, A bibliography of the survivals of the classics (London 1938).

ABY WARBURG: Gesammelte Schriften. Die Erneuerung der heidnischen Antike, Beiträge zur Geschichte der europäischen Renaissance, edited by GERTRUD BING (2 vols., 745 p., Leipzig 1932; Isis 23, 602). This contains all of WARBURG's published writings. The editor, Dr. BING, is planning an additional volume which will include a selection of WARBURG's letters and notes and a biography.

Corpus platonicum Medii aevi. RAYMOND KLIBANSKY: The continuity of the Platonic tradition during the Middle Ages (58 p., 5 pl. 1939; Isis 33, 129). RAYMOND KLIBANSKY: Plato Latinus, vol. 1. Meno (114 p., 1940; Isis 33, 86). FRANZ ROSENTHAL and RICHARD WALZER: Plato Arabus. Vol. 2. Alfarabius (1943; Isis 34, 425).

Journal of the Warburg Institute, edited by EDGAR WIND and RUDOLF WITTKOWER, later called Journal of the Warburg and Courtauld Institutes (1937, 8 vols. to 1949).

Mediaeval and Renaissance Studies edited by RICHARD HUNT and RAYMOND KLIBANSKY (vol. 1, 1941).

Annual reports of the Institute are published in pamphlet form.

— MANCHESTER —

1781: **Manchester Literary and Philosophical Society** (36 George Street):
The Manchester Society is the oldest scientific society in England, next to the Royal Society. Its beautiful home was destroyed by enemy action on Dec. 24, 1940. It contained many relics of JOHN DALTON, THOMAS PERCIVAL, CHARLES WHITE, ROBERT OWEN, JAMES PRESCOTT JOULE, STURGEON, ROSCOE, WILLIAMSON, BALFOUR STEWART, OSBORNE REYNOLDS, SCHUSTER, HORACE LAMB, ELLIOT SMITH, RUTHERFORD and others. Most of that has perished. The Dalton collection was especially rich.

List of articles salvaged (Memoirs and Proceedings of the Society, 1939-41, p. xxxiv-xxxvii).

— OXFORD —

1926: **Museum of the History of Science** (Old Ashmolean Building, Broad Street):
The Ashmolean Museum, the oldest British Museum of Natural History, was founded in 1683 by ELIAS ASHMOLE (1617-92); the collections having been gathered largely by JOHN TRADESCANT sr. (d. 1637?) and his son, JOHN TRADESCANT, jr. (1608-62), who published a description of them, Museum Tradescantianum (1656). ROBERT THEODORE GUNTHER: Early science in Oxford (chiefly vol. 3, Oxford 1925; Isis 8, 375-77); The Old Ashmolean. Prepared for the 250th anniversary of its opening (156 p., Oxford 1933).

In 1924, the Old Ashmolean was reopened to house the collections relative to the history of science, most of them given to the university by LEWIS EVANS, others donated by several Oxford colleges. In 1935, the Lewis Evans Collection became the Museum of the History of Science. The first curator was ROBERT THEODORE GUNTHER (1869-1940), who made considerable use of them for his work Early science in Oxford (14 vols. Oxford 1920-45; Introd. 3, 1886) and his Astrolabes of the world (2 vols., Oxford 1932; Isis 20, 310-16, 492-95). See also GUNTHER's Handbook of the Museum of the history of science (162 p., Oxford 1935). GUNTHER has published a series of Old Ashmolean Reprints.

GUNTHER's successor as curator of the museum until 1950 was F. SHERWOOD

TAYLOR, who described the museum in Endeavour (vol. 1, no. 2, 3 p., April 1942) and published the Catalogue of an exhibition of scientific apparatus pertaining to medicine and surgery (840 items, 36 p., Oxford 1947). Dr. TAYLOR was assisted by Dr. S. F. MASON. See TAYLOR's note in Nature (164, 738-39, 1949).

HUNGARY

— BUDAPEST —

Historical section of the museum for hygiene:
The section was directed by Professor TIBOR GYÖRY of NÁDUDVAR (1869-1938). The present situation of the museum is not known to me, because a polite request for information addressed to the Director on 15 Feb. 1949 received no answer.

The following note was kindly sent to me by CLAUDIUS F. MAYER in March 1951. The full title of the museum was Népegészségügyi Intézet és Muzeum (Public Health Institute and Museum). Address: Eötvös ucca 4, Budapest. The museum was intended to be an exhibit for health education. It was very rich in material related to industrial hygiene and industrial medicine. It was under the direction of GEORG GORTVAY, M.D., a public health officer and a medical officer of the Health Ministry of Hungary.

The museum had a small collection of old medical and surgical instruments which was much enlarged at the time of an International Exposition held in 1927. The enlargement was chiefly by collection of material on Hungarian medical folklore, again for purposes of public health-education. A special exhibit was arranged for showing the history of quackery. This exhibit was under my immediate direction and arrangements (in 1927-29).

I do not know what happened in recent years. I met GORTVAY in 1937 but, at that time, he was already the head of another group in the State Health Insurance system of Hungary. GYÖRY died next year; but he had very little to do with the museum, except as a higher government employee in matters of supervision.

ITALY

— FLORENCE —

Istituto e Museo di storia della scienza (Palazzo Castellani, Piazza dei Giudici, Firenze):
The Museum owns a very rich collection of instruments, some of them used by GALILEO, TORRICELLI, members of the Accademia del cimento, etc.

The director is Prof. Dott. ANDREA CORSINI, assisted by Dott. MARIA LUISA BONELLI. The latter published an illustrated description of it in the Archives internationales (no. 6, Janv. 1949, p. 452-56, 2 pl.).

— PAVIA —

Istituto di farmacologia:
Includes a Raccoltà di storia della farmacia, described by P. MASCHERPA in Chimica 1943, no. 8, 34 p.

— ROME —

Musaeum Kircherianum:
This museum was created about the middle of the seventeenth century by the Jesuit father ATHANASIUS KIRCHER (1602-80). According to KIRCHER's encyclopaedic tendencies, the museum included objects of every kind—antiquities, archaeology, ethnography, natural history, etc. It also included a number of mathematical and physical instruments. The Museum does not exist any more as such, its collections having been divided among the other Roman museums; it is possible, however, to reconstruct it in one's imagination, because of the elaborate description of it by another Jesuit, FILIPPO BUONANNI or BONANNI (1638-1735): Musaeum Kircherianum (522 p., folio, with 169 engraved plates, Roma 1709). Pp. 302-12, fig. 65-81, describe the Instrumenta mathematica.

Information kindly obtained from GIORGIO LEVI DELLA VIDA and PIETRO BARO-

CELLI, both of Rome. I was not able to ascertain whether the scientific instruments of the Kircher Museum still exist, and if so where they are at present.

Istituto di storia della scienza dell'Università.
Institute which is a part of the University of Rome. The first director was the mathematician, FEDERIGO ENRIQUES (1871-1946), who began in 1932 (with GIORGIO DE SANTILLANA) the publication of a general history of science. The first vol. only was published (antiquity; Isis 23, 467-69).

1920-1936: Istituto storico italiano dell'arte sanitaria.
Established in Rome in 1920. Published a Bollettino (q.v.) from 1921 to 1934. The Istituto then became the Accademia di storia dell'arte sanitaria, and the Bullettino became Atti e memorie (q.v.). It was replaced in 1936 by the Instituto di storia della medicina.

1936: Istituto di storia della medicina dell'Università di Roma.
Institute which is a definite part of the faculty of medicine and is organized for study, teaching, bibliographic documentation. It includes library, archives, museum, and is responsible for many publications.
The director is Prof. ADALBERTO PAZZINI; assistant, LUIGI STROPPIANA.
A. PAZZINI: I primi dieci anni d'insegnamento e di attività dell'Istituto (Annali di medicina navale e coloniale, vol. 3, 44 p., ill., Ministero della marina militare, 1946), with full bibliography.

THE NETHERLANDS
— HAARLEM —

Teylers Stichting (Teyler Foundation):
Foundation established by the bequest of PIETER TEYLER VAN DER HULST in 1778; it provided for two societies, the first called "Société théologique," the second, "la Seconde Société de Teyler," dedicated to the study (in the order given) of physics, poetry, history, painting, numismatics. In order to realize that second purpose a Museum was founded containing collections of physical instruments, natural curiosities, drawings and medals.
MARTINUS VAN MARUM: Description d'une très grande machine électrique placée dans le Muséum de Teyler et des expériments (sic) faits par le moyen de cette machine (quarto, 235 p., pls., Haarlem 1785; supplement 11 p., 1787); Première continuation des expériences faites par le moyen de la machine électrique teylerienne (quarto, 286 p., 1787). Both volumes in Dutch and French.
Guide for visitors to the Museum by ADRIAAN DANIEL FOKKER and A. M. MUNTENDAM (not seen, date unknown).
The most interesting among early "natural curiosities" is the giant fossil salamander which the Swiss palaeontologist, JOHANN JAKOB SCHEUCHZER (1672-1733) mistook for "homo diluvii testis."

— LEIDEN —

Rijksmuseum voor de geschiedenis der natuurwetenschappen (National Museum for the History of Science at Leiden, Steenstraat 1 A):
This museum, not connected with the Leiden University, was started by a private Foundation on the initiative of Dr. CLAUDE AUGUST CROMMELIN, Lecturer on Physics at the Leiden University and opened the 5th of June 1931 under the directorship of Dr. CROMMELIN and the vice-directorship of Prof. Dr. C. J. VAN DER KLAAUW, Professor of Zoology at the Leiden University. Dr. CROMMELIN's inaugural address was published in Dutch in Physica 11 (1931) p. 152 (German translation in Die Naturwissenschaften 19 (1931) p. 673). A guide for visitors was published by him and the Conservator Dr. MARIA ROOSEBOOM in 1947. Dr. CROMMELIN has devoted many articles to individual instruments, physical and astronomical, to the Dutch instrumentmaking in the 17th and 18th centuries, etc.
Since the 1st of January 1947 the museum is organized on a national basis and bears the above name. Dr. CROMMELIN retired from the Directorship the 1st of January 1949 and was succeeded by Dr. ROOSEBOOM.

This museum contains a large number of scientific and medical instruments, memorials and manuscripts which illustrate the development of Dutch science from the seventeenth century on. A section is devoted to CHRISTIAN HUYGENS. Dr. CROMMELIN has published recently a catalogue of the Huygens collection (32 p., 4 pl., Leiden 1949). MARIA ROOSEBOOM: The National Museum of the history of science (Archives intern. d'hist. des sci. 29, 129-35, ill., 1950).

In addition to its publications it has for sale a large number of photographs representing objects on exhibition, portraits, autographs, etc. Typewritten list (May 1949).

Instituut voor geschiedenis der geneeskunde, wiskunde en natuurwetenschappen
(Institute for the history of medicine, mathematics, and natural sciences):

This institute was established in 1913; it is attached to the University of Leiden, to the Museum described above and to the Dutch society for the history of science. A special committee is in charge of contacts with the University. The library was established in 1928, and a collection of medals (Scientia medica et naturalis in nummis) in 1942. The institute is located in the Museum. Its proceedings appear in the Bijdragen voor de geschiedenis der geneeskunde.

D. BURGER: Gedenboek by het 35-jarig bestaan van het Genootschap (Amsterdam 1949); Institut d'histoire de la médecine, des mathématiques et des sciences (Archives 1, 513-16, 1948).

— THE HAGUE —

Het Nederlandse Postmuseum (Netherlandish Postal Museum):

Postal museum including not only post stamps but a number of objects illustrating every aspect of postal, telegraphic and telephonic communications. Its inception goes back to 1924, but its development was stopped by the war. The director, Dr. R. E. J. WEBER, described its purpose and realization in a Dutch brochure Karakter en ontwikkeling van het Nederlandse Postmuseum, reprinted from Het PTT-bedrijf (Jaargang 1, no. 2, p. 60-68), not dated but Dr. WEBER's covering letter was dated June 1950.

NORWAY

Norway's main contribution was the invention of *"open-air museums"* which have developed considerably in Scandinavia. These collections of old buildings (churches, public and private houses) are very important for the study of architecture and folkarts; they always include exhibits illustrating the history, if not of science, at least of agriculture and technology.

One of the first *"open-air museums"* was created at Maihaugen, Lillehammer, by ANDERS SANDVIG (1862-1950). It contains over 100 buildings.

Dr. JEAN ANKER, Editor of *Centaurus*, in a letter dated Copenhagen 3 Oct. 1950, has kindly added the following correction:—

"It is not quite right to say that ANDERS SANDVIG was the pioneer of the 'open-air' museum, although he was one of the pioneers for the idea in Scandinavia.

"The idea on which the open-air museum is based, viz., an endeavour to preserve historical buildings by moving them to an undisturbed place, can undoubtedly be traced far back. Thus in the 16th century the Danish King FREDERIK II had a log house moved from Halland (a part of South Sweden, at that time belonging to Denmark) to Zealand; in 1528 FRANÇOIS I is said to have moved a dwelling-house from Morel near Fontainebleau to Cours-la-Reine near Paris, etc. In 1844 FRIEDRICH WILHELM of Prussia moved Vang's old 'stave-kirk' from Telemarken in Norway to Brückenberg in Riesengebirge (Silesia), where I have seen it myself.

"World exhibitions have also contributed to the furtherance of this idea, e.g., when the Crystal Palace of the first exhibition in London in 1851, in 1854, after having been moved to Sydenham, was reopened with a number of courts containing reproductions in reduced size of the prominent buildings of the civilized world.

"The idea proper of real 'open-air museums' (park museums) originates from Scandinavia, however, and Norway seems to have shown the way, while to Sweden belongs the honour of having created the first real collections in this form.

"This much, however, can be stated that already in 1881 Gol's old 'stave-kirk' together with another building from Telemarken was moved to Bygdö near Oslo, and at the same place the Norwegian Popular Museum (Norske Folkemuseum) in 1898 acquired a large area for an open-air museum, which in 1907 was united with the above-mentioned and other buildings.

"It was probably the Bygdö Museum you have seen on your visit to Norway, that is if it was not the Sandvigske collections near Lillehammer, which in 1902 was taken over by 'the Society of the Welfare of the Town of Lillehammer.'

"The oldest and one of the biggest open-air museums is 'Skansen' in Stockholm which was founded in 1891 by ARTHUR HAZELIUS as a branch of the Nordic Museum (Nordiska Museum).

"1895 saw the first preparations for an open-air museum in Denmark, and in 1897 the first building for the purpose was erected in Rosenborg Garden in Copenhagen. The place was unsuitable, however, and the museum did not acquire the desired conditions until 1901, when the Folkemuseum opened its open-air museum near Lyngby north of Copenhagen, where it is still to be found. It has developed into a very large museum with a great number of buildings from the whole country as well as from our former Swedish and German provinces.

"The museum near Lyngby (Sorgenfri) is the greatest, but gradually we have developed quite a number scattered all over the country. The best known is our Town Museum, 'Den gamle By,' in Århus. A number of open-air museums is now to be found also in Sweden and Norway.

"As far as I know, no review of the history of individual open-air museums exists (I just asked the head of the Lyngby Museum, Dr. ULLDAL); we have, however, a number of publications about the individual museums. From the Swedish literature the following may be mentioned: L. SVENSSON: Hembygdens arv (1929); Från landskapsmuseer och hembygdsgårder (in 'Fataburen' 1931, sqq.); G. BERG: ARTHUR HAZELIUS (1933); S. ERIXON & Å. CAMPBELL: Svensk bygd och folkkultur, 1-4 (1946-48)."

POLAND

After the reconstitution of Poland in 1919, chairs for the history of medicine, each of them connected with an institute ad hoc, were established in the five Polish Universities:

CRACOVIA (KRAKOW).—Institute directed by Professor W. SZUMOWSKI (Isis 31, 183).

POSEN.—Institute directed by Professor ADAM WRZOSEK (Isis 31, 184, 190).

WILNO (VILNA).—Institute directed by Professor S. TRZEBINSKI (Isis 7, 243; 8, 559; 31, 184).

VARSAW (WARSZAWA).—Institute directed by Professor FRANCISZEK GIEDROYC (Isis 11, 564; 12, 437).

LWOW (LEMBERG).—No information.

H. E. SIGERIST: Forschungsinstitute (vol. 1, 402, 1930).

Polite letters of inquiry addressed on 10 June 1949 to the five Polish universities remained unanswered.

ROMANIA

— BUCHAREST —

National Institute of the History of Medicine:

The institute of Bucureşti was founded by V. GOMOIU in 1935. Includes library, archives, and objects concerning the history of medicine and pharmacy (Isis 40, 182).

— CLUJ —

1921: Institutul de istoria medicinei şi farmaciei şi de folklor medical (Institute for the history of medicine, pharmacy, and medical folklore):

Founded in 1921 by Dr. JULES GUIART of Lyon; directed by Dr. VALERIU L. BOLOGA. Publishes the Biblioteca medico-istorica; studies by members of the institute are published also in medical journals, Romanian or French. Descriptions by BOLOGA in Archeion (9, 517-20, 1928).

Cluj, the main city of Transylvania, was called in Latin, Claudiopolis; in German, Klausenburg; in Hungarian Kolozsvár. Cluj is the official (Romanian) name since 1918.

SOVIET UNION

— LENINGRAD —

Institute for the history of science:

The All-Union Institute for experimental medicine in Leningrad organized in 1933 a Bureau of the history of science (President, Prof. K. M. BYKOV). The activities of that bureau are the same as that of an institute: Library and museum activities, organization of research, various types of publications.

HENRY E. SIGERIST (Bull. of the Institute of the history of medicine 3, 92-93, 1935).

The following information which we owe SEMYON P. RUDNYKH was first published in Isis (37, 77), but is so relevant that we reprint it in extenso:

"The study of the history of science, with a special emphasis on the history of science in Russia, is to be concentrated in a special institute of the Academy of Sciences of the USSR set up by decision of the Soviet Government in the end of 1944. The Institute is headed by Academician V. L. KOMAROV, President of the Academy of Sciences, and a Council consisting of Honorary Academician, N. A. MOROZOV; Academicians S. I. VAVILOV, V. P. VOLGIN, B. D. GREKOV, A. M. DEBORIN, N. D. ZELINSKY, A. N. KRYLOV, L. A. ORBELI, V. P. POTEMKIN and E. V. TARLE; Corresponding Members of the Academy L. S. BERG and H. S. KOSHTOYANTZ, and Professors G. F. ALEXANDROV, V. G. KUZNETSOV (Assistant Director), T. I. RAINOV and V. I. SVETLOV.

"The study of the history of science in general will be combined with the study of particular branches of science (physics, astronomy, mathematics, mechanics, chemistry, biology, etc.). One of the aims of the Institute is to spread knowledge on the history of science among the people, particularly among the youth. The Institute will have a museum, library and bibliographical bureau.

"The Institute for the Study of the History of Science plans to issue the following publications:

" 'Scientific Heritage,' collection of hitherto unpublished or little known documents relating to the history of science in Russia and abroad. The first volume, now being prepared for the press, contains unpublished documents of general interest, including a manuscript by MENDELEYEV discovered shortly before the present war and some unpublished manuscripts of outstanding West-European scientists;

" 'Transactions,' a periodical in which will be published articles and essays on questions of the history of science;

" 'Classics of Russian science';

" 'History of Russian science,' a collective work in several volumes;

" 'Coryphaei of Russian science'—series of volumes, each containing the selected works of a Russian scientist, a life of the scientist, bibliography, and comments;

" 'Classics of natural sciences'—individual classical works which are landmarks in the history of science, with comments and notes.

"Monographs dealing with individual questions of the development of science in Russia and in the West.

"Textbooks for colleges and popular publications.

"The Institute is preparing to produce a work of many volumes on the general history of science, to publish critical and bibliographical works, collect exhibits and documents and hold conferences on the history of science."

For publications, see chapter 20, under Trudy.

SWEDEN

My information on Swedish Museums was largely obtained thanks to the courtesy of Dr. ARNE HOLMBERG, Librarian of the Royal Swedish Academy of Science. The courtesies of other colleagues are mentioned in separate notes.

— FALUN, DALARNE (DALECARLIA) —

Bergslagets Museum (Mining Museum) founded c. 1898:

Owned by Stora kopparbergs Bergslags A. B. (Stora kopparbergs mining district Co., inc.), superintendent: Dr. ALVAR SILOW.

Mining in that district of Dalecarlia began at least as early as the thirteenth century; the museum contains documents dated 1288, 1347.

Brief guide in Swedish (24 p., Falun 1947; Isis 39, 124). Reprinted 1949.

History by SVEN TUNBERG: Stora kopparbergets historia. I. Förberedande Undersökningar (198 p., 39 ill., Uppsala 1922; Isis 39, 124). Introd. (3, 219).

Information kindly communicated to me by Dr. ANDRIES MacLEOD of Vintjärn, Dalarne, and Dr. ALVAR SILOW of Falun.

— STOCKHOLM —

1921: **Museet för de exakta vetenskapernas historia** (Museum for the history of exact sciences):
Founded in 1921 and owned by the Royal Academy of Sciences. It is not yet open to the public and is temporarily housed in the Riksmuseum, Stockholm 50. Superintendent: Prof. GUSTAF ISING.
Annual reports in the Annual of the Academy (K. Svenska vetenskapsakademiens Årsbok) beginning in 1922. Thanks to the great kindness of Dr. ARNE HOLMBERG I obtained the collection of those reports from 1922 (for 1921) to 1948 (for 1947); each of them is an offprint from the Academy's yearbook, varying in length from a few pages to some 60. The longest one, for 1927 (Yearbook 1928, p. 259-316) contains an account of other museums on the history of science such as those of London, Paris, Prague, Vienna, Munich, Nuremberg, Dresden.

1897: **The Berzelius Museum of the Royal Academy of Sciences:**
Founded in 1897. Located in the Academy's building, Stockholm 50. Superintendent: Prof. ARNE WESTGREN.
Kungl. vetenskapsakademiens Berzelius-Museum (21 p., Uppsala 1928).
This Museum collects books, MSS and memorials of every kind concerning the chemist BERZELIUS (1779-1848). The Academy has published an elaborate biography of BERZELIUS (3 vols., 1929-31) and his correspondence, and has devoted various other books to his memory (summary in Isis 36, 134-35).

1924: **Tekniska museet** (Museum of technology):
Private institution founded in 1924. The present Museum is established in a building of very large size and itself of great technical interest, built in 1934-36.
From the description I gather that the aim is primarily technical (to illustrate and explain modern technicalities) but there are various exhibits of historical interest, for example, those concerning "the father of Swedish technology," CHRISTOPHER POLHEM (1661-1751) and his disciples.
Superintendent: TORSTEN ALTHIN.
S. SÖDERBERG: Tekniska museet (Industria 1947); Tekniska museet (undated guide, Stockholm).

Järnvägsmuseum (Railway museum):
Opened in 1915. One part of it is at the Central Railway Station in Stockholm (temporarily closed since 1946), another part at Tomteboda Station, 3 km. north.
Includes remains of the first Swedish-built engine, 1853 (the first Swedish railway for steam engine traction was opened in 1856). There are many other engines, passenger cars, the first autobus, signal installations, etc.
Järnvägsmuseum (Stockholm 1946). Das Eisenbahnmuseum (Stockholm 1939). The Swedish Railway museum (Stockholm 1939).

Telegrafmuseet (Telegraph museum).
Open since 1937. No literature.

Open-air Museums.—*See* the letter of JEAN ANKER, printed above under "Norway."

SWITZERLAND

— BASEL —

Historisches Museum (Steinenberg, 4):
There is as yet no section of the history of science in this museum, but I understand that one may be organized in the near future (Letter from Dr. WOLFGANG SCHNEEWIND, assistant curator, dated 27 Dec. 1948). The Museum owns two Mercator globes, terrestrial and celestial, dated 1541 and 1551, plus other globes, telescopes, etc. It also owns three sixteenth century reckoning tables, which are very rare objects (FRANCIS PIERREPONT BARNARD: The casting-counter and the counting board, p. 231, Oxford 1916; Isis 5, 553).

Die Schweizerische Sammlung für historisches Apothekenwesen an der Universität Basel:

The nucleus of this museum is the private collection of Dr. Josef Anton Häfliger, who became in 1926 Privatdozent at the University for the history of pharmacy. In 1927 the collection was taken over by the Swiss "Apothekerverein," and greatly increased by the acquisition of another private collection gathered by Dr. Th. Engelmann. Elaborate catalogue by J. A. Hälfliger: Pharmazeutische Altertumskunde (204 p., 53 ill., Zürich 1931). The Museum is housed in the Pharmaceutical Institute of the University.

In Häfliger's book (p. 27-40) there is a long list of collections relative to the history of pharmacy. Many of these collections are included in large museums of a much wider scope; others are to be found in the old pharmacies which have been preserved in many European cities.

My attention was first drawn to the Basel collection by Dr. Emil Walter of Zürich (his letter of 30 Dec. 1947).

— Zürich —

Medizingeschichtliche Sammlung der Universität Zürich:

The nucleus of this museum was the private collection of Dr. G. A. Wehrli (1888-1949) begun in 1915. It was acquired by the canton of Zürich in 1932 and is housed in one of the University buildings. It concerns the history of medicine in all its aspects, not only scientific medicine but also medical folklore and charlatanry.

Information received from Dr. Emil Walter (his letter of 30 Dec. 1947; Isis 41, 57).

UNITED STATES OF AMERICA

— Baltimore, Maryland —

1927: Institute for the History of Medicine:

This institute was created as a part of the Johns Hopkins University at the initiative of Dr. William Henry Welch, about 1927-28. The organization of the institute was inspired by that of the Leipzig institute which Welch visited in 1927. It includes a fairly large library, the Welch Memorial Library, partly collected by Welch himself. Dr. Sigerist was director of the institute from 1932 to 1947; Prof. Richard H. Shryock succeeded him in 1949.

The institute publishes a Bulletin (q.v.) and various series of books. For its history, see Simon Flexner: W. H. Welch (425, 443; New York 1941; Isis 34, 381).

— Cambridge, Massachusetts —

1918-49: Section of the history of science of the Carnegie Institution of Washington in Cambridge, Massachusetts:

The work of this section began with George Sarton's appointment on July 1, 1918 and ended with his retirement on August 31, 1949.

This section was the center for the study of the history of science in America. The main publication is Sarton's Introduction to the history of science (3 vols. in 5, 1927-48).

The Carnegie Institution sponsored the publication of various other books on the history of science the list of which appeared in Osiris (9:624-38, 1950).

Progress of the work done by Sarton year by year may be read in the Year Books of the Institution beginning with no. 18 (for 1919) and ending with no. 48 (for 1948-49).

Sarton works in the Harvard (Widener) Library, rooms 185-189. His library and apparatus have been given to that library; the books bought for him by the Carnegie Institution have also been given to Harvard and will thus remain mixed with the other books used by him (books bought with his own money or presented to him).

This library includes a card catalogue of all the notes published in Isis; that is, a bibliography of the history of science all over the world from about 1910. The cards fill 72 drawers of the standard size.

This section was entirely supported by the Carnegie Institution, Harvard providing two rooms in Widener Library for its collections. At the time of SARTON's retirement from the Carnegie Institution an arrangement was made with Harvard University and with the Widener Library making the continuation of SARTON's work possible for a few more years.

1949: Harvard Museum of the History of Science:
An exhibition of scientific instruments used at Harvard in the eighteenth century and later, was held in the Edward Mallinckrodt Chemical Laboratory, on Oxford Street, from 12 February 1949 on.

The exhibition has been arranged by DAVID P. WHEATLAND, I. BERNARD COHEN and SAMUEL ELIOT MORISON. It is probably the nucleus of a permanent museum.

The period covered is 1764-1837. There are no instruments anterior to 1764, for a conflagration occurring in that year destroyed Harvard Hall which included the "philosophical chambers" (where the instruments were kept) as well as the college library.

Isis (6, 543). DAVID PINGREE WHEATLAND and I. BERNARD COHEN: Some early scientific instruments at Harvard University (32 p., ill., Harvard University Press 1949). I. B. COHEN: Some early tools of American science. An account of the early scientific instruments and mineralogical and biological collections in Harvard University (222 p., 32 pl., Harvard University Press 1950; Isis 41, 233-34).

— CHICAGO, ILLINOIS —

1933: Museum of Science and Industry (57th Street at Lake Michigan):
Founded by JULIUS ROSENWALD; its exhibits were opened to the public in 1933 in the reconstructed Fine Arts Building, an immense palace which had originally been built in stucco for the Chicago Fair of 1893. Total floor area, 14 acres. The Museum was partly inspired by the Deutsches Museum of Munich, e.g., it includes like the latter a coal mine wherein visitors can obtain some idea of what a real mine is and how it functions. It is a museum of science rather than of the history of science, yet many exhibits are (or will be) of historical interest.

The organizer and first director of the Museum was WALDEMAR BERNHARD KAEMPFFERT, author of A popular history of American invention (2 vols., New York 1924; improved German translation Berlin 1927; Isis 11, 533). KAEMPFFERT denied the imitation of the Deutsches Museum and claimed that the Chicago museum was the development of new ideas. See his paper Revealing the technical ascent of man in the Rosenwald Industrial Museum (Scientific Monthly 28, 481-98, 10 ill., 1929).

No publications except a short guide (Exhibit finder, 16 p.) for visitors.

1930: Adler Planetarium and Astronomical Museum (Chicago Park District):
The building specially made to accommodate a planetarium made in Jena (the first of its kind in America) and given by MAX ADLER, was opened to the public on 12 May 1930. It includes in the rooms around and below the planetarium, a large collection of astronomical instruments which was brought together and described by PHILIP FOX (1878-1944). See the Brief guide prepared by him 4th ed., 64 p., ill., Chicago, Sept. 1937; Isis 34, 450).

Of course, collections of astrolabes, ancient telescopes and other instruments, old books, may be found in many observatories, such as the Harvard Observatory in Cambridge, Mass., or the Library of the Mount Wilson Observatory, Pasadena, Calif., or in other planetariums such as the one attached to the American Museum of Natural History, in New York (like every great museum of natural history, the American Museum contains a good many historical exhibits).

— CINCINNATI, OHIO —

Lloyd Library and Museum (309 West Court St., Cincinnati 2):
These collections were begun in 1864 by the two brothers, JOHN URI LLOYD (1849-1936) and CURTIS GATES LLOYD.

The publications are most of them scientific (mycological, pharmaceutical, botanical, entomological) but they include also a "reproduction series" begun in 1900 (nine nos. by 1931, reproducing older works), a number of botanical bibliographies and books on the history of pharmacy.
CASWELL A. MAYO: The Lloyd library and its makers (Bull. no. 28 of the Lloyd Library, 72 p., ill., 1928). Mrs. CORINNE MILLER SIMONS: Lloyd Library and Museum. A history of its resources. (Special libraries p. 481-86, Dec. 1943).

— CLEVELAND, OHIO —

Museum of historical and cultural medicine (11,000 Euclid Avenue):
This museum is owned by the Cleveland Medical Library Association. It was initiated by D. P. ALLEN and developed by H. DITTRICK, as described by himself in Bull. Hist. Med. (1940, 8, 1214-45).

— DOYLESTOWN (near Philadelphia), PENNSYLVANIA —

1916: Mercer Museum of the Bucks County Historical Society:
The Society was organized in 1880 and incorporated in Pennsylvania in 1885. The main collections were gathered by one of its charter members, HENRY CHAPMAN MERCER (1856-1930; Isis 14, 424). He presented the existing building in 1916, and additions were made to it in 1933 and 1936.
The objects exhibited are chiefly tools and utensils of every kind, age and provenance; added to them are other objects of archaeological interest illustrating the life of the people using those tools.
There are other historical and folkloric societies and museums in Pennsylvania, which evoke the life and activities of the old "Dutch" (German) settlers: the Schwenkfelder Historical Library at Pennsburg, the Pennsylvania State Museum at Harrisburg, the Berks County Historical Society at Reading, the Hershey Museum at Hershey, the Landis Valley Museum at Lancaster. The last-named one boasts a large collection of Lancaster Rifles (the Pennsylvania German rifles). The other museums contain many tools and instruments similar to those of the Mercer Museum, but less numerous and generally restricted to the local varieties.
A description of all of those museums was published by the Pennsylvania German Folklore Society (vol. 7, 1942), with many illustrations.
The Mercer Museum has published many books and papers explaining some parts of the collections, e.g., H. C. MERCER: Ancient carpenter tools (1929; Isis 18, 400), Light and fire making (1898), Tools of the nation maker (1897); RUDOLF P. HOMMEL: China at work (1937; Isis 31, 219).
There are small guides for visitors, e.g., subject 1, Food (4 p., 1921), subject 2, Tools (4 p., 1923).
HENRY CHAPMAN MERCER (1856-1930) Memorial services (40 p., ill., Doylestown, 1930).

— KANSAS CITY, KANSAS —

Department of medical history:
Includes a small collection of medico-historical objects founded by LOGAN CLENDENING (1884-1945), author of popular books on medicine and the history of medicine. Bull. Hist. Med. (1940, 8, 742-48).

— MADISON, WISCONSIN —

1941: American Institute for the History of pharmacy:
The institute was founded on 22 Jan. 1941, but its organization had been prepared many years before by the teaching and collecting of Dr. EDWARD KREMERS (1865-1941), the building up of the pharmaceutical section of the Library of the University of Wisconsin (that section is very rich, not second even to the Lloyd Library), the collections of Dr. RICHTMANN, and other collections preserved within the Museum of the Wisconsin Historical Society.
The organizer and director of the Institute is Dr. GEORGE URDANG, who collabo-

rated with Dr. KREMERS and continued the latter's teaching in the history of pharmacy.

The museum of the Institute was described by Dr. URDANG in The scope of pharmacy. An exhibit (61 p., ill., Madison, 1946).

— NEW HAVEN, CONNECTICUT —

1940: Historical Library of the Yale University, School of Medicine:
The Library was created by the bequest of Dr. HARVEY CUSHING (1869-1939); it includes CUSHING's own library and that of ARNOLD C. KLEBS (1870-1943). The organizer and first director is Dr. JOHN F. FULTON. The Yale Historical Library is not only a collection of books, MSS and other documents and monuments relative to the history of medicine, it is also a center of research and publication.

See the Reports of the Historical Library for 1940-41, 1941-44, 1944-45, 1945-46, 1947-48, etc.

See also FULTON's biography of CUSHING (Springfield, Ill., 1946; Isis 37, 92-93).

1947: Yale Museum of Science:
A catalogue of surviving early scientific instruments of Yale College. Placed on display in the Sterling Memorial Library, October 1947 (12 p.).

Many of the items are now preserved in the Historical Library.

— NEWPORT NEWS, VIRGINIA —

1930: The Mariner's Museum:
Founded by ARCHER M. HUNTINGTON "It is devoted to the culture of the sea and its tributaries, its conquest by man, and its influence on civilization." It includes many objects concerning the history of navigation, etc.

There is no general guide but the Museum has published some twenty booklets describing separate exhibits, historical ships or places, etc.

— NEW YORK, NEW YORK —

New York Academy of Medicine (2 East 103rd St., New York 29):
In addition to its rich collection of books, prints, medals, the Academy has for a good many years been accumulating old instruments and other objects illustrating medical research and practice. There is enough material for a medical museum, but the latter is not organized and ready for public exhibition (Letter from Miss JANET DOE, librarian, dated Feb. 8, 1949).

Museum of the Peaceful Arts in the City of New York:
This Museum is quoted here only pro memoria. The idea was originated by GEORGE FREDERICK KUNZ (1856-1932): The projected Museum of the peaceful arts (paper read before the American Museum Association's meeting, New York 1912, 12 p.). Great efforts were made to obtain sufficient capital but failed. It was more or less replaced by the New York Museum of Science and Industry.

G. SARTON has in his archives a considerable correspondence on the subject.

New York Museum of Science and Industry (RCA Building, Rockefeller Center):
This Museum is more concerned with the exhibition of modern discoveries and inventions than with their history.

It was founded by a bequest of HENRY R. TOWNE in 1924 and opened to the public in 1927.

— PHILADELPHIA, PA. —

The Henry Charles Lea Library and Reading Room (University of Pennsylvania, 34th and Locust St.):
This is the library collected and used by HENRY CHARLES LEA (1825-1909), historian of the Inquisition and witchcraft, and given to the University by his children.

It is a rich collection of books and MSS dealing with the subjects to which LEA devoted a good part of his life.

EDWARD SCULLEY BRADLEY: H. C. LEA (Philadelphia 1931), including bibliog-

raphy of LEA's writings.   H. C. LEA: Materials toward a history of witchcraft, edited
by ARTHUR C. HOWLAND, introduction by GEORGE LINCOLN BURR (3 vols., 1592 p.,
Philadelphia 1939; Isis 34, 235-36); Minor historical writings edited by the same
(420 p., Philadelphia 1942; Isis 34, 235-36).

There is a Lea Professorship of History in the University of Pennsylvania.   The
present incumbent, JOHN L. LA MONTE, is more interested in the Crusades than in
the Inquisition, yet he kindly wrote to me (9 Feb. 1949) that the Library is always
open to special students and visiting scholars.   Dr. HOWLAND, emeritus professor
and curator of the Lea Library, is cataloguing and analyzing the Lea MSS and other
items, and the library is kept up-to-date.   LA MONTE died in 1949 (Isis 41, 202).

1931: Edgar Fahs Smith Memorial Collection (University of Pennsylvania):
Collection of books, MSS and prints relative to the history of chemistry, made by
EDGAR F. SMITH (1854-1928), professor of chemistry and sometime provost of the
university.   It was reorganized in 1931 as an institute for research in the history of
chemistry, and publishes Chymia (vol. 1, 1948).

Curator and secretary, EVA V. ARMSTRONG.

1933: The Franklin Institute:
The Institute dates from 1824; the idea of building a Museum of science originated in 1928 and the Museum was opened in 1933.   The Museum includes the Fels
Planetarium and many exhibits illustrating the wonders of modern science and technology.   Many of the exhibits are of historical interest, the chief of them being
FRANKLIN's printing shop and other Frankliniana, early machines, tools, and instruments of every kind.

SYDNEY L. WRIGHT: The story of the Franklin Institute (105 p., ill., 1938).
Brief guide to the Museum (62 p., ill., no date).

See also Doylestown, Pa.

— WALTHAM, MASSACHUSETTS —

Chronica Botanica Library and Archives (977 Main Street and 79 Sartell Road):
One of the largest biological historical libraries in private hands and an institute
for the history of biology in statu nascendi.   Special sections include: (1) History
of botanical gardens, (2) Botanical exploration, (3) Method and philosophy of the
natural sciences, (4) Emblem books of a biological interest, (5) Chinese and Japanese classics, (6) Natural history poetry, (7) Early horticulture.

Chronica Botanica Archives (at Sartell Road): (1) Autographs, (2) Portraits,
(3) Various memorabilia, (4) Older nursery catalogues, (5) Prints of gardens, and
(6) Early plant geographical maps.

Card indices: (1) References to published (as well as unpublished) biographical
data about plant scientists of the past (ca. 3 million cards), (2) Literature of the
history of biology, (3) Bibliography of collective biographical literature, (4) Data
on the history of botanical gardens, (5) Literature of historical plant geography, (6)
Literature of biological methodology, museum, and garden technique, (7) Literature
of hepaticology.

See Arch. Int. Hist. Sci. 29: 785-787, 1950.

— WASHINGTON, D. C. —

Army Medical Library and Army Medical Museum (also called Surgeon General's
Library and Museum):
The Library and Museum are two separate institutions, once located in the same
building (7th St. and Independence Ave., Washington 25) and operated as departments of the U. S. Army Medical Services under the authority of the Surgeon General.

The library is perhaps the richest medical library in the world, and it is known
everywhere because of its Index Catalogue which is one of the fundamental tools
of the medical historian.   EDGAR ERSKINE HUME: The Army medical library (Isis
26, 423-47, 2 portr., 1937).   See also CLAUDIUS F. MAYER (Isis 40, 119).

The museum is rather a museum of medicine than of the history of medicine, yet
it includes a number of exhibits illustrating the development of medicine and of

medical instruments (stethoscopes, microscopes, hearing aids, syringes, surgical and dental instruments, military medical kits, etc.). There is also a fine collection of coins, stamps, medals and plaquettes of medical interest. The collections are well catalogued and classified, but there is no general description of them.

The Army Medical Museum is now a subdivision of the Armed Forces Institute of Pathology which unites under one general head: a) Institute of pathology (at old address); b) Army Medical Museum (old address but in another building, on other side of the street); c) Registry of Pathology (at old address), and d) Medical Illustration Service (in building of the museum). Both museum and library originated after the Civil War and were developed by JOHN SHAW BILLINGS (1838-1913), about whom see the article in Isis 26 referred to above.

Smithsonian Institution—United States National Museum:

Collections concerning the history of science and technology are found in at least three departments, Ethnology or Anthropology, Engineering and Industries, and the recently created National Air Museum. Reports concerning the activities of these departments appear every year in the Annual Report of the Smithsonian Institution.

The activities of the first-named of these departments are well illustrated by its publications. OTIS T. MASON (Curator of Ethnology): The origins of invention (419 p., ill., London 1895). WALTER HOUGH (Curator of Anthropology): Synoptic series of objects in the U. S. National Museum illustrating the history of inventions (Proc. USNM, 60, art. 9, 47 p., 56 pl., 1922), Fire as an agent in human culture (USNM, Bull. 139, 284 p., 41 pl., 1926); Collection of heating and lighting utensils (USNM, Bull. 141, 118 p., 99 pl., 1928); Fire-making apparatus (Proc. USNM, vol. 73, art. 14, 72 p., 11 pl., 1928), etc.

The Museum of engineering and industries is one of the four divisions of the Department of Engineering and Industries. It has a very large collection of objects and instruments illustrating technical inventions, chiefly those made within the nation after the Revolution. Some of the early items are models such as were necessary at the beginning of last century in support of an application for a U. S. patent. Particular items or groups of items have been described by the former curator, CARL W. MITMAN, or by his assistants, in engineering or industrial journals, but there is no general catalogue.

Though the Department collections include some of the earliest accessions of the Smithsonian Institution (founded in 1846), its history begins about 1880; its organization was conceived by G. BROWN GOODE, who was much interested in the history of American science. The present curator is FRANK A. TAYLOR. See his articles The background of the Smithsonian Institution's Museum of engineering and industry (Science 104, 130-32, 1946); A National Museum of science, engineering and industry (Scientific Monthly 63, 359-65, 1946), plans for a larger Museum to be built in Washington.

The National Air Museum:

The objects illustrating ballooning and aviation were detached in 1946 from the Department of Engineering and Industry, in order to constitute the kernel of a new museum (Public Law 722, 22 August 1946).

The present curator is CARL WEAVER MITMAN "Assistant to the Secretary [of the Smithsonian Institution] for the National Air Museum."

Carnegie Institution. See Cambridge, Massachusetts.

COMPANY MUSEUMS

A good many industrial firms have established museums relative to their own past achievements or to the achievements of the branch of industry which they represent. That custom originated in Germany where intense industrial activities were combined with a deep sense of tradition and a genuine historical spirit. It was strengthened by the zeal of FRANZ MARIA FELDHAUS,[109] who organized investigations in the

---

[109] His methods are explained and illustrated in his journal Geschichtsblätter für Technik, Industrie und Gewerbe (vol. 11, 1-10, 1927).

history of technology on a commercial basis and produced a number of studies to celebrate the jubilee of various German companies.   Many of these studies have been listed in Isis (e.g., 4, 216-17; 26, 572; 28, 585).

According to LAURENCE VAIL COLEMAN:[110] Company museums (1943), there were at the time of his writing 80 company museums in the United States and Canada, some of them, it is true, very small and not open to the public, others on the contrary quite considerable.   Each of those museums is important, for it helps to preserve more accurately some technological and industrial traditions.   COLEMAN's book contains a brief description of each and all of them.   It will suffice here to enumerate a few in alphabetical order of subjects:

Abrasives.—Norton Co., Norton Hall Museum (Worcester, Mass.).

Agricultural machinery. — J. I. Case Co. Farm machinery collection (Racine, Wisc.).

Aluminum. — Aluminum Co. of America.   Aluminum Museum (230 Park Ave., New York).

Arithmetical machines. — Felt & Tarrant Mfg. Co. (1735 N. Paulina St., Chicago, Ill.).

Asbestos. — Asbestos Ltd. (8 W. 40 St., New York).

Automobiles. — Ford Motor Co.   Ford Rotunda (Dearborn, Mich.). Studebaker Museum (South Bend, Ind.). General Motors Corporation.   Parade of progress (traveling exhibits, headquarters, 1775 Broadway, New York).

Chemistry. — Rumford Chemical Works.   Rumford Museum (Rumford, R. I.). Fisher Scientific Co., Fisher Collection of alchemical and historical pictures (711 Forbes St., Pittsburgh, Pa.).

Electricity. — The Old Edison Laboratory (West Orange, N. Y.), established soon after the death of THOMAS ALVA EDISON in 1931.   This is the most important museum of its kind in America. General Electric Co.   Research Laboratory Exhibits (Schenectady, N. Y.).

Explosives. — E. I. du Pont de Nemours & Co.   Du Pont Museum (Wilmington, Del.).

Firearms. — Colt's Patent Fire Arms Manufacturing Co.   Colt Museum (Hartford, Conn.). CHARLES T. HAVEN and FRANK A. BELDEN: History of the Colt revolver and other arms (711 p., ill., 1940).

Fire engines. — The Home Insurance Co., The H. V. Smith Museum (59 Maiden Lane, New York, N. Y.).   Insurance Co. of North America (1600 Arch St., Philadelphia).

Forestry. — See Logging equipment.

Fur trade. — Hudson's Bay Co. (Winnipeg, Manitoba).

Glass. — United States Glass Co. (Tiffin, Ohio).   Libbey Glass Co. (Foot of Ash St., Toledo, Ohio).

Gyroscopes. — Sperry Gyroscope Co. (Manhattan Bridge Plaza, Brooklyn, N. Y.).

Logging equipment. — Wisconsin Land & Lumber Co.   Paul Bunyan Museum (Blaney Park, Blaney, Mich.).

Meteorological instruments. — Taylor Instrument Co. (Rochester, N. Y.).   The News Syndicate Co.   The News Lobby Exhibit (220 E. 42nd St., New York).

Mining. — See Rock drilling.

Paper. — Crane & Co., Crane Museum (Dalton, Mass.).   Hammermill Paper Co. (Erie, Pa.).

Pharmacy. — Burroughs Wellcome & Co.,Wellcome exhibition galleries (11 E. 41 St. New York).   These galleries were discontinued about 1946.

Two catalogues of special exhibitions were published.   The romance of exploration and emergency first-aid from STANLEY to BYRD (160 p., ill., Chicago, Cen-

---

110 We owe to COLEMAN a whole series of important reference books on American museums: Manual for small Museums (New York, Putnam 1927).   Directory of Museums in South America (1929).   Historic House Museums (1933).   The Museums in America (3 vols. 1939).   College and University Museums (1942).   Company Museums (1943).   All these books, except the first, published by the American Association of Museums, Washington, D. C.

tury of Progress Exhibition 1934). The Reichert Collection illustrative of the evolution and development of diagnostic instruments (70 p., 1942).

The Squibb ancient pharmacy (Squibb Building, corner of 58th St. & Fifth Ave., New York City, 28th floor).

Collection made in Europe for E. R. Squibb and Sons, manufacturing chemists, and brought to America in 1932. GEORGE URDANG and F. W. NITARDY: The Squibb ancient pharmacy (190 p., ill., New York, Squibb, 1940; Isis 32, 493). There are many such collections in Europe, but this is the largest available in America. For a list of other collections, too many to be enumerated here, *see* JOSEF ANTON HÄFLIGER: Pharmazeutische Altertumskunde (p. 27-39, Zürich 1931).

Photography. — Eastman Kodak Co. (Kodak Park, Rochester, N. Y.).

Printing and Publication. — The New York Times, The John H. Finley Museum of the Recorded Word (229 W. 43rd St., New York). Chillicothe Newspapers (Chillicothe, Ohio). See also typesetting.

Railroads. — The Baltimore & Ohio Co. (Bailey's Roundhouse, Baltimore, Md.). Union Pacific System (Headquarters Bldg., Omaha, Neb.). Norfolk & Western Railway (Roanoke, Va.).

Rock drilling. — Ingersoll-Rand Co. Rock Drill Museum (Phillipsburg, N. J.).

Scales. — Toledo Scale Museum (Telegraph Rd., Toledo, Ohio).

Shoes. — United Shoe Machinery Corporation Shoe Museum (140 Federal St., Boston, Mass.).

George E. Keith Co., Old Red Shop (Campello, Brockton, Mass.).

Steel. — Worcester Pressed Steel Co., John Woodman Higgins Steel Museum (Worcester, Mass.).

The Museum is located on 100 Barber Avenue in Worcester. It was briefly described by JOHN W. HIGGINS: The industrial museum (Industrial Education Mag., March 1935).

Bethlehem Steel Exhibit (Bethlehem, Pa.). See also Wires.

Surgical instruments. — V. Mueller & Co. (408 S. Honore St., Chicago).

Telegraph. — Western Union Telegraph Co. Engineering Museum (60 Hudson St., New York).

Telephone. — Bell System Historical Museum (463 West St., New York). Museum established in 1913, controlled by the American Telephone and Telegraph Company, illustrating the history of electrical communications.

WILLIAM CHAUNCEY LANGDON: The American Telephone Historical Collection (Bell Telephone Quarterly, Jan. 1924, 12 p.); The growth of the historical collection (*ib.*, April 1925, 14 p.). W. C. FARNELL: The Bell System historical museum (50 p., ill., Bell Telephone Laboratories, Dec. 1936), this is a guide to the main exhibits.

The Bell Telephone Co. of Canada. Telephone Museum (1050 Beaver Hall Hill, Montreal, P. Q.).

Textiles. — Crompton & Knowles Loom Works (Worcester, Mass.).

Typesetting. — Mergenthaler Linotype Co. (Park Ave. & Ryerson St., Brooklyn, N. Y.).

Typewriters. — Underwood Elliott Fisher Co. (Hartford, Conn.).

Watches. — Elgin National Watch Co. (Elgin, Ill.). Waltham Watch Co., Franklin Dennison Collection (Waltham, Mass.).

Wires. — American Steel and Wire Co. (Worcester, Mass.).

SMALL REGIONAL OR LOCAL MUSEUMS

To these "company museums" should be added a few of the "local" museums, of which there are now many thousands in the United States. The purpose of these museums is to exhibit objects illustrating the history and archaeology of a definite locality and of the region surrounding it. When that region was the cradle of a definite industry, the local history of that industry will in all probability be represented. For example, I remember seeing industrial exhibits in the Museum of Rochester, N. Y., and of course many of them in the two regional historical museums of New York City, the Museum of the City of New York (Fifth Ave. at

104th St.) and the Museum of the New York Historical Society (Central Park W., between 76 and 77th Sts.). Some of the Massachusetts Museums illustrate maritime industries and fishing. For example, the Peabody Museum in Salem, and the two whaling museums of New Bedford and of Nantucket (*see* Isis 16, 115-23, 1931). We may refer again to the Mariners' Museum in Newport News, Virginia to which a separate note is devoted above.

HISTORICAL HOUSES OF INTEREST TO THE HISTORIAN OF SCIENCE

The only houses listed below are those open to the public and including collections or at least a few memorabilia. All of them, except BARTRAM, are listed among a great many others (some 400) which do not concern the historian of science in L. V. COLEMAN: Historic House Museums (Washington, D. C. 1933); the account of each house in COLEMAN's book is far too meager.

The houses are listed in the alphabetic order of their localities.

Fredericksburg, Virginia:
Mercer Apothecary shop (c. 1750).

Greenfield Village, Michigan:
The Menlo Park group of houses, moved from Menlo Park, New Jersey. EDISON's Laboratory, EDISON's Office Library, carbon shed, carpenter shop, glass house, machine shop.
EDISON's Fort Myers Laboratory (moved from Fort Myers, Florida). For other EDISON memorabilia *see* West Orange.
Sandwich Glass Plant.
Village blacksmith shop, etc.
FORD's shop (moved from Detroit).
STEINMETZ cottage (moved from Schenectady, N. Y.).
The whole of Greenfield Village, which includes many American houses and two English ones, was developed by HENRY FORD. It is a very large open-air museum, like the Scandinavian museums briefly described by Dr. JEAN ANKER, above, in the section devoted to Norway.

Hastings-on-Hudson, New York:
Observatory Cottage of HENRY DRAPER (1837-82).

Mitchell, Indiana:
Apothecary shop of c. 1830.

Nantucket, Massachusetts:
Birthplace of MARIA MITCHELL (1818-89), astronomer.

Philadelphia, Pennsylvania:
House of the botanist, JOHN BARTRAM (1699-1777), in BARTRAM's garden on the W. bank of the Schuylkill.

West Orange, New Jersey:
The old EDISON laboratory, organized some time after the death of THOMAS ALVA EDISON (1847-1931).

Woburn, Massachusetts:
Birthplace of BENJAMIN THOMPSON, count RUMFORD (1753-1814).

OTHER TECHNICAL MUSEUMS

F. M. FELDHAUS published in Archeion (11, 348-357, 1927) a short list of 46 technical museums, many of which do not exist any more, and are represented only by old catalogues or references in literature. For example, the museum of the Jesuit father ATHANASIUS KIRCHER is known through the catalogue of Father FILIPPO BUONANNI, Musaeum Kircherianum (Rome 1709), the collection of NICOLAS

GROLLIER DE SERVIÈRES made at Lyon c. 1675 was described by his grandson, GASPARD GROLLIER DE SERVIÈRES: Recueil d'ouvrages curieux de mathématique et de mécanique (quarto 111 p., pl. fig., Lyon 1719; 2nd ed., Lyon 1733; 3d ed. Paris 1751). The objects included in the old collections have often been dispersed, and some of them (sometimes a great many of them) reappear sooner or later in the other larger museums. For example, a wire drawing bench of the Dresden landgravian collection is now in the Musée de Cluny, Paris; a terrestrial sphere of 1725 previously kept in the Gottorp castle of the duke FRIEDRICH III of Schleswig is now in Leningrad; some of the objects originally collected by the archduke FERDINAND of Tirol c. 1581 and kept in Ambras Castle (near Innsbruck) were moved to the Kunsthistorische Sammlungen, Burgring, Vienna; etc.

Each large museum is a collection of collections. It might be worthwhile eventually to compile a list of all the historical collections which have thus lost their identity in larger assemblages. This was done for collections of natural history by CHARLES DAVIES SHERBORN: Where is the . . . Collection (148 p., Cambridge 1940; Isis 36, 77-78, 229).

25. INTERNATIONAL CONGRESSES

International congresses of the history of science have been organized from time to time by the International Academy; a list of them and of their publications is given on p. 255. Let us repeat briefly that there have been thus far six such congresses, to wit:

I. Paris 1929
II. London 1931
III. Portugal 1934
IV. Prague 1937

V. Lausanne 1947
VI. Amsterdam 1950
(VII. Jerusalem, Israel 1953)

Other international congresses of the history of science have been organized as sections of international congresses devoted to philosophy, to history, or to particular sciences. In spite of being "sections" of other congresses instead of being independent, some of these congresses have been very important. That is especially true of the three congresses organized in Paris 1900 and Geneva 1904 as parts of the first and second congresses of philosophy, and in Rome 1903, as a part of the second congress of history. These particular congresses were so important (and they all met before the first congress of the Academy) that they might be called the first three international congresses of the history of science. Let us give some information about them.

I. Paris 1900: **Congrès international de philosophie.**
The proceedings were published in four thick volumes. Vol. 1. Philosophie générale et métaphysique (1900). Vol. 2. Morale générale. La philosophie de la paix. Les sociétés d'enseignement populaire (1903). Vol. 3. Logique et histoire des sciences (688 p., 1901). Vol. 4. Histoire de la philosophie (1902).
In vol. 3, the papers devoted to the logic of the sciences are far more numerous than those on the history of the sciences. Yet, the latter were delivered by such men as Moritz Cantor, Gaston Milhaud, Siegmund Günther and Henri Bouasse. P. Tannery took part in these deliberations but his own paper (on Aristotelian science) was included among those relative to the history of philosophy.

II. Rome 1903: **II. Congresso internazionale di scienze storiche.**
The proceedings, Atti, fill 12 volumes (Roma 1904-07). Vol. X. History of geography and geography of history. Vol. XI. History of philosophy and history of religions. Vol. XII. History of physical, mathematical, natural and medical sciences (354 p., Roma 1904). The nine meetings of that section were presided over by Pietro Blaserna, Paul Tannery, Karl Sudhoff, Raphael Blanchard, Siegmund Günther, Emil Lampe, K. Benedikt.

III. Genève 1904: **IIe Congrès international de philosophie.**
Rapports et comptes rendus publiés par Ed. Claparède (Genève 1905). The congress was divided into the following sections. 1) History of philosophy, 2) General philosophy and psychology, 3) Applied philosophy, 4) Logic and philosophy of sciences (p. 675-772). 5) History of sciences (p. 773-964). Paul Tannery was the leader of section 5 and papers were read by H. Berr, P. Duhem, V. Mortet, K. Sudhoff, H. G. Zeuthen, etc. The proceedings of that fifth section bear the title "Histoire des sciences" (IIIme Congrès international d'histoire des sciences).
If that designation of the Genève congress of 1904 as "third international congress" were internationally accepted, then the ordinal number of each congress listed above would have to be increased by three units (the Amsterdam congress of 1950 would then be not the sixth but the ninth).

On account of the two world wars which broke the family of nations in two or more groups, similar difficulties occur in the enumeration of many other congresses, *e.g.*, the mathematical congresses. As historians are primarily interested in the existence of congresses and their sequence, and only secondarily in their official enumeration, an effort has been made to give a list of the congresses without bothering about the different methods of enumerating them.

As most international congresses of science and learning devote some attention to the history of their own discipline, we publish here a list of the most important. Even when an international congress, say, of chemistry, did not include a special historical section, its publications are still valuable for the historian of chemistry, for they reveal the intellectual climate obtaining at the time of its meeting. Presidential and other general addresses are often reminiscent, retrospective, and in various degrees historical and philosophical. An examination of the archives of a series of international congresses of a definite science or discipline, enables one to understand better the evolution of that science or discipline, its development into more and more branches, or on the contrary its unification under a new synthetic point of view. Of course, the international congresses enable one to measure the progress of international coöperation and integration. It is of great interest also for historians to know which were at this or that date the central or leading problems. The proceedings of the international congresses help to answer such questions.

The periodic meeting of international congresses of any kind implies the existence of a central office preserving the continuity of the meetings within a definite (though changeable) frame, implementing the decisions and wishes of each congress and preparing carefully the deliberations of the next one. Sometimes, international congresses have been organized "hors série," [111] outside of the frame already provided for them; such irregularities, which may be due to national, regional or linguistic vindications or to jealousies between various groups or schools, should be deprecated. If the creation of a new discipline requires the organization of a congress ad hoc, one should give the new congress a name sufficiently different from other names already in use in order to prevent ambiguities or confusions.

Some of the congresses had too broad a scope to be truly useful, that was the case for the Congress of arts and sciences of St. Louis (1904) and for congresses organized to celebrate the centenary of universities. "Qui trop embrasse mal étreint." On the other hand, many congresses have too narrow a scope to be of interest to others than the specialists taking part in them. However important they may be within their own sector, the historian of science and the philosopher cannot be expected to study their publications. Moreover, such very special congresses[112] are far too numerous to be enumerated here.

Irrespective of their scope or even of their subject some international congresses have been far more successful than others, while other congresses have failed to establish themselves. The miscarriages were generally due to bad organization, or to jealousies or at least lack of coöperation between the leaders. Success was generally due to the personal qualities of skilful organizers, as well as to the relative popularity of certain disciplines.

It is noteworthy that the longest traditions (in number of meetings) were built by the Americanists (29 congresses, 1875-1949), the Botanists (28 congresses 1864-1954), the Orientalists (21 congresses 1873-1948). Then follow the Chemists (20 congresses, 1860-93, 1894-1938), the Prehistorians (18 congresses, 1866-1939), the Geologists (18 congresses, 1878-1948), the Physicians (17 congresses, 1867-1913), the Physiologists (18 congresses, 1889-1950), the Architects (16 congresses, 1867-1949), the Geographers (16 congresses 1871-1949), the Historians of art (15 congresses 1873-1939), the Ophthalmologists (16 congresses, 1857-1950), the Veterinarians (14 congresses, 1863-1949), the Historians of medicine (13 congresses, 1920-50), the Surgeons (13 congresses, 1905-49), the Psychologists (12 congresses, 1889-1940), the Zoologists (12 congresses, 1889-1935), the Pharmacists (12 congresses 1865-1935), the Mathematicians (11 congresses, 1897-1950).

---

[111] For example, *see* congresses of the history of religion and congresses of philosophy, below.

[112] *E.g.*, many medical congresses dealing with special problems or diseases, such as gout, blood transfusion, cancer, brucellosis, etc. Of course, the historian of each of those problems or diseases will have to consult the publications of those special congresses, but he will be led to that naturally without need of our help.

The following congresses began in the nineteenth century (but some of them did not continue until now):

1853	STATISTICS	1875	AMERICANISM
1857	OPHTHALMOLOGY	1878	GEOLOGY
1860	CHEMISTRY	1884	ORNITHOLOGY
1863	VETERINARY ART	1889	FOLKLORE
1864	BOTANY	1889	PHOTOGRAPHY
1865	PHARMACY	1889	PHYSIOLOGY
1866	PREHISTORY	1889	PSYCHOLOGY
1867	ARCHITECTURE	1889	ZOOLOGY
1867	MEDICINE	1897	MATHEMATICS
1871	GEOGRAPHY	1900	HISTORY
1873	ORIENTALISM	1900	PHILOSOPHY [113]
1873	HISTORY OF ART	1900	HISTORY OF RELIGIONS [114]

The titles of congresses are generally given in many languages, but even in any one language they vary from time to time;[115] in the list below we do not try to give exact titles but simply indicate the general subject (chemistry, medicine, etc.), and the congresses are listed for the reader's convenience in alphabetical order of those subjects.   The names of cities are generally given in English; to give them in the language of each country would have caused difficulties (even typographical ones, in the case of Copenhagen).

No attempt has been made to mention the official publications of each congress, for that would extend our list considerably.   When the reader knows that a congress of physiology took place say, in Cambridge 1898, he may take for granted that the proceedings were actually published within a few years, and he will trace them without too much trouble in the catalogue of any large library.   He may find bibliographical references also in International congresses and conferences 1840-1937.   Union list, edited by WINIFRED GREGORY (folio 229 p., New York, Wilson 1938), or more briefly in the list compiled for the Army Medical Library by CLAUDIUS F. MAYER: Congresses.   Tentative chronological and bibliographical reference list of national and international meetings of physicians, scientists and experts (288 p., Index-Catalogue, 2nd Suppt., 4th series, Washington 1938; First addition, p. 29-51, Index-Catalogue, vol. 3, 4th series).

The following list is restricted to only a few international congresses, those which are the most interesting for historians of science.

The publications of those congresses contain a large number of papers concerning our studies, which are somewhat forgotten (as are the papers published in Festschriften); at any rate, they cannot be as well known as the papers published in journals devoted to the history of science.   It would be worthwhile to compile a bibliography of them and thus rescue them from oblivion and integrate them in the general bibliography of the history of science.

As the congresses are listed below for the student's convenience in alphabetical order, a methodical classification of them will be useful (the capitalized word determines the alphabetical order):

    I. Mathematics
    II. Physical sciences: Astronomy, applied Mechanics, Crystallography, Chemistry, Biochemistry. Geodesy and geophysics, Geography, Geology. Photography. Architecture. Weights and measures. Chronometry.
    III. Natural sciences: Botany, Zoology, Entomology, Ornithology.
    IV. Medical sciences: Anatomy, Physiology, Medicine, Surgery, Ophthalmology, Pharmacy, Veterinary medicine.
    V. Anthropology and archaeology: Anthropology and ethnology, prehistoric Anthropology and archaeology, Archaeology and history, Prehistory and protohistory. Americanism. Folklore.

---

[113] Including the first congress of the history of science.

[114] The inception of so many congresses in 1889 and 1900 was caused by the International Fairs held in Paris in those years. The three congresses of 1900 took place in Paris, as well as four of 1889 (the congress of physiology, however, began in that year not in Paris but in Basel).

[115] E.g., some congresses of the history of medicine were called in French Congrès de l'histoire de l'art de guérir! The effort to preserve those subtleties in our list would distract the reader instead of helping him.

VI. History: History, History of art, History of medicine, History of religion, History of science. Orientalism. Byzantine history. Classical studies. Papyrology. Toponymy and anthroponymy.

VII. Sociology: Statistics, Sociology.

VIII. Philosophy: Philosophy, Psychology, unity of Science. Philosophy of sciences.

International Congresses of Americanists:

I. Nancy 1875	XVI. Vienna 1908
II. Luxemburg 1877	XVII. Buenos Aires 1910
III. Bruxelles 1879	XVIII. London 1912
IV. Madrid 1881	XIX. Washington 1915
V. Copenhagen 1883	XX. Rio de Janeiro 1922
VI. Torino 1886	XXI. Göteborg 1924
VII. Berlin 1888	XXII. Roma 1926
VIII. Paris 1890	XXIII. New York 1928
IX. Huelva 1892	XXIV. Hamburg 1930
X. Stockholm 1894	XXV. La Plata 1932
XI. Mexico 1895	XXVI. Seville 1935
XII. Paris 1900	XXVII. Mexico and Lima 1939
XIII. New York 1902	XXVIII. Chile 1942?
XIV. Stuttgart 1904	XXIX. New York 1949
XV. Quebec 1906	

International Congresses of Anatomists:

I. Genève 1905	IV. Milano 1936
II. Bruxelles 1910	V. Oxford 1950
III. Amsterdam 1930	VI. Alger 1935

International Congresses of Anthropology and Ethnology:

Unnumbered congresses in Paris 1878, Vienna 1889, Chicago 1893, Cologne 1907, Basel 1933.

I. London 1934	II. Copenhagen 1938

International Congresses of Prehistoric Anthropology and Archaeology:

I. Neuchatel 1866	X. Paris 1889
II. Paris 1867	XI. Moscow 1892
III. Norwich & London 1868	XII. Paris 1900
IV. Copenhagen 1869	XIII. Monaco 1906
V. Bologna 1871	XIV. Genève 1912
VI. Bruxelles 1872	XV. Coimbra, Lisbon 1930
VII. Stockholm 1874	XVI. Bruxelles 1935
VIII. Budapest 1876	XVII. Bucharest 1937
IX. Lisbon 1880	XVIII. Istanbul 1939

See below, Congresses of Prehistory and Protohistory

International Congresses of Archaeology and History:

I. Bonn 1868	III. Alger 1930
II. Rome 1912	

For art, see history of art, below.

International Congresses of Architects:

I. Paris 1867	IX. Rome 1911
II. Paris 1878	X. Bruxelles 1922
III. Paris 1889	XI. Netherlands 1927
IV. Bruxelles 1897	XII. Budapest 1930
V. Paris 1900	XIII. Rome 1935
VI. Madrid 1904	XIV. Paris 1937
VII. London 1906	XV.[116] Paris 1942
VIII. Vienna 1908	XVI. Cairo 1949

International Astronomical Union:

This union does not organize international congresses but is very active in organizing international collaboration in various undertakings (including the history and bibliography of astronomy). There are international conferences from time to time, but no congresses as is the case for other branches of science.

---

[116] The 15th Congress was announced to take place in Washington 1939 but did not materialize.

An international congress of astronomical societies took place in Paris, in 1914. Comité international permanent pour l'exécution de la carte photographique du ciel (1889-1909). Conférence internationale des étoiles fondamentales 1896. Congrès astrophotographique international 1887. Congrès international des éphémérides astronomiques 1911. Congrès international des sociétés astronomiques 1914.

International Astronomical Conferences:

I. ROME 1922	V. PARIS 1935
II. CAMBRIDGE 1925	VI. STOCKHOLM 1938
III. LEYDEN 1928	VII. ZÜRICH 1948
IV. CAMBRIDGE, MASS. 1932	

International Congresses of Biochemistry:

I. CAMBRIDGE 1949   II. PARIS 1952

International Biometric Conferences:

I. WOODS HOLE, MASSACHUSETTS 1947 (1)   III. ITALY 1953 (2)
II. GENEVA 1949

(1) At that time the Biometric Society was formed, An international society devoted to the mathematical and statistical aspects of biology. Secretary: Box 1106, New Haven 4, Connecticut.

(2) A Biometric Symposium will take place somewhere in India in 1951 and help prepare the third congress.

International Botanical Congresses:

Some of the early congresses were called international congresses of horticulture and botany. About twenty meetings took place between 1864 and 1892:

I. BRUSSELS 1864	XI. AMSTERDAM 1877
II. AMSTERDAM 1865	XII. PARIS 1878
III. LONDON 1866	XIII. LEYDEN 1879
IV. PARIS 1867	XIV. BRUSSELS 1880
V. ST. PETERSBURG 1869	XV. ANTWERP 1881
VI. LONDON 1871	XVI. GHENT and PARIS 1883
VII. GHENT and VIENNA 1873	XVII. ST. PETERSBURG 1884
VIII. FLORENCE 1874	XVIII. ANTWERP 1885
IX. COLOGNE 1875	XIX. PARIS 1889
X. BRUSSELS 1876	XX. GENOA 1892

A new series began in 1900:

I. PARIS 1900	V. CAMBRIDGE 1930
II. VIENNA 1905	VI. AMSTERDAM 1935
III. BRUSSELS 1910	VII. STOCKHOLM 1950
IV. ITHACA, N. Y. 1926	(VIII. PARIS 1954)

Secretary of the Interim Commission (Botanical Section of the International Union of Biological Sciences): FRANS VERDOORN, Chronica Botanica House, Waltham, Mass. Dr. VERDOORN recently prepared a historical review of the plant science congresses which will be published in the Proceedings of the Stockholm Congress. This congress passed a resolution, proposed by VERDOORN, according to which future international botanical congresses will have a special section for the history of the plant sciences.

International Congresses of Byzantine Research:

I. BUCHAREST 1924	V. ROME 1936
II. BELGRADE 1927	VI. PARIS 1948
III. ATHENS 1930	VII. BRUXELLES 1948
IV. SOFIA 1934	VIII. PALERMO 1951

The VIth Congress replaced the one which was scheduled to meet in Alger 1939; it took place in Paris from July 27 to August 2, 1948, and was immediately followed by the VIIth Congress in Bruxelles from 4 to 15 August same year. This is the only example of two international congresses of the same series taking place in immediate succession in two different countries. It was done to compensate for the very long interruption caused by the war.

International Chemical Congresses:

I. KARLSRUHE 1860	VI. PARIS 1878
II. PARIS 1867	VII. DÜSSELDORF 1880
III. MOSCOW 1872	VIII. MILANO 1881
IV. VIENNA 1873	IX. PARIS 1889
V. PHILADELPHIA 1876	X. CHICAGO 1893

Succeeded by the International Congresses of pure and applied Chemistry:

I. BRUXELLES 1894	VII. LONDON 1909
II. PARIS 1896	VIII. WASHINGTON & NEW YORK 1912
III. VIENNA 1898	IX. MADRID 1934
IV. PARIS 1900	X. ROMA 1938
V. BERLIN 1903	XI. NEW YORK & WASHINGTON 1950
VI. ROMA 1906	

The congress organized in Karlsruhe in Sept. 1860 upon KÉKULÉ's initiative was one of the first scientific congresses; it was very small (some 140 members) but it is very important in the history of the atomic theory (*Isis* 9, 373).

International Conferences of Chemistry:

I. ROMA 1920	VIII. WARSAW 1927
II. BRUXELLES 1921	IX. THE HAGUE 1928
III. LYON 1922	X. LIÉGE 1930
IV. CAMBRIDGE 1923	XI. MADRID 1934
V. COPENHAGEN 1924	XII. LUZERN & ZÜRICH 1936
VI. BUCHAREST 1925	. . . .
VII. WASHINGTON 1926	XV. AMSTERDAM 1949
	XVI. NEW YORK, WASHINGTON 1951

International Congresses of Chronometry:

1. PARIS 1889	(x). PARIS 1949.
2. PARIS 1900	

To these meetings must be added the annual meetings of the Conférence internationale de l'heure, organized by the Bureau des longitudes, Paris 1912. The Bureau international de l'heure is located since 1913 (officially 1919) in the Observatoire of Paris.

For the meeting of 1949 *see* Revue des questions scientifiques (10, 408-10, 1949).

International Congresses of Crystallography:

The first congress of the International union of crystallography took place in Cambridge, Mass., in 1948. The proceedings of it are published in the Acta crystallographica.

The second congress will be held in Stockholm in 1951.

Address: Dr. R. C. EVANS, Cavendish Laboratory, Cambridge, England.

International Congresses of Classical Studies:

The first congress took place in Paris 28 August—3 Sept. 1950 in connection with the IXth International Congress of historical studies. The original French title is Premier congrès de la Fédération internationale des Associations d'Etudes classiques.

Secretary: M. A. DAIN, 42 rue de Dantzig, Paris 15.

International Congresses of Entomology:

I. BRUXELLES 1910	VI. MADRID 1935
II. OXFORD 1912	VII. BERLIN 1938
III. ZÜRICH 1925	VIII. STOCKHOLM 1948
IV. ITHACA, N. Y. 1928	IX. AMSTERDAM 1951
V. PARIS 1932	

International Congresses of Ethnography:

I. PARIS 1878	III. PARIS 1900
II. PARIS 1889	

International Congresses of Folklore (Congrès des traditions populaires):

    I. Paris 1889   III. Chicago 1893
    II. London 1891   IV. Paris 1900

At that time the continuity was broken. An International Congress for Folktale Study was held at Lund, Sweden, in 1935. As a result of the Lund meeting a more general folklore congress called International Congress for European Ethnology and Folklore was held at Edinburgh in 1937. In the same year an International Folklore Congress took place in Paris. The Continuation Committee appointed at the Paris congress of 1937 never had the opportunity to function.

A Mid-century International Folklore Conference was held at Indiana University, Bloomington, Indiana in 1950. Another International Congress is announced to take place in Stockholm, 1951. (Part of the information was kindly provided by Professor Stith Thompson in letters dated Bloomington, Ind., 15 Nov., 16 Dec. 1950).

International Congresses of Geodesy and Geophysics:
First conference in Berlin 1864, 17th in Hamburg 1912.

After the First War, astronomers, geodesists and geophysicians meeting in Rome decided upon the creation of two international unions (1) the International Astronomical Union, (2) the International Geodetic and Geophysical Union.

The second of these unions has organized congresses in

    I. Rome 1922   VI. Edinburgh 1936
    II. Madrid 1924   VII. Washington 1939
    III. Prague 1927   VIII. Oslo 1948
    IV. Stockholm 1930   IX. Bruxelles 1951
    V. Lisbon 1933

General Secretary, Dr. J. M. Stagg, 34 King's Road, Richmond, Surrey, England.
The union is divided into seven sections: Geodesy, Seismology, Meteorology, Atmospheric Electricity and Magnetism, Physical oceanography, Volcanology, Hydrology.

International Congresses of Geography:

    I. Antwerpen 1871   IX. Genève 1908
    II. Paris 1875   X. Roma 1913
    III. Venezia 1881   XI. Cairo 1925
    IV. Paris 1889   XII. London & Cambridge 1928
    V. Bern 1891   XIII. Paris 1931
    VI. London 1895   XIV. Warsaw 1934
    VII. Berlin 1899   XV. Amsterdam 1938
    VIII. St. Louis 1904   XVI. Lisbon 1949
                       XVII. Washington 1952

An international congress of historical geography took place in Bruxelles in 1930.

International Congresses of Geology:

    I. Paris 1878   X. Mexico 1906
    II. Bologna 1881   XI. Stockholm 1910
    III. Berlin 1885   XII. Toronto 1913
    IV. London 1888   XIII. Bruxelles 1922
    V. Washington 1891   XIV. Madrid 1926
    VI. Zürich 1894   XV. South Africa 1929
    VII. St. Petersburg 1897 XVI. Washington 1933
    VIII. Paris 1900   XVII. Moscow 1937
    IX. Vienna 1903   XVIII. London 1948
                      XIX. Algiers 1952

International Congresses of History:
In addition to two international meetings—at Chicago 1893 and The Hague 1898 —which are not counted in the regular series, the international congresses of historical sciences have taken place as follows:

    I. Paris 1900   VI. Oslo 1928
    II. Rome 1903   VII. Warsaw 1933
    III. Berlin 1908   VIII. Zürich 1938
    IV. London 1913   IX. Paris 1950
    V. Bruxelles 1923

International Congresses of the History of Art:

I. VIENNA 1873	IX. MUNICH 1909
II. NUREMBERG 1893	X. ROME 1912
III. COLOGNE 1894	XI. PARIS 1916 (1921) [117]
IV. BUDAPEST 1896	XII. BRUXELLES 1930
V. AMSTERDAM 1898	XIII. STOCKHOLM 1933
VI. LÜBECK 1900	XIV. SWITZERLAND 1936
VII. INNSBRUCK 1902	XV. LONDON 1939
VIII. DARMSTADT 1907	

International Congresses of the History of Medicine (Congrès de l'Histoire de l'Art de Guérir):

I. ANTWERPEN 1920 [118]	VIII. ROMA 1930
II. PARIS 1921	XI. BUCHAREST 1932
III. LONDON 1922	X. MADRID 1935
IV. BRUXELLES 1923	XI. YUGOSLAVIA 1938 [119]
V. GENÈVE 1925	XII. NICE 1949
VI. LEIDEN & AMSTERDAM 1927	XIII. AMSTERDAM 1950 [120]
VII. OSLO 1928	

International Congresses of the History of Religions:

I. PARIS 1900	V. LUND 1929
II. BASEL 1904	VI. BRUXELLES 1935
III. OXFORD 1908	VII. AMSTERDAM 1950
IV. LEIDEN 1912	

The Congress held in Paris in 1923 under the title Congrès international des religions (Société Ernest Renan) was not a regular meeting of the international organization.

International Congresses of the History of Science:
See p. 255, 290.

International Congresses of Mathematicians:

I. ZÜRICH 1897	VII. TORONTO 1924
II. PARIS 1900	VIII. BOLOGNA 1928
III. HEIDELBERG 1904	IX. ZÜRICH 1932
IV. ROMA 1908	X. OSLO 1936
V. CAMBRIDGE 1912	XI. CAMBRIDGE, MASS. 1950
VI. STRASBOURG 1920	XII. AMSTERDAM 1954

International Congress of Applied Mechanics:
First series: Paris 1889, 1900.
Second series:

I. DELFT 1924	V. CAMBRIDGE, MASS. 1938
II. ZÜRICH 1926	VI. PARIS 1946
III. STOCKHOLM 1930	VII. LONDON 1948
IV. CAMBRIDGE 1934	VIII. ISTANBUL 1952

International Congresses of Medicine:

I. PARIS 1867	X. BERLIN 1890
II. FLORENCE 1869	XI. ROME 1894
III. VIENNA 1873	XII. MOSCOW 1897
IV. BRUXELLES 1875	XIII. PARIS 1900
V. GENÈVE 1877	XIV. MADRID 1903
VI. AMSTERDAM 1879	XV. LISBON 1906
VII. LONDON 1881	XVI. BUDAPEST 1909
VIII. COPENHAGEN 1884	XVII. LONDON 1913 [121]
IX. WASHINGTON 1887	

---

[117] The congress of 1916 was indefinitely postponed on account of the war; it was replaced by another congress held in Paris in 1921.

[118] A previous congress was held in London 1913, being section XXIII of the 17th Congress of Medicine.

[119] Congresses XII and XIII planned to be held in Berlin 1940, Rome 1942 did not take place, or were not international.

[120] The meeting of Amsterdam was in the form of a section of the VI. Congress of the History of Science.

[121] Special volume for the history of medicine Section XXIII (475 p., London 1914), analyzed in the Vth Critical Bibliography (Isis, 2, 248-310). Only the XVIIth congress had a special section for the history of medicine; the history of medicine was taken care of later in a congress ad hoc; see under history, above.

International Congresses of Ophthalmology:

I. BRUXELLES 1857	IX. UTRECHT 1899
II. PARIS 1862	X. LUCERNE 1904
III. PARIS 1867	XI. NAPLES 1909
IV. LONDON 1872	XII. WASHINGTON 1922
V. NEW YORK 1876	XIII. AMSTERDAM, THE HAGUE 1929
VI. MILANO 1880	XIV. MADRID 1933
VII. HEIDELBERG 1888	XV. CAIRO 1937
VIII. EDINBURGH 1894	XVI. LONDON 1950

Confusion is caused by a meeting held in May 1947 which was called the *4th* international.   (C. F. M.)

International Congresses of Orientalists:

I. PARIS 1873	XII. ROME 1899
II. LONDON 1874	XIII. HAMBURG 1902
III. ST. PETERSBURG 1876	XIV. ALGIERS 1905
IV. FLORENCE 1878	XV. COPENHAGEN 1908
V. BERLIN 1881	XVI. ATHENS 1912
VI. LEYDEN 1883	XVII. OXFORD 1928
VII. VIENNA 1886	XVIII. LEYDEN 1931
VIII. STOCKHOLM and OSLO 1889	XIX. ROME 1935
IX. LONDON 1892	XX. BRUXELLES 1938
X. GENEVA 1894	XXI. PARIS 1948
XI. PARIS 1897	XXII. ISTANBUL 1951

International Congresses of Ornithology:

I. VIENNA 1884	VII. AMSTERDAM 1930
II. BUDAPEST 1891	VIII. OXFORD 1934
III. PARIS 1900	IX. ROUEN, PARIS 1938
IV. LONDON 1905	X. UPPSALA 1950
V. BERLIN 1910	XI. SWITZERLAND 1954
VI. COPENHAGEN 1926	

International Congresses of Papyrology:

I. Bruxelles 1930 (as a part of the Semaine égyptologique)
II. Leyden 1931 (as a part of the 18th Congress of Orientalists)
III. Munich 1933 (first independent meeting)
IV. Firenze 1935
V. Oxford 1937
VI. Paris 1949.

International Congresses of Pharmacy:

I. BRAUNSCHWEIG 1865	VII. CHICAGO 1893
II. PARIS 1867	VIII. BRUXELLES 1897
III. VIENNA 1869	IX. PARIS 1900
IV. ST. PETERSBURG 1874	X. BRUXELLES 1910
V. LONDON 1881	XI. THE HAGUE 1913
VI. BRUXELLES 1885	XII. BRUXELLES 1935

An international congress for the history of pharmacy was held in Basel 1934. It was called international because it was held in Switzerland, not in Germany, but it was chiefly German.

The International Federation of Pharmacists began to hold meetings in 1925. These meetings were also called International Congresses of Pharmacists; of these the *12th* was held in Zürich 1947.   (C. F. M.)

International Congresses of Philosophy:

I. PARIS 1900	VII. OXFORD 1930
II. GENEVA 1904	VIII. PRAGUE 1934
III. HEIDELBERG 1908	IX. PARIS 1937
IV. BOLOGNA 1911	X. AMSTERDAM 1948
V. NAPLES 1924	XI. BRUXELLES 1952
VI. CAMBRIDGE, MASS. 1926	

The so-called international congresses of philosophy held in Rome in November 1946 and in Barcelona in October 1949 were "hors série." Of course, it is easy enough to organize in any large city meetings or symposia where representatives of many nations are gathered, but such meetings are not international congresses in the technical sense. An international congress, one should bear in mind, is a congress organized by an international committee ad hoc, it is one of many congresses organized more or less periodically by the same committee for the same general purpose.

As an example of meetings, gathered in a small city, year after year and truly international in scope, consider Eranos, a philosophical symposium taking place every summer in Ascona (Ticino, Switzerland) since 1933 (Isis 41, 97, 138, 410). There is no limit to the number of meetings which might thus be organized almost anywhere by private or local initiative, but regardless of their interest or importance, we should not call them "international congresses of philosophy," for that phrase has a technical meaning established by a long tradition.

International Congress of the Philosophy of Sciences:

Congress announced to meet in Paris, 17-22 Oct. 1949. As its prospectus refers to no preceding meeting, it is presumably the first of a new series. It is organized by the Institut International de Philosophie in Paris, Administrateur permanent; Raymond Bayer.

The Congress is divided into eleven sections: Logic, Mathematical Philosophy, Calculus of probabilities, Mechanics and astronomy, Theoretical physics, Physicochemistry, Biology, Earth sciences, Epistemology, History of sciences, Pedagogy of sciences, General synthesis. (Archives internationales 28, 1270-71, 1949).

Mlle. SUZANNE DELORME, Secretary of the Institut International de Philosophie, is also Secretary of the Congress. Address: 61 rue du Mont Cenis, Paris 18.

The Secretary of the section devoted to the history of science is RENÉ TATON, 64 rue Gay-Lussac, Paris 5.

For the philosophy of science *see* also the Congresses on the Unity of Science, below.

International Congresses of Photography:

I. PARIS 1889	VI. PARIS 1925
II. BRUXELLES 1891	VII. LONDON 1928
III. PARIS 1900	VIII. DRESDEN 1931
IV. LIÉGE 1905	IX. PARIS 1935
V. BRUXELLES 1910	

International Congresses of Physiology:

I. BASEL 1889	XI. EDINBURGH 1923
II. LIÉGE 1892	XII. STOCKHOLM 1926
III. BERN 1895	XIII. BOSTON 1929
IV. CAMBRIDGE 1898	XIV. ROME 1932
V. TORINO 1901	XV. LENINGRAD & MOSCOW 1935
VI. BRUXELLES 1904	XVI. ZÜRICH 1938
VII. HEIDELBERG 1907	XVII. OXFORD 1947
VIII. VIENNA 1910	XVIII. COPENHAGEN 1950
IX. GRONINGEN 1913	XIX. MONTREAL 1953
X. PARIS 1920	

International Congresses of Prehistory and Protohistory:

I. LONDON 1932	[III. BUDAPEST 1949] [122]
II. OSLO 1936	III. ZÜRICH 1950

See above, Congresses of Prehistoric Archaeology.

International Congresses of Psychology:

I. PARIS 1889	VII. OXFORD 1923
II. LONDON 1892	VIII. GRONINGEN 1926
III. MUNICH 1896	IX. NEW HAVEN, CONN. 1929
IV. PARIS 1900	X. COPENHAGEN 1932
V. ROME 1905	XI. PARIS 1937
VI. GENÈVE 1909	XII. VIENNA 1940

For religion, see under history of religion above.

---

[122] Withdrawn!

International Congress for the Unity of Science: [123]

I. Paris 1935   IV. Cambridge 1938
II. Cophenhagen 1936   V. Cambridge, Mass., 1939 (Isis 32, 340-44)
III. Paris 1937

International Congresses of Sociology:

I. Torino 1921   III. Roma 1924
II. Vienna 1922   IV. Panama 1926

International Congresses of Statistics:

I. Bruxelles 1853   VI. Florence 1867
II. Paris 1855   VII. The Hague 1869
III. Vienna 1857   VIII. St. Petersburg 1872
IV. London 1860   IX. Budapest 1876
V. Berlin 1863   X. Paris 1878

In 1885, the International Statistical Institute was founded with organized biennial sessions, Roma 1887, etc.

The Belgian ADOLPHE QUETELET (1796-1874) was the president of the first of these congresses, of the third, the fourth, the fifth, the sixth, the seventh and the eighth; he could not preside over the second congress because of illness, and over the ninth because he had died in the meanwhile. This is a unique example in the international organization of science; it proves that QUETELET was really recognized as the founder and the great master, without peer (Isis 23, 10). QUETELET did not originate only the congresses of statistics, for the example which he had given was followed gradually by the representatives of other studies (*see* table p. 292); he may be called the founder of international scientific congresses.

International Congresses of Surgery:

I. Bruxelles 1905   VIII. Warsaw 1929
II. Bruxelles 1908   IX. Madrid 1932
III. Bruxelles 1911   X. Cairo 1936
IV. New York 1914   XI. Bruxelles 1938
V. Paris 1920   XII. London 1947 [124]
VI. London 1923   XIII. New Orleans 1949
VII. Roma 1926

International Congresses of Toponymy and Anthroponymy:

I. Paris 1938   III. Bruxelles 1949
II. Paris 1947

For more information *see* the journal Onomastica which began to appear in 1947 under the direction of ALBERT DAUZAT, 10 rue de l'Eperon, Paris 6. The international center is now at the University of Louvain.

International Congresses of Veterinary Medicine:

I. Hamburg 1863   VIII. Budapest 1905
II. Vienna 1865   IX. The Hague 1909
III. Zürich 1867   X. London 1914
IV. Bruxelles 1883   XI. London 1930
V. Paris 1889   XII. New York 1934
VI. Bern 1895   XIII. Zürich, Interlaken 1938
VII. Baden-Baden 1899   XIV. London 1949

Weights and Measures:

The Commission internationale du mètre met in Paris 1869, 1870, 1872.

The Comité international des poids et mesures met yearly in Paris from 1875/76 on. No meetings in 1893, 1896, 1898.

The Congrès international pour l'unification des poids et mesures met in Paris in 1878.

---

[123] This might be called Congress of the Philosophy of Science. Of course, every Congress of Philosophy devotes at least one of its sections to the Philosophy of Science.

[124] The London meeting replaced a meeting planned to be held in Stockholm 1941. The Stockholm meeting did not materialize; a meeting was held in that year 1941 in Boston, hors série.

The Conférence générale des poids et mesures met in Paris 1889, 1895, 1901, 1907, 1913, 1921, 1927, 1933, 1948.

The Congrès international pour l'unification des titres de l'or et de l'argent met in Paris in 1900.

International Congresses of Zoology:

I. Paris 1889	VII. Boston 1907
II. Moscow 1892	VIII. Graz 1910
III. Leiden 1895	IX. Monaco 1913
IV. Cambridge 1898	X. Budapest 1927
V. Berlin 1901	XI. Padua 1930
VI. Bern 1904	XII. Lisbon 1935.

❀ ❀ ❀ ❀ ❀

The organization of the international congresses, especially the early ones, was largely due to the initiative of enthusiastic individuals such as Kekulé or Quetelet. Their efforts were facilitated by the existence of national or international societies, and in many cases by governmental help. Indeed, during the nineteenth century the national (governmental) organization of science was extended considerably. Some kind of governmental influence had existed from the seventeenth century on, as is shown by the history of the Royal Society, and more obviously by that of the Académie des Sciences, by the creation of the first Observatories and the planning of cartography on a national scale. In the nineteenth century a number of geological surveys were established (Isis 2, 369-79). While the national organizations were developing, the international organization began, first in fields wherein international coöperation was essential for everybody's advantage (*e.g.*, meteorology, astronomy, statistics, geodesy, oceanography), later in almost every field of knowledge. The international congresses were only a part albeit an important one, of the international organization.

Special bodies were created to establish the international coöperation as efficiently as possible. It will suffice to name the International Geodetic Association (1864), the International Seismological Association (1901), etc. The international organization was not by any means restricted to science and learning, a network of good will was gradually spreading over the whole earth, and just before the first World War it was already so extensive and so complex that an enormous volume was needed in order to describe it. I am referring to the Annuaire de la Vie Internationale[125] edited by Albert Marinus under the leadership of Henri La Fontaine.[126] The organization of scientific research was more naturally international, however, than that of every other activity, and therefore the history of science is essentially the history not of any one nation but of mankind.[127] The network was broken and the good will partly lost or shattered after the First War.

In order to reestablish them two new overall international bodies were created in 1919, the Union Académique Internationale (International Union of Academies) and the International Research Council.[128] The later was inaugurated at Brussels in July 1919, "Each state was advised to set up or recognize a central scientific body capable of representing the country in the International Council. International Unions were also organized in the major fields of science to co-ordinate and develop activities hitherto scattered among numerous small international societies with overlapping functions and membership. There are at present ten International Unions, namely: Astronomical Union, Union of Geodesy and Geophysics, and Union of

---

[125] Annuaire de la Vie Internationale publié pour l'Union des Associations Internationales avec le concours de la Fondation Carnegie pour la Paix internationale et de l'Institut international de la Paix (vol. 2, 2,652 p., Bruxelles 1912; Isis 1, 289-90).

[126] Henri La Fontaine (1854-1943), Belgian senator and statesman, one of the main advocates of international arbitration and of the Permanent Court of International Justice, who was awarded the Nobel prize for peace in 1912-13 (Isis 34, 412).

[127] I explained those views just before the first World War, L'histoire de la science et l'organisation internationale (Bruxelles 1913) and reprinted my appeal twenty-five years later before the second World War (Isis 29, 311-25, 1938).

[128] Renamed Conseil International des Unions scientifiques, International Council of Scientific Unions (ICSU) in 1932.

Chemistry, all organized in 1919; Scientific Radio Union, Union of Pure and Applied Physics, Union of Biological Sciences, and Union of Geography, organized in 1922, and in 1925 after provisional meetings earlier; Union of Crystallography, Union of Theoretical and Applied Mechanics, and Union of History of Science, added in 1947 after preliminary meetings in 1947." [129]

An International Union of Mathematics organized in 1922, was discontinued in 1932; it is planned to reestablish it (in 1952?). It is also planned to establish an International Union of Physiology (in 1952?). Applications for the organization of new unions must be passed upon by the executive board of ICSU. The present tendency of ICSU is to restrict the number of unions and to organize joint commissions covering a larger field. For example the History of Science has been amalgamated with the Philosophy of Science.

All this concerns the administration of science rather than research itself, but the line is not always easy to draw and it is clear that the future development of science will imply collective efforts of greater and greater complexity, and that means more and more administration. This is very sad, yet unavoidable, and we must make the best of it. There will be a growing body of administrators, or of men whose points of view are administrative rather than purely scientific or individual, yet there will always be room for men of initiative and of genius.

To return to our main subject, the international congresses, their organization will be regulated more and more (if only for financial reasons) by the ICSU, through whose intermediary the necessary subsidies may be obtained.

The historian of science is not concerned with the organization of international congresses but with their publications which provide convenient syntheses of this or that discipline at regular intervals. However, it may be worth his while to know how the international congresses are organized and managed; the ICSU or any special scientific union, or their committees in his own nation will give him all the information which he may need at any time. Americans may obtain information from the National Research Council, Division of International Relations, Washington, D. C.

Unesco has recently published a Directory of International Scientific Organizations (238 p., Paris, May 1950).

---

[129] This statement is taken from the memorandum prepared on 19 December 1949 by the Committee on International Scientific Unions (chairman, Dr. JOHN A. FLEMING) of the U. S. National Research Council. Additional information kindly provided by Dr. FLEMING in a private letter (Washington, D. C., 17 Jan. 1951).

26. PRIZES

I. Prix Binoux (1889) for the History or Philosophy of Science.—Founded by bequest of LOUIS FRANÇOIS BINOUX to the Académie des Sciences, Paris, to reward outstanding work in the history and philosophy of the sciences. It was given for the first time in 1903 (to H. G. ZEUTHEN). For the prizes awarded from 1903 to 1924, *see* Isis 8, 161-63, from 1925 to 1935, Isis 25, 136-37, from 1936 to 1945, Isis 37, 79, from 1945 to 1949, Isis 41, 303.

II. Sudhoff Medal (1923).—Medal awarded by the German Society of the history of science. At the time of SUDHOFF's seventieth birthday (1923; *see* Mit. 22, 305-07, 1923), a plaquette was published in his honor. Later, his portrait (as it was in that plaquette) was published in medal form to be given to eminent historians of science. I do not know when the first award was made.

III. Dutch Medal (1940).—Medal awarded by the Dutch Society of the History of Science. A medal of honor is awarded by the Dutch Society at irregular intervals. It was first awarded in 1940, then in 1941; three medals were given in 1946 (Archives 1, 514, 1948).

IV. Prix Arnold Reymond for Philosophy of Science (1941).—The full name of the prize is "Prix Arnold Reymond, foundation Charles Eugène Guye." It was founded by GUYE's bequest to the University of Lausanne (15 May 1941). CHARLES EUGÈNE GUYE (1866-1942) was a Swiss physico-chemist, professor of physics at the University of Geneva, much interested in the philosophy of science; the prize was named in honor of ARNOLD REYMOND, professor of philosophy in Lausanne, president of the Academy from 1937 to 1947.

This prize is meant to reward the memoir "which explains in the clearest and most impartial manner the progress and tendencies during the last ten years of scientific philosophy in its wholeness or in one of its fields." It will be awarded by the University of Lausanne.

The first award was made in 1944 to PIERRE LECOMTE DU NOÜY (1883-1947; Isis 38, 246). Further awards will be made at intervals of five to ten years. More details in Archives (1, 156, 1947).

V. Prizes for Students (1947).—In order to encourage the study of the history of science among university students the History of Science Society was enabled by the generosity of one of its members to offer each year a "History of Science Essay Prize" of one hundred dollars.

The prize was awarded for the first time in October 1947. It is restricted to undergraduates or first year graduate students in American and Canadian colleges. For more details *see* the advertisements appearing frequently in Isis (the first one in Isis 37, p. 4).

INDEX *

* Prepared by FRANCES SIEGEL.